D0414991

Earth and life through time

10

Illustration on title page In this coastal scene from the Cretaceous Period, a pterosaur snatches a fish from the jaws of a giant plesiosaur. Many pterosaurs — flying reptiles — were far larger than the birds of the day.

The Open University, Walton Hall, Milton Keynes MK7 6AA

First published 1998

Copyright © 1998 The Open University

All rights reserved; no part of this publication may be reproduced, stored in a retrieval system, transmitted or utilized in any form or by any means, electronic, mechanical, photocopying, recording, or otherwise, without written permission from the publisher or a licence from the Copyright Licensing Agency Ltd. Details of such licences (for reprographic reproduction) may be obtained from the Copyright Licensing Agency Ltd of 90 Tottenham Court Road, London W1P 0LP.

Written, edited, designed and typeset by The Open University.

Printed and bound in Great AABritain by Jarrold Book Printing, Norfolk, England.

ISBN 0 7492 8196 0

This text forms part of an Open University course, S103 *Discovering Science*. The complete list of texts that make up this course can be found on the back cover. Details of this and other Open University courses can be obtained from the Course Reservations Centre, PO Box 724, The Open University, Milton Keynes MK7 6ZS, United Kingdom: tel. (0044) 1908 653231.

For availability of this or other course components, contact Open University Worldwide Ltd, The Berrill Building, Walton Hall, Milton Keynes MK7 6AA, United Kingdom: tel. (00 44) 1908 858585, fax (00 44) 1908 858787, e-mail ouwenq@open.ac.uk. Alternatively, much useful course information can be obtained from the Open University's website http://www.open.ac.uk

s103block10i1.1

Contents

Introduction

1

The Earth is an intensely dynamic planet, as we saw in Block 3. Unlike our nearest neighbour, the Moon, the surface of our world is not only teeming with life, but reveals its ceaseless activity in countless other ways: rough seas, surging tides, thunderstorms, waterfalls, avalanches, landslides, volcanoes and earthquakes. Nowhere on Earth is immune from change, and on a geological time-scale such changes can be hard to believe based on the experience of a single human lifetime. The highest rocks in the world, at the top of Everest, were once under the sea; the Earth's driest deserts will some time be covered by ocean waters, and one day lava will probably spew out over what in its present arrangement of land and sea we call the British Isles.

Certain events in the geological past have far exceeded anything known in human history. But for the pioneers of geology in the 18th and 19th centuries, the principle that 'the present is the key to the past' became the best approach to understanding the features of the Earth, and it remains the quickest way to unravel really ancient history. By looking at geological processes operating today, and what they produce, we can learn to recognize their ancient counterparts in the rock record. Such knowledge can be of great practical value in locating resources such as oil, gas and metals.

In Blocks 4 and 9 you learnt about the processes of organic evolution occurring today. The fossil record is the only *direct* evidence of the course of evolution through time that we have; without it, for example, we would not know that dinosaurs ever existed. In Section 2, we shall see how organisms can be preserved as fossils. Then, in an overview of the history of life, we shall find out just how long after life's inception it took for complex animals and plants to emerge. In a sudden burst of evolution, an amazing range of animals appeared around 545 million years (Ma) ago. We shall get glimpses of early life in the sea, its eventual move onto land, and its expansion into the spectacular diversity we see today (Block 4).

You've probably already looked at the fossil replicas in the Practical Kit. Major activities in Sections 2 and 3 use these replicas and will enable you to develop the core skills of making and recording observations of three-dimensional specimens, and of interpreting aspects of the biology and environment of ancient organisms.

Extinction, as we learnt in Blocks 4 and 9, is the natural fate of the vast majority of species that have ever lived. As we shall see in Section 3, now and then mass extinctions have wiped clean much of life's slate, leaving survivors blessed perhaps more by good luck than good genes.

The story of the Earth and its life through time is preserved in rocks, and in Sections 4 to 7 we continue the study of rocks begun in Block 3. Revisiting the geological specimens in the Kit will develop further the skills of observing, recording and interpreting different types of rock. In Section 4 we look at minerals — the building blocks of rocks. Without being able to extract some of the chemical elements contained in minerals, humans would not have progressed beyond Stone Age technology to the Bronze Age, the Iron Age and now the Age of the Silicon Chip. Minerals, and in particular the way that their chemical composition and internal structure affect their properties, are explored in two CD-ROM activities.

Igneous rocks such as granite and basalt are formed from the cooling of molten magma, as was explained in Block 3. Different igneous rocks reflect different processes involved in the formation and crystallization of magma, a theme of Section 5. The chemical and physical breakdown of igneous rocks (or any other type of rock) produces sediments, which can in turn become sedimentary rocks, as discussed in Section 6. Sedimentary strata are the diaries of Earth history, containing as they do a record laid down one layer upon another, like pages in a journal. Many such pages are, however, missing from the diary, and recognizing these omissions is part of the detective work required to assemble the story of the Earth.

In Section 7 we study metamorphic rocks and the settings that produce them. When rocks are squeezed and heated, new minerals are often formed as the chemical elements in the rock rearrange themselves into more stable arrangements. The older a rock is, the greater the chance that it has been subjected to high pressures and high temperatures, such as those induced during the collision of continents.

Section 8 explains how we can date rocks (and their fossils), not just in relative terms — this limestone is older than that one — but also in absolute terms, enabling us to declare, for example, that the last volcano in Scotland erupted about 52 Ma ago.

For its size, Britain has a greater variety of rock types and rock ages exposed at the surface than almost anywhere else in the world. In Section 9, we look at scenes from Britain's eventful geological past; for example, the crust that now forms Britain once lay south of the Equator and was in two main parts with an ocean in between. A CD-ROM activity explores evidence that about 275 Ma ago Britain experienced a climate as hot and dry as the Sahara Desert today.

In Section 10, we take stock and investigate some of the intimate connections between the solid Earth, its oceans, its atmosphere and its life through time.

In this block you will develop some fundamental skills within the context of Earth sciences that can be applied elsewhere in science. An over-arching theme of the block is that understanding the nature and history of the Earth is a multidisciplinary science that constantly involves changing scales of time and space. For example, atoms build into minerals, minerals into rocks, and rocks into continents, which themselves, like life, are continually changing. Being able to handle changing scales of time and space is a valuable skill to acquire, as is the ability to make and record observations of three-dimensional objects or features, and to interpret them and the sequence of events they reveal.

There are, of course, uncertainties in all branches of science. In Earth sciences, there may be many uncertainties when reconstructing events that happened millions of years ago. Some aspects are not amenable to controlled experiments, there can be huge numbers of variables, and observations may be incomplete. This means that interpretations of complex events may have significant — albeit unquantifiable — uncertainties. Learning to deal with these uncertainties, and to be aware of the assumptions underlying any interpretation, are important skills developed in this block.

'The past is the key to the future' has become today's geological cliché because of concerns over climate change (Block 2) and the effect it will have on life, human and otherwise. This block will help to equip you with some of the background knowledge and skills that, taken further, can enable Earth scientists to address these and other important issues.

Fossils and the early history of life

2

As we learnt in Block 2 (Section 3.2), a fossil is evidence of ancient life, and such evidence is usually found within a sedimentary rock. Interestingly, several early thinkers, such as the Greek historian Herodotus, deduced as early as the 5th century BC that shells now found on mountains were the remains of ancient sea creatures. Herodotus went on to reason that the rocks containing these fossils must have been formed under the sea. However, along with many other perceptive ideas of the ancient Greeks, this theory became lost for about 2 000 years. By the time the ideas of evolution by natural selection were being debated in the 19th century (Block 4, Sections 9–11), fossils were seen as providing the only direct evidence of the course of life's evolution through time.

In this section, we see how organisms become preserved as fossils, and how they can be interpreted as once-living organisms. We then look at the fossil record of early life, and, in a practical activity, study some animals from an ancient sea.

2.1 Getting into the fossil record

A fossil can be part of the body of an ancient organism, such as the bones of a fish (Figure 2.1a), or the signs of an organism's activities, such as the footprints left by a dinosaur in wet sediment, now a hard rock (Figure 2.1b). In some rocks the only evidence of life may be chemicals that can only have been produced by life processes — so-called 'chemical fossils'.

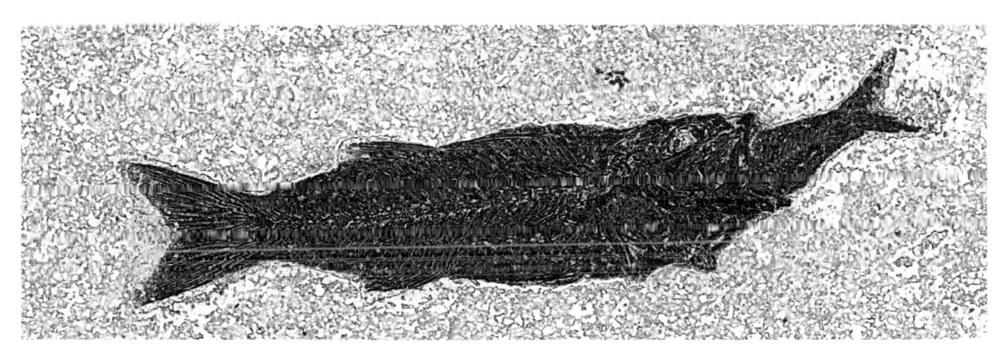

(a)

(b)

Figure 2.1 (a) Fossil fishes that were living about 50 Ma ago, revealing a clear case of greed. The larger fish overestimated its appetite and choked to death trying to swallow the smaller fish. (b) Trace fossils: the tracks of five dinosaurs that walked across what is now part of Colorado, USA about 150 Ma ago. The lateral spacing and parallel direction of the tracks suggest that these dinosaurs moved around in social groups.

Body fossils preserve something of the *bodily remains* of animals or plants, such as shells, bones and leaves, or their impression in the enclosing sediment. **Trace fossils** preserve evidence of the *activity* of animals, such as their tracks, trails, burrows, or borings. Trace fossils are often the only evidence we have of extinct organisms whose bodies lacked any hard parts.

- Which of the following fossils are body fossils, and which are trace fossils? (i) the hair of a woolly mammoth; (ii) bite marks of the greedy fish on the smaller fish in Figure 2.1a; (iii) the moulted shell of a lobster; (iv) the footprint of a bird.

- (i) and (iii) are body fossils. The shell moulted by the lobster (iii) was part of its body, so it is a body fossil. Any marks made in the sediment as it struggled to shed its shell would be trace fossils. Both (ii) and (iv) are trace fossils. The bite marks of the greedy fish are a trace fossil, but the rest of the bitten fish is a body fossil.

Although the fossil record represents a very small proportion of past life, some types of organism leave a pretty good record. An organism's **preservation potential** — the chance that it has of getting into the fossil record — varies a great deal according to a range of factors, such as whether its body has any durable parts, where it lives and whether it becomes buried in sediment.

Figure 2.2 A coastal scene near St David's, South Wales.

Look at Figure 2.2, which shows a scene on the coast of South Wales near St David's. Somewhere in the scene are the following organisms: (i) a rabbit in the fields above the cliffs; (ii) a flower growing in the foreground; (iii) a thick-shelled limpet attached to the rocks along the shoreline; (iv) a cockle burrowing in sand out at sea. Think for a moment about the chances that each has of getting preserved in the fossil record.

(i) A rabbit certainly has hard, potentially fossilizable bones and highly resistant teeth, but if it dies a natural death its remains will probably be chewed and dispersed by scavengers, and exposed to the elements. Any remaining soft tissues will soon be eaten and decomposed by small organisms, especially bacteria. The bones and teeth may be worn down by movement in a stream, and possibly covered over by sediment.

Any burial is likely to be very short-lived, however, and the remains may soon be exhumed by erosion during the next storm and, eventually, after many such episodes, be completely weathered away.

(ii) The flowers growing in the foreground do not generally have durable parts, and their petals, stem, roots, etc. will rot away quickly in this exposed environment. One part of them, however, has a high preservation potential — their pollen (Block 2, Section 3.2.1). Some of the pollen grains are likely to be blown far out to sea and settle into the sediment accumulating there. Pollen is exceedingly resistant to decay, and fossil pollen grains can be released by dissolving sedimentary rocks in hydrofluoric acid — the powerful acid capable of etching glass. The pollen grains survive this treatment, and can be studied under a microscope. As we saw in Block 2 (Section 3.2.2), changes in types of pollen in the fossil record can indicate changing climates, such as a shift from wet to dry conditions, or from warm to cold.

(iii) The shell of a limpet, being hard and relatively thick, protects the animal from attack by the sea and from predators. This thick shell might at first seem to give the organism a good chance of fossilization. However, once dead, the shell would soon fall off the rock, and then usually be broken up by waves and strong currents along the rocky shoreline.

(iv) A cockle burrowing in sand out at sea has the highest preservation potential of these four organisms. It has a hard shell, and it is already living within sediment and making potential trace fossils (its shallow burrows).

The land tends to be a site of net erosion, and the sediment that starts off in rivers and lakes mostly ends up in the sea, especially the shallow seas on the edges of continents. This opportunity for long-term burial is one of the main reasons why animals from shallow marine environments dominate the fossil record, and why fossils of land-based organisms are scarce.

Question 2.1 Consider the following individual organisms, and assess their likely long-term preservation potential as fossils, taking into account the structure of their bodies and the environment they live in: (i) a garden slug; (ii) a garden snail; (iii) a whale; (iv) a jellyfish. ◀

So, the preservation potential of an *individual organism* depends mainly on: (i) its *morphology* (i.e. structure and composition), particularly the presence or absence of robust hard parts; (ii) where it lives and the circumstances of its death, and especially whether or not it is buried in a marine environment where sediments tend to accumulate; and (iii) whether or not its activities are likely to produce trace fossils. Box 2.1, *Is there such a thing as perfect preservation?*, discusses just how good fossil preservation can be.

- The preservation potential of any particular *species*, rather than just an individual member of it, is affected by one other crucial factor. What is it?

- The number of individuals in the species.

The more abundant the species, the higher its preservation potential. With animals, the fossil record is biased in favour of the most abundant ones near the base of food chains, and against scarce animals such as large vertebrates at the top of food chains. A wide geographic distribution also increases the chances of a species being found in the fossil record.

Question 2.2 Consider the following species and, ignoring any effects of human predation, assess their *overall* preservation potential as a species: (i) the blue whale (population a few thousand individuals); (ii) the garden earthworm; (iii) an early species of our genus, *Homo*, with a very small population that lived in the tropics a million years ago; (iv) a common species of oyster with a thick shell. ◀

Box 2.1 Is there such a thing as perfect preservation?

Given all the factors that act against preservation, it is surprising that some extremely delicate forms of life have found their way into the fossil record; examples range from the cells lining the stomach of a 100 Ma-old fish, and the soft tissues of its last meal, to the butterfly in Figure 2.3.

Consider for a moment what must have occurred for this particular butterfly to have been preserved so well.

For a start, it had to be sealed off quickly from various agents of destruction.

- What general kinds of agents of destruction can you think of that the butterfly must have been protected from?

- The butterfly must have been sealed off from (i) some of the *biological* agents of destruction, such as scavengers that might have eaten it; (ii) *physical* agents of destruction such as strong winds or water currents that would have broken up its fragile body; (iii) *chemical* agents of destruction such as oxygen (which enhances decomposition), or solutions that might have dissolved away all its organic remains.

In fact, the butterfly came to rest on very fine-grained sediment at the bottom of a stagnant (oxygen-poor), current-free lake, and was gently covered over by a rain of further fine sediment. As we shall see in Section 6, very fine-grained sediment indicates weak or absent currents which would be unlikely to damage the butterfly.

- Can you suggest another reason why *fine*-grained sediment is significant for the preservation of this butterfly?

- Small grains favour the preservation of delicate structures and fine details, because the grains can fit closely around them.

Figure 2.3 A butterfly that was flapping its wings about 25 Ma ago, in what is now Colorado, USA.

Imagine that the butterfly had instead come to rest on a bed of gravel, and been covered over by more gravel. Apart from the fact that currents strong enough to transport gravel would break up the butterfly, the large gravel particles could not mould closely around its delicate structures, and it would soon be obliterated. The durability and preservation quality of any potential fossil thus decreases as the grain size of the enclosing sediment *increases*.

Rapid, permanent burial by fine sediment in oxygen-poor environments is one of the most favourable situations for fossil preservation. Although extremely fine details can be fossilized in the right physical and chemical conditions, there is no such thing as the *perfect* preservation of an entire organism. DNA has been recovered from some fossils less than 100 000 years old, such as the frozen flesh of mammoths, but it is degraded into short fragments. It is virtually certain that *no* DNA can have survived from organisms alive millions of years ago, such as Jurassic dinosaurs.

Hard biological materials such as bones, shells and wood often contain pores (open spaces). When hard parts are lying buried in sediment, any such pores tend to be filled up with minerals that precipitate out (Block 6, Section 3.1) from the water seeping through the sediment. The original biological materials (such as the cell walls of bone or wood) may sometimes be replaced by these minerals. Both the filling up of pores and the replacement of biological materials may occur in a single fossil. Neither of these processes, which are a kind of 'turning into stone', *has* to occur for something to be called a fossil; sometimes the fossil can still be composed of the original, barely altered shell or bone. A shell entombed in rock may be dissolved away at any time by percolating waters, especially acidic ones, leaving only the impression of the shell's surfaces on the adjacent rock.

- Sharks have exceptionally durable, though porous, teeth. Suppose that there are two shark teeth on a table, each of the same size, shape and colour. One is a fossil and the other isn't. How might you expect to tell the two apart, and why?

- Pick them both up. The fossil is likely to feel heavier. Its density will probably have been increased by additional minerals that have filled up the pore spaces in the tooth whilst it was within the sediment or sedimentary rock.

2.2 Interpreting fossils as living organisms

Now that we have considered what fossils are, and how and where they tend to be preserved, let's look at the ways in which a knowledge of modern organisms can be used to interpret the biology of ancient organisms and the environments they lived in. Although soft parts are rarely preserved in the fossil record, the form of any hard parts is always related to an animal's soft-part anatomy, the way it grows and its mode of life.

As shallow marine invertebrates dominate the fossil record, let us take two phyla that have hard parts, starting with the phylum Mollusca. (Phyla are the major divisions of animal life; Block 4, Section 4.3.) Three classes of **molluscs** are abundant and diverse, both today and in the fossil record: bivalves, e.g. cockles and mussels; gastropods, e.g. snails and slugs; and cephalopods (pronounced 'keffallo-pods'), e.g. squid and octopus. Although at first sight these animals might seem completely unrelated to each other, they actually represent variations on the same theme — the bodyplan (Block 4, Section 4.3) of the phylum Mollusca. All the various classes of molluscs have diverged in different directions away from a common ancestor.

In most groups of molluscs, the body secretes an external shell (such as that of a snail). **Bivalves**, as their name declares, have a shell in two parts known as valves. Except in a few bivalve groups such as oysters, the valves are of equal size and shape, one being the mirror image of the other. From the outside one can see growth lines, such as those visible on the cockle (Figure 2.4a, *overleaf*). Each growth line represents the outer edge of the shell at an earlier stage in its life.

On the *inside* of each valve there is evidence that can be used to interpret the bivalve's mode of life. Although the soft parts may have long decayed away, bivalve shells have distinct areas where muscles for closing the shell were attached. The size, shape and location of these muscle scars reveal aspects of the animal's mode of life. Each valve of the cockle shell (Figure 2.4b, *overleaf*) has two muscle scars, between which is a thin groove that runs roughly parallel to the edge of the shell. This groove is where part of the fleshy tissue that secreted the shell was attached.

(a)

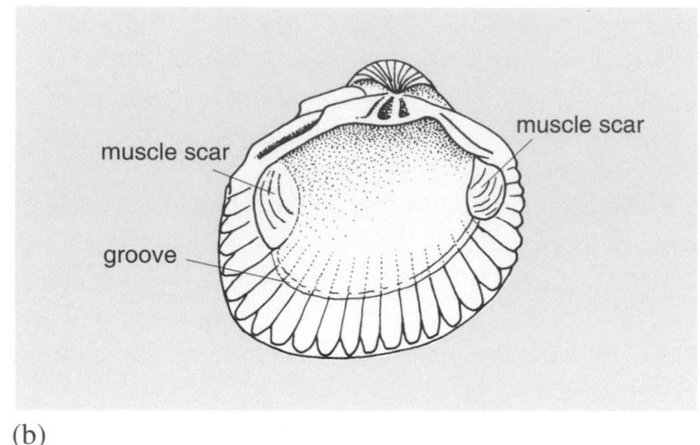

(b)

Figure 2.4 (a) A living cockle, its shell and siphons clearly visible as it lies partly buried in sand. (b) The interior of one valve of a cockle shell.

In the living cockle, Figure 2.4a, two soft tubular siphons can be seen. One is used for taking in water to structures that absorb oxygen and strain off tiny food particles suspended in the water. The other siphon ejects water containing waste products. Bivalves that live in a burrow have long siphons that protrude up above the entrance of the burrow during feeding. A distinct notch in the course of the groove between the muscle scars, if present, indicates where the bivalve could retract its siphons when disturbed.

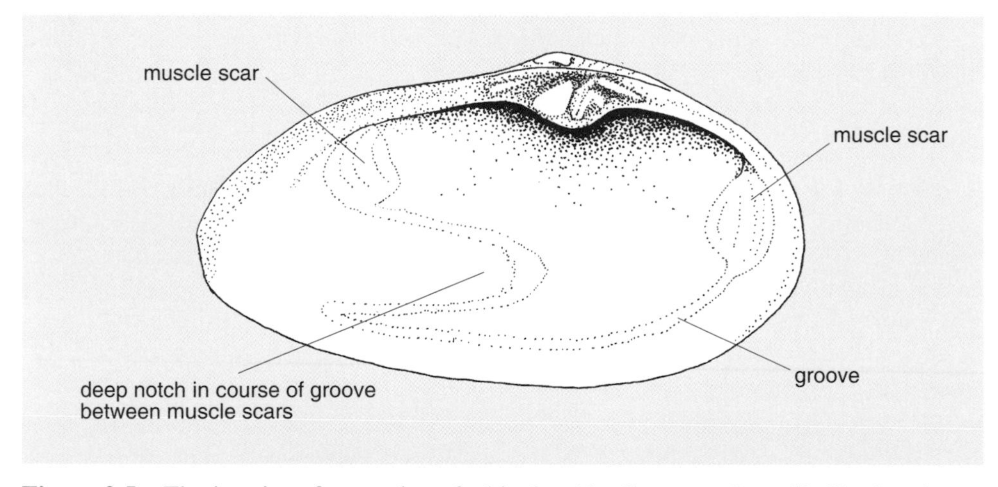

Figure 2.5 The interior of one valve of a bivalve (the Common Otter Shell), showing a deeply notched groove between the muscle scars.

- Imagine that you have found an isolated fossil bivalve shell, similar to that in Figure 2.5, and you are trying to interpret its mode of life. You notice it has a deeply notched groove between the muscle scars. What inference would you make from this observation?

- The species was probably a deep burrower.

The deeper the notch, the longer the siphons that were retracted into it. Long siphons are needed if the animal burrows deeply below the sediment surface (as does the species in Figure 2.5). The cockle, by contrast, is a shallow burrower, and so its shell has no such notch (Figure 2.4b).

Echinoderms ('eck-eye-no-derms') are members of another phylum, and so have a fundamentally different bodyplan to that of the molluscs. Among the groups in the exclusively marine phylum Echinodermata are sea-urchins (**echinoids**) and starfish. Echinoderm skeletons are made of many interlocking plates of the mineral calcite (calcium carbonate). In sea-urchins, movable spines used for locomotion and defence are attached by muscles to knobs on the plates.

Figure 2.6 shows two views of the edible sea-urchin — a living animal covered in spines (Figure 2.6a), and a dead animal with its spines partially missing (Figure 2.6b). The thin tentacles projecting out beyond the calcite spines (Figure 2.6a) are soft, multi-purpose organs called tube-feet which the animal uses for feeding, respiration, locomotion and, in some species, constructing burrows. The tube-feet project through little pores in the plates of the skeleton. Most of the round sea-urchins live by browsing on plant and animal growths covering rocks, whereas oval or heart-shaped ones (with a front and back end) are adapted to burrowing and usually have smaller spines. The mouth is located on the underside.

- Which parts of sea-urchins mentioned above are most *unlikely* to be found in the fossil record, but which can nevertheless be inferred to have been present because of features of the sea-urchin's skeleton?

- The tube-feet, which are indicated by pores in the plates, and the muscles that connected the spines to the rest of the skeleton.

spines
tube-feet

(a)

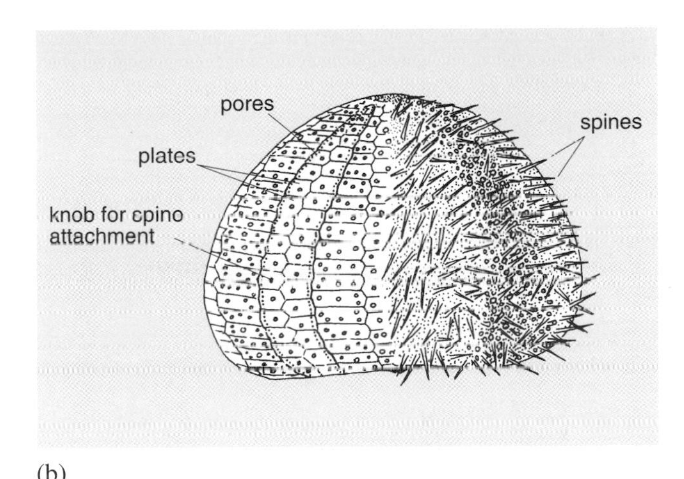

(b)

Figure 2.6 (a) A living edible sea-urchin, with long tube-feet extending beyond its spines. (b) A dead edible sea-urchin with its tube-feet decayed. The spines, which usually soon fall off naturally, have been removed from the left side, revealing the plates of which the skeleton is made.

Question 2.3 Which of the following aspects associated with a fossil organism should make it easier to reconstruct the once living individual, its activities, and its environment? (i) It has few relatives alive today; (ii) it left abundant trace fossils; (iii) there are several other fossil groups in the same rock; (iv) its hard parts became separated from each other after death; (v) its hard parts are complex, with many detailed structures. ◀

You will soon be applying some of the points in this section when interpreting the Kit fossil replicas as living organisms in Activities 2.1 and 3.1.

2.3 Life's long fuse to the Cambrian explosion

As we begin to study the history of life, we need to be able to place important events in the perspective of geological time. Geologists have subdivided the history of the Earth into time intervals of varying duration. The major boundaries between these time intervals were chosen in the 19th century, largely on the basis of biological events recorded in the fossil record, such as mass extinctions, and on other events such as mountain-building episodes which left features in the sedimentary record that could be recognized over a wide area. Initially, there was only a *relative* time-scale — a sequence of events — but today we can give approximate dates to these in millions of years. We shall return to the various ways of ordering and dating events in geological time in Sections 3 and 8.

Figure 2.7 shows the geological time-scale. In such diagrams, the earliest (oldest) events are placed at the bottom of the diagram, and the latest (youngest) at the top, reflecting the relative age of layers in a pile of sedimentary rocks. This convention was followed in the pollen diagrams of Block 2, Section 3.2.2. The way that the time-scale is divided up is discussed in Box 2.2, *The divisions of geological time*.

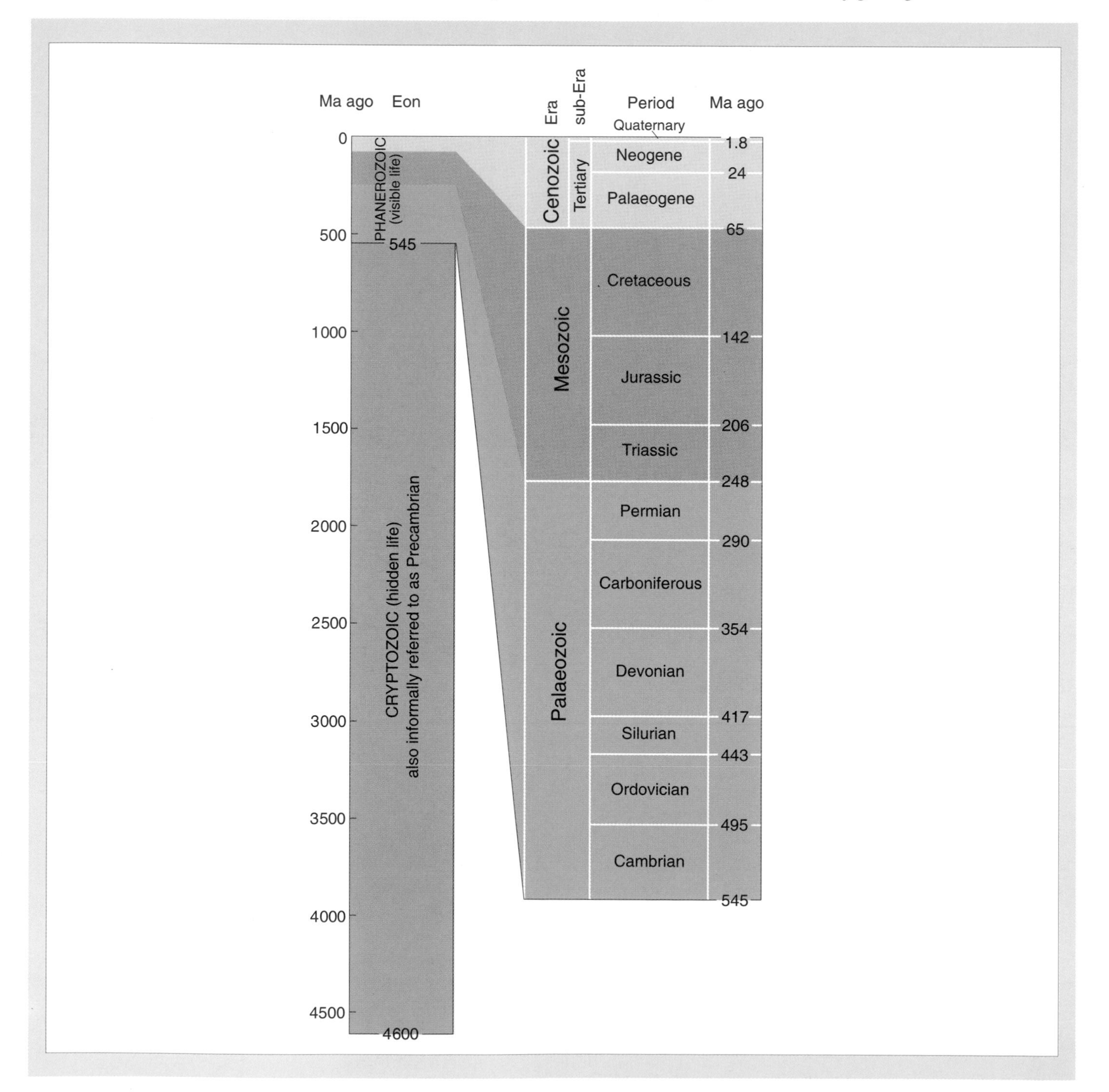

Figure 2.7 The geological time-scale, with space at the sides to write in the answers to Questions 2.5 and 3.2. You will need to refer back to this figure frequently as you study the block.

Box 2.2 The divisions of geological time

The broadest division of Earth history is into two intervals (called eons) of very different length: the **Cryptozoic** Eon and the **Phanerozoic** Eon. (The word 'Eon' does not need to be mentioned each time.) The Cryptozoic is a vast amount of time — from the origin of the Earth, 4 600 Ma ago, to the start of the Phanerozoic, 545 Ma ago. This interval — the Cryptozoic Eon — is very widely, albeit informally, known as 'the **Precambrian**', and we shall use the term Precambrian rather than Cryptozoic in the rest of this block.

Question 2.4 What percentage of the Earth's history does the Precambrian represent? ◀

Cryptozoic is derived from Greek words meaning 'hidden life'. In contrast, Phanerozoic is derived from Greek words meaning 'visible life', reflecting the obvious presence of life since the start of this eon, when fossils first become abundant (Section 2.4). The Phanerozoic Eon is divided into three **eras** — the **Palaeozoic**, **Mesozoic** and **Cenozoic*** Eras (meaning 'ancient life'; 'middle life', and 'recent life', respectively). Each of these eras is divided into a number of **periods** of unequal length (Figure 2.7). The names of periods are variously derived, ranging from the Latin for Wales, 'Cambria'; an area of Russia, Perm; to the Latin for chalk, 'creta'. You are *not* expected to memorize the order of the periods, although this would prove useful. The Palaeogene and Neogene Periods together form the Tertiary Sub-Era, and the current period, which started 1.8 Ma ago, is the Quaternary Period.

So how old is life on Earth? The oldest sedimentary rocks, from west Greenland, dated 3 850 Ma old, contain carbon in a form interpreted as evidence of biological activity, i.e. a chemical fossil. As you will read in Block 12, however, life probably appeared almost as soon as Earth's physical conditions permitted it, by 4 000 Ma ago if not before.

The oldest fossil structures in the world, 3 500 Ma old, come from Western Australia and South Africa. Some are so small you need a microscope to find them, but others are much larger fossils called stromatolites (Figure 2.8a, *overleaf*). **Stromatolites** are mound-like structures formed by various bacteria. We know this because some stromatolites are still forming today in a few places, such as in Shark Bay, Western Australia (Figure 2.8b, *overleaf*). The main bacteria involved are cyanobacteria, which produce oxygen during photosynthesis, i.e. they use light as an energy source, carbon dioxide as a carbon source, and release oxygen into the atmosphere as a by-product. The cyanobacteria live in mat-like layers at the top of the structure, trapping sediment and forming mounds 0.5–2 m high; each mound is mostly sediment.

In addition to these large-scale stromatolites, Precambrian sedimentary rocks also contain fossils of bacteria themselves: single cells and groups of cells, some joined together in chains. Many types of bacteria would have existed then, as today. Some, like the cyanobacteria, seem to have changed remarkably little in their morphology for at least 2 000 Ma. Figure 2.9 (*overleaf*) shows a comparison of living and fossil cyanobacteria. Such cells, being prokaryotes, lack a nucleus, as we saw in Block 4, Section 3.1.

*You will find the alternative spellings Caenozoic or Cainozoic in some textbooks.

(a)

(b)

Figure 2.8 (a) One of the world's oldest fossils — a 3 500 Ma-old stromatolite from Western Australia in cross-section. The specimen is 20 cm across. (b) Living stromatolites from Shark Bay, Western Australia. They are about 0.5–1.5 m across.

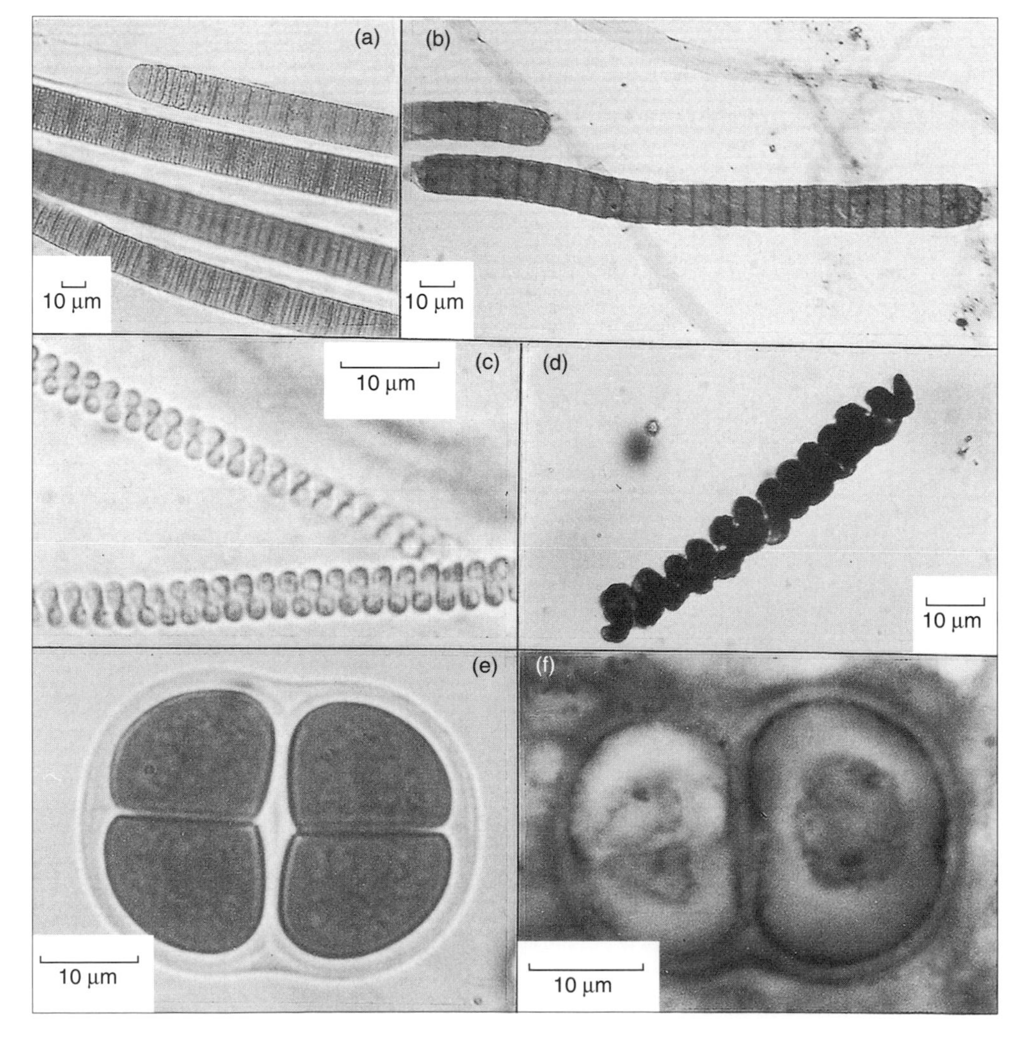

Figure 2.9 Comparison of living and fossil cyanobacteria. (a), (c) and (e) are from stromatolites growing today in Mexico; (b), (d) and (f) are from rocks in the former Soviet Union. (b) is 950 Ma old; (d) is 850 Ma old and (f) is 1 550 Ma old.

According to evidence from Precambrian rocks, the Earth's atmosphere originally lacked oxygen, but it eventually changed to being oxygen-rich, probably as a result of photosynthesis by cyanobacteria. Some oxygen may also have been formed by non-biological mechanisms, such as the breakdown of water into hydrogen and oxygen by ultraviolet (UV) radiation. It was, however, not until about 2 000 Ma ago — about half the age of life itself — that oxygen in the atmosphere started to build up into permanent accumulations. Some of the oxygen (O_2) was converted into ozone (O_3), forming a protective layer in the upper atmosphere that shielded life from harmful ultraviolet radiation; previously seawater alone had this protective role.

The first eukaryotic cells (i.e. cells with DNA enclosed in a nucleus; Block 4, Section 3.1) do not appear in the fossil record until about 2 100 Ma ago (though evidence from molecular biology suggests eukaryotes may have evolved earlier). Initially, these eukaryotes were mainly slowly-evolving, photosynthetic plankton, but about 1 200 Ma ago they diversified rapidly, and multicellular algae (small primitive seaweeds) arose by about 1 000 Ma ago. Eventually, eukaryotic cells became larger, and more specialized, and with the protection from harmful radiation afforded by a thicker ozone layer, a wide variety of shallow-water environments at the edges of the oceans became accessible to eukaryotes.

One of life's largest gear-changes came when, according to the fossil record, multicellular animals made their first appearance about 610 Ma ago. Life on the Earth, for the first time, now included relatively large individual organisms with a range of specialized cells (though still lacking hard parts). This group of animals, the *Ediacaran fauna* (Figure 2.10), named after Ediacara in South Australia, and found in many places around the world (including Charnwood Forest in Leicestershire, England), was widespread by 565 Ma ago. Some of the fossils resemble modern animals such as jellyfishes, but many have a peculiar quilted structure unknown in animals today. Most of these puzzling Ediacaran organisms seem to have left no descendants.

Figure 2.10
A reconstruction of the Ediacaran fauna that lived at the end of the Precambrian, just before the Cambrian explosion. The largest organisms are about 15 cm long.

Figure 2.11 First signs of the Cambrian explosion: a variety of small shelly fossils. None is more than a few mm long.

2.4 The Cambrian explosion

One of the most important events in the history of life began about 545 Ma ago, i.e. some four billion years after the origin of the Earth. The term **Cambrian explosion** reflects a sudden burst of evolution, when a wide variety of organisms, especially those with hard, mineralized parts, first appear in the fossil record. Thus began the Phanerozoic Eon — 'the time of visible life'. Very small (1–2 mm) shelly fossils appeared in the earliest part of the Cambrian Period — assorted shapes such as tubes and cones (that presumably enclosed soft tissue), as well as spines, scales, and knobs (Figure 2.11). It's often difficult to tell, however, whether a fossil is the complete skeleton of a single organism or an isolated part of some larger creature. It is clear, though, that by about 530 Ma, most phyla that are in existence today had appeared (though life was still confined to the sea). Not surprisingly, a few entirely soft-bodied phyla living today have no known fossil record, so we don't know when they evolved. Evidence from genetics, and from some remarkably preserved fossil embryos in the early stages of division from China, suggests that some animal phyla diverged from each other much earlier than the start of the Cambrian explosion, but the timing remains uncertain.

The main stimulus for the acquisition of hard parts seems likely to have been the rise of predation.

- From the information given above, which aspects of the small shelly fossils from the earliest Cambrian are consistent with a rise in predation?

- The appearance of features that could be used for protection, such as spines and scales, and tubes and conical shells that could protect vulnerable soft parts inside.

Natural selection, however, can only act on variation that is already there (Block 4, Section 10; Block 9, Section 13), so how did these useful hard parts ever get started? One plausible idea is that the hard parts may have originated as crystalline products of excretion. The slightest toughening of soft parts by mineral deposition would have been of selective advantage, either in defence or attack.

There is little evidence of special, widespread environmental changes that could have directly triggered the Cambrian explosion. Whatever the causes, once triggered, a wide range of ecological opportunities presumably became available for exploitation, promoting the rapid evolution of new, quite different types of animals. Many of the newly-evolved phyla show organization of the body into specialized areas — especially a head end with food-trapping and sensory organs, a tubular gut and limbs. There is no doubt that many Cambrian animals were equipped with adaptations for preying, and were able to pursue food much more actively than could the Ediacaran fauna — such as by scuttling over the sea floor, swimming actively, and burrowing.

- A greatly increased variety of types of trace fossils, especially burrows of soft-bodied animals, are found around the start of the Cambrian explosion. What is the significance of this finding?

- It reflects the evolution of much more complex patterns of behaviour, some of it probably related to the avoidance of predators.

2.4.1 The Burgess Shale animals

High in the Canadian Rockies is exposed a deposit of middle Cambrian age, about 520 Ma old, called the Burgess Shale. It contains the fossils of animals that lived on a muddy sea floor, and which were suddenly transported into deeper, oxygen-poor water by submarine landslides. Their catastrophic burial has given us an exceptional view of Cambrian life. Not only have animals with hard shelly parts been preserved but entirely soft-bodied forms are present as thin films on the sediment surface. Only about 15% of the 120 genera present in the Burgess Shale are shelly organisms that dominate typical Cambrian fossil assemblages (fossils that occur together) elsewhere. The shelly component was therefore in a minority, and organisms with hard parts probably formed less than 5% of individuals in the living community.

- If the soft-bodied fossils of the Burgess Shale are taken away, all that remains is a typical Cambrian assemblage of hard-bodied organisms. Why is this important to bear in mind when trying to interpret other Cambrian fossil assemblages?

- The other Cambrian assemblages may also have been dominated by soft-bodied animals, even if the only fossils they now contain are of hard-bodied ones.

Another important revelation of the Burgess Shale lies in the wide diversity of animal bodyplans that were around in middle Cambrian time, about 520 Ma ago. There are representatives of about a dozen of the phyla that persist to the present day, including *Pikaia* (Figure 2.12a), one of the earliest known chordates (the group to which vertebrates belong; Block 4, Box 5.1). Two forms closely related to early arthropods include *Opabinia*, which had five eyes perched on the top of its head (Figure 2.12b), and *Anomalocaris* (Figure 2.12a), the largest known Cambrian animal, which may have reached two metres in length. Its extraordinary jaw consisted of spiny plates encircling the mouth, which probably constricted down on prey in much the same way that the plates of an iris diaphragm cut down the light in a camera. About a dozen other types of fossils have been said to be so unlike anything living today and so different from each other that, had they been living now, each would have been placed in a separate phylum. With further study, however, the relationships of these puzzling animals are becoming clearer; some forms are hard to classify simply because the boundaries between major categories of animal life were still blurred shortly after the Cambrian explosion, as a result of their recent common ancestry.

Figure 2.12 Reconstructions of some of the Burgess Shale animals. (a) *Anomalocaris* (1 m long) dwarfs all the other organisms, which include *Pikaia*, top left, one of the earliest known chordates (5 cm). (b) The five-eyed *Opabinia*, preying with its long mobile jaw on a small (2 cm) gelatinous animal, *Amiskwia*, of unknown relationships. Note that the colours of organisms shown in this and other such reconstructions are conjectural.

Burgess Shale-type faunas have been found in about 30 sites ranging from North America and Greenland, to China and Australia. The wide range of animals they contain seems to reflect an unpruned 'bush of diversity' resulting from the Cambrian explosion. Not long after, extinction lopped off some of the branches, leaving more distinct phyla that have remained to this day.

Activity 2.1 Life in the Silurian sea

Let us now move on in time to some of the life that was thriving in the sea during a later part of the Palaeozoic Era — the Silurian Period. In this activity, and Activity 3.1, you will be studying the fossil replicas in the Practical Kit, and will develop some very important skills of observation and interpretation. ◀

Question 2.5 Write in the following 11 events, listed here in random order, in their appropriate position beside the geological time-scale in Figure 2.7:

- first animals (Ediacaran fauna)
- permanent accumulation of free atmospheric oxygen
- rapid diversification of eukaryotes
- origin of the Earth
- first multicellular organisms (algae)
- first evidence of life (chemical fossils) in oldest sedimentary rocks
- Burgess Shale fossils
- Wenlock Limestone fossils in the Kit
- first eukaryotic cells in the fossil record
- Cambrian explosion
- first fossil structures (including stromatolites) 

2.5 Summary of Section 2

The fossil record is the only direct evidence of the course of life's evolution through time.

The preservation potential of an individual organism depends mainly on the durability of its body parts, and where it lives and dies. The preservation potential of a particular species also depends on its abundance and geographic distribution. Marine animals with hard parts, such as those represented by replicas in the Practical Kit, form the bulk of the fossil record.

During fossilization, the pore spaces in biological materials tend to be filled in, and the materials themselves sometimes replaced, by minerals precipitating from solutions seeping through the enclosing sediment. Fossilized hard parts such as shells, bones and teeth can often yield information about the soft parts of an organism, its mode of life and environment. Examples of this were revealed during observation and interpretation of the Silurian specimens in the Kit.

The fossil record suggests that life had begun by at least 3 850 Ma ago. Life probably consisted only of prokaryotes until about 2 100 Ma ago, when simple eukaryotes first appear in the fossil record. Photosynthetic bacteria produced most of the oxygen that eventually formed a permanent accumulation in the atmosphere. Multicellular algae had evolved by about 1 000 Ma ago.

Only about 610 Ma ago did the first multicellular animals appear (the Ediacaran fauna). During the Cambrian explosion, starting about 545 Ma ago, animals with hard parts, and animals capable of making complex trace fossils, first appeared in a sudden burst of evolution, when most animal phyla arose. The Burgess Shale fossils reveal a very wide diversity of Cambrian animals, but it is important to remember that life was still confined to the sea.

3 More of life's comings and goings

The Cambrian explosion left the seas teeming with animal life, and you have now studied some of the marine fauna that was thriving about 120 Ma later in the Silurian Period. In this section, we look at some of the other major entrances — and exits — in the saga of life, and at some marine animals of the Jurassic Period.

3.1 Invasion of the land

It was not until about 430 Ma ago — during the Silurian Period, and about 3.5 *billion* years after the origin of life — that the main invasion of freshwater and land environments by plants and animals really got going. Long before then, in the later parts of the Precambrian, some algae and bacteria may possibly have lived on land, and there is evidence that some small plants, and possibly some small animals too, lived on land in the Ordovician Period.

There were all sorts of environmental challenges to which plants and animals had to adapt to live out of the sea. For example, if a marine plant cell is directly surrounded by fresh water, the water tends to flow into it, causing it to burst. Alternatively, if the cell is directly surrounded by air, it loses all its water, just as seaweeds become hard and crisp when stranded above high tide and exposed to the wind and the sun. So, to survive in air, plants had to acquire an effective outer coat to keep the right amount of water in. They also had to evolve small, controllable pores (called stomata; Block 1, Section 6.4.1, and Block 9, Section 6.2) to enable gases to be exchanged through this coat.

To grow up off the land surface, plants had to develop groups of special plumbing cells to conduct water, nutrients and the products of photosynthesis around their bodies. Without the buoyancy provided by immersion in water, adaptations in both plants and animals were needed to support a body on land against the pull of gravity. Expressed this way, it is all too easy to give the impression, quite wrongly, that such innovations could be achieved intentionally, almost as if by some directed effort. On the contrary, as in all evolutionary explanations, natural selection (Block 4, Section 10; Block 9, Section 13) would have favoured those organisms that were, *by chance*, better adapted to these new environmental challenges.

A fossil of a very early land plant is shown in Figure 3.1a. Only about 5 cm tall, it lacked roots and leaves, and sent short shoots upward to capture sunlight and release spores (reproductive cells) into the wind. These first land plants, which lived in swamps and on riverbanks and floodplains, provided food for the animals that, by chance, were best adapted to life on land — the arthropods, which already had an almost waterproof outer skeleton and were very strong for their size. Small millipedes and wingless insects were apparently tempted on to land to eat rotting plant debris, and they and their remains were eaten in turn by predatory or scavenging carnivorous arthropods such as centipedes, scorpions and small spider-like creatures (Figure 3.1b).

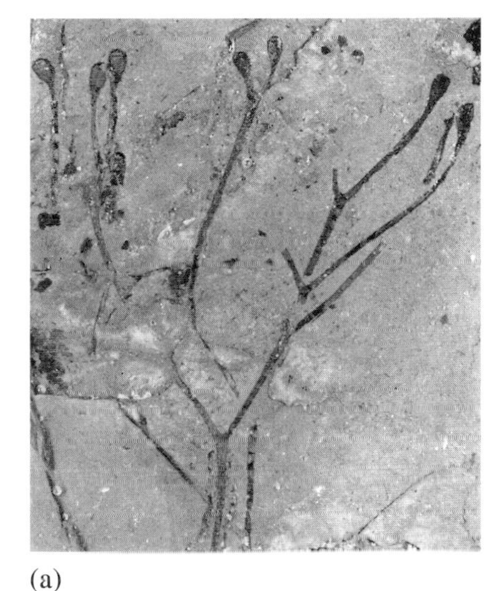

(a)

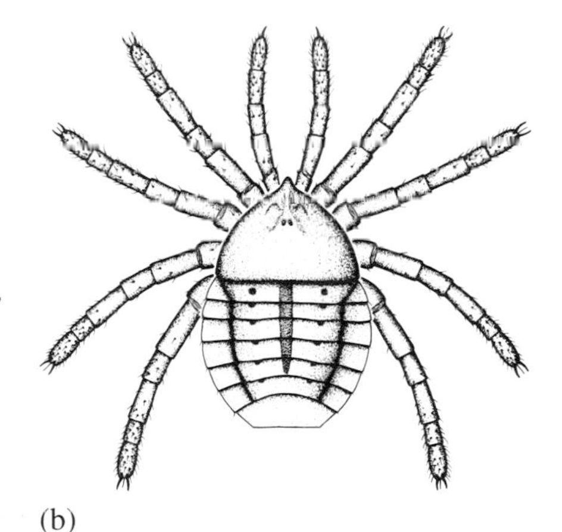

(b)

Figure 3.1 Early life on land. (a) A very early land plant from Silurian rocks in Wales, about 5 cm tall. Notice the spore-bearing structures at the end of each simple-branching stem. (b) One of the earliest known land animals — a spider-like creature (4 mm long including legs) from Silurian rocks in Shropshire, England.

So what would a typical land scene from the Silurian have looked like? A low, mossy-looking carpet of green, primitive land-plants flanked the rivers, lakes and ponds. Small, early land-arthropods roved among them, unmolested by vertebrates, which were still restricted to water. Beyond, inland, was mostly bare rock and debris from weathering and erosion.

Figure 3.2 An early Devonian scene with a plant species (height 45 cm) fringing a lake.

A slightly more advanced plant, about 45 cm tall, is shown in Figure 3.2; it had an underground or surface-lying horizontal stem with tiny root hairs. The species grew beside shallow pools early in the Devonian Period in what today we call Scotland, which was then just south of the Equator, as we saw in Activity 16.1 (the CD-ROM 'Plate motion in the past and future') in Block 3. The local area was occasionally flooded by mineral-rich waters from nearby hot springs, which helped to fossilize the plants (and associated animals) and preserve them in exquisite detail.

By the end of the Devonian Period, lowland flood plains were dominated by plants sufficiently tall to be called trees, with wood, true roots, and complex branching patterns. Some of these giant fern-like trees had evolved *seeds* that protected the fertilized ovules and supplied them with a food store, giving them independence from water and allowing inland areas to be colonized. By the end of the Devonian, many features of today's land plants had already evolved, though flowers and fruits (enclosing the seed) appeared much later with the first flowering plants in the early Cretaceous Period.

3.1.1 The delayed invasion of the vertebrates

As we've seen, the first chordates such as *Pikaia* (Figure 2.12a) appeared on the scene during the Cambrian explosion. By the late Cambrian they had diversified into the first vertebrates, including small, eel-shaped creatures known mainly from their microscopic teeth, and other jawless fishes. (**Vertebrates** are chordates with backbones, and today include five classes: fishes, amphibians, reptiles, mammals and birds.)

Although the first fishes appeared in the late Cambrian, they remained rare and did not start their main diversification until the late Ordovician. Fishes became increasingly diverse through the Silurian, but only became abundant in the Devonian. And it was not until the late Devonian that vertebrates first evolved features that enabled them to live, at least partly, on land. Fossils of the first amphibians, such as the sturdy *Ichthyostega* (pronounced 'ickthy-o-steega') and the more slender *Acanthostega* (Figure 3.3) are found in freshwater rocks of this age, laid down in warm swamps in what is now Greenland.

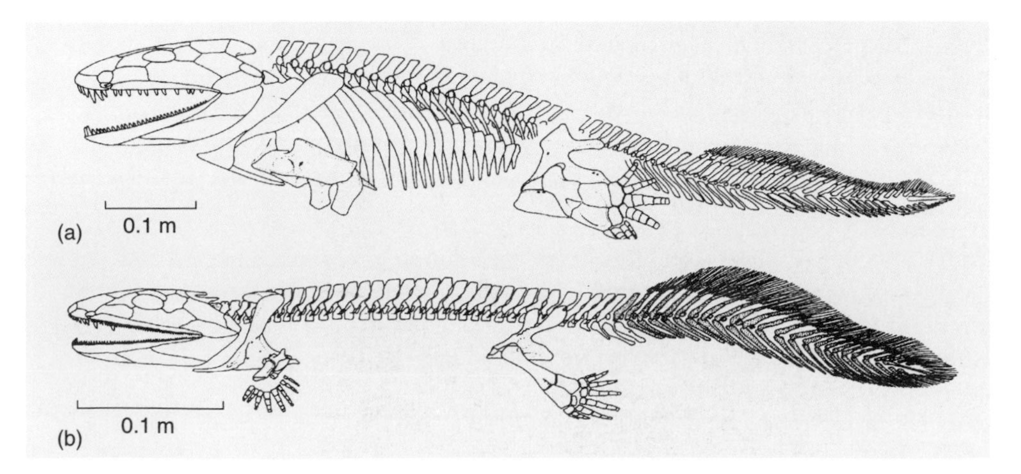

Figure 3.3 Two of the earliest known amphibians from the late Devonian. (a) *Ichthyostega* (1 m); (b) *Acanthostega* (60 cm). Note that where the digits ('fingers' or 'toes') are known, they number 8, not 5 as soon became the norm.

Ichthyostega and *Acanthostega* had a rather fish-like body outline, including a tail fin. Their limbs, however, show that these carnivorous animals could waddle about on land, although their lifestyle was mostly aquatic. We shall never be certain of the selection pressures that drove this transition to life on land, but plausible advantages include the escape from predatory fishes and the utilization of unexploited food sources.

Amphibians remained large during the Palaeozoic Era, often reaching 1 or 2 metres long — huge by the standards of today's frogs, toads and newts. By 350 Ma ago, in the early Carboniferous Period, the first reptiles had appeared. Unlike amphibians, which are dependent on being near lakes or ponds to lay their eggs and develop their tadpoles, reptiles evolved a crucial adaptation — a shelled egg that did not dry out in air.

Among the huge trees of the dense late Carboniferous forest (Figure 3.4) were reptiles, amphibians and insects such as dragonflies and cockroaches. The trees and other plants growing in these equatorial forests and in swamps trapped the energy of sunlight during photosynthesis. This energy became stored in plant debris that accumulated on the floor of the forests and in swamps (as you may remember from the discussion of the carbon cycle, Block 2, Section 8). Eventually, this debris was buried, compressed and converted by heat and pressure into coal; 300 Ma later the energy from Carboniferous sunlight fuelled the Industrial Revolution.

To place these events in a better perspective, study Figure 3.5 (*overleaf*), which shows an outline of vertebrate evolution, including the branching points from which new major groups originated. As usual with diagrams depicting events in geological time, this figure should be read from the bottom (oldest) upwards.

Figure 3.4 Scene from a late Carboniferous forest. The animals in the foreground (from left to right) are a cockroach, a reptile and an amphibian.

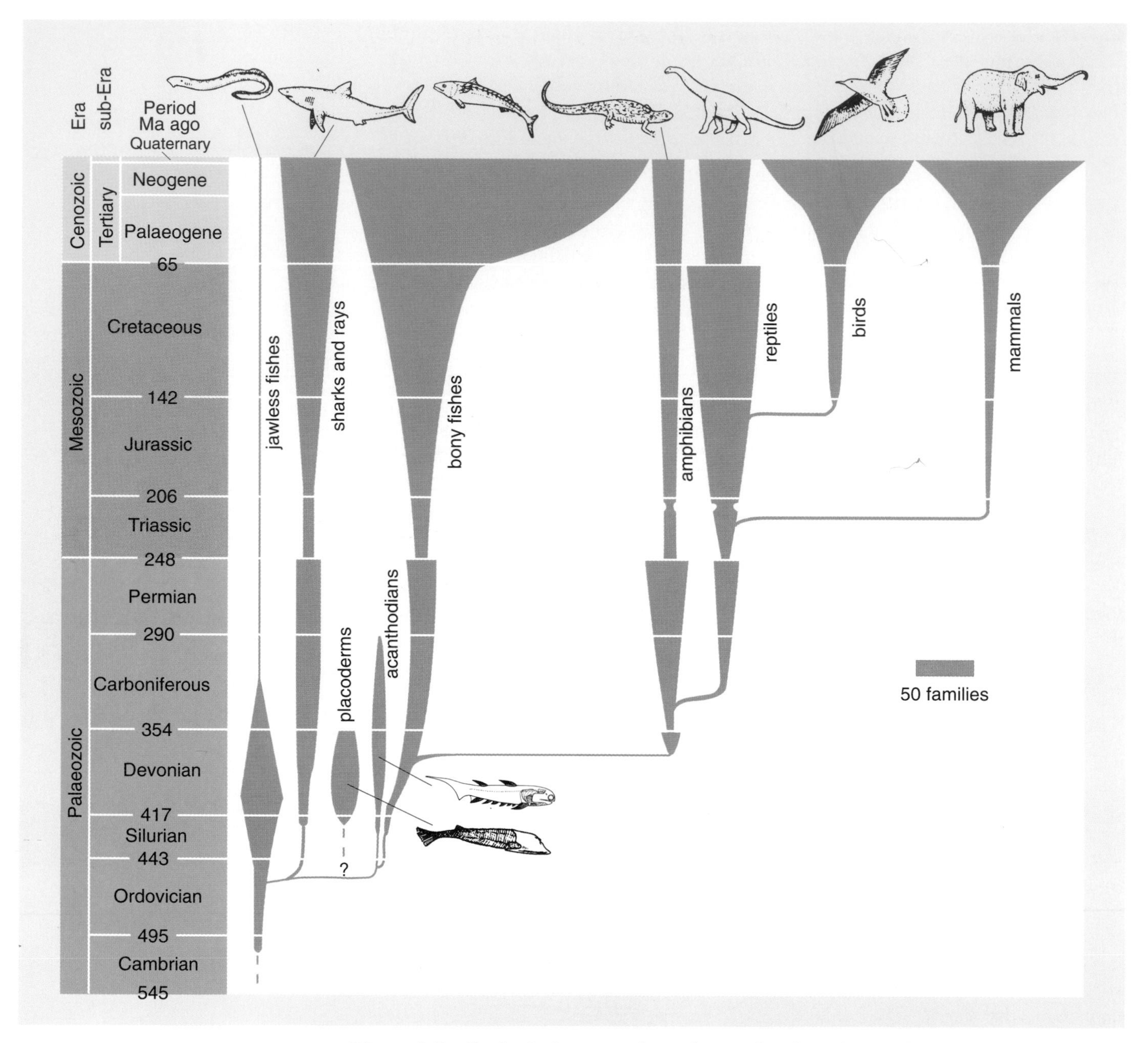

Figure 3.5 Geological ranges of vertebrates showing when various groups evolved from each other during the Phanerozoic. The width of each group indicates its approximate diversity (as number of families); note the scale bar. The wide horizontal separation of some newly-evolved groups from their ancestors (e.g. mammals from reptiles) does *not* indicate huge, abrupt change but is simply a consequence of the way the diagram is drawn. Placoderms were a group of jawed fishes with thick external armour, and acanthodians were slender jawed fishes with many spines.

Which of today's classes of vertebrates were in existence by the end of the Triassic Period?

Fishes, amphibians, reptiles *and* mammals had all evolved by this time, about 206 Ma ago.

When were (i) jawless fishes, and (ii) amphibians at their highest diversity (in terms of number of families)?

(i) in the Devonian; (ii) in the Permian.

In which geological period did birds first appear, and from which vertebrate group did they evolve?

Birds evolved from reptiles in the late Jurassic.

Much evidence suggests that birds, whose distinctive feature is the possession of feathers, evolved from dinosaurs. Dinosaurs were a special group of reptiles — special not least because, after their origin in the middle Triassic, they became the dominant land animals for over 150 Ma. They filled almost every niche possible for large land vertebrates. They included carnivores, herbivores and omnivores (mixed diet), and ranged in size from that of a chicken to vast plant eaters, such as the 25 m-long, 40-tonne *Brachiosaurus*. Dinosaurs never, however, took to the air or to the oceans: other large reptiles — the pterosaurs ('terro-saurs') — dominated the skies, and marine reptiles such as ichthyosaurs ('ickthy-o-saurs') and plesiosaurs ('please-ee-o-saurs') flourished in the sea (see title page).

Activity 3.1 Life in the Jurassic sea

You should now continue to develop your skills of observation and interpretation by studying the Jurassic fossil replicas in the Kit. ◀

3.2 Extinctions are forever

The vast majority of species that have ever existed — probably around 95% — have become extinct. As we saw in Block 4, Section 5.2, and Block 9, Section 14.1, extinction, like death, is a normal aspect of the history of life. Extinction is the complete, global end of the line for a species; it leaves no descendant individuals anywhere. It's very important to distinguish the *local* extinction of a species from true, *global* extinction. For example, the Large Blue butterfly used to be seen in English meadows earlier this century. Its life cycle was intimately associated with a species of ant that itself died out locally due to a change of grazing practice. The Large Blue became locally extinct in Britain in 1979, but it still lives in France, and elsewhere in Europe, and may yet do so again in England if conditions improve for it. Also, a species that has with time evolved directly *into* another species has also not become extinct in one crucial sense: it is not the end of the line. In this case the lineage has simply been sufficiently transformed for the descendants to be recognized as a different species. For example, modern humans, *Homo sapiens*, probably evolved directly from a species called *Homo erectus*, so *Homo erectus* did not become truly extinct.

At any time in the history of life some species will be becoming extinct, and others will be originating. The fossil record shows that there has always been a normal, 'background' rate of both speciation (the formation of new species, Block 9, Section 14.3) and extinction, i.e. there has been a *turnover* of species (Block 4, Section 5.2).

The majority of past species extinctions have been part of this 'background' rate of extinction. Early in the 19th century, however, it was recognized that, from time to time, many groups disappeared from the fossil record more or less together, never to be found again in younger rocks. It was partly for this reason that many of the boundaries between one geological period and another were constructed. Geologically rapid, major reductions in the diversity of life on a global scale are called **mass extinctions**. There have been five especially severe mass extinctions in the Phanerozoic — the 'Big Five': in the late Ordovician, late Devonian, late Permian, late Triassic, and late Cretaceous (see Box 3.1, *Some casualties of the Big Five Phanerozoic extinctions*).

- Indicate with an asterisk each of these mass extinctions beside the geological time-scale in Figure 2.7. Now consider the sequence of eras and periods. Which two of the Big Five extinctions would you expect to have been the most severe?

- The most severe extinctions were those used to mark the end, not just of periods, but of eras — the Palaeozoic Era and the Mesozoic Era, i.e. at the end of the Permian Period and the end of the Cretaceous Period.

In these two mass extinctions, the loss of marine animal species has been estimated to be as high as 95% in the late Permian and 70% in the late Cretaceous.

Box 3.1 Some casualties of the Big Five Phanerozoic extinctions

Late Ordovician Many types of trilobites, brachiopods, echinoderms and corals.

Late Devonian Many marine families, especially those of tropical reef-dwelling organisms such as corals, brachiopods, bivalves and sponges.

Late Permian Nearly 60% of marine families, especially those from low latitudes. Virtually all corals became extinct, and reefs were eliminated. Trilobites and water-scorpions disappeared totally. Crinoids, brachiopods, bivalves and gastropods suffered huge losses. Many groups of amphibians and reptiles perished.

Late Triassic Major losses among cephalopods, gastropods, brachiopods, bivalves, sponges and marine reptiles. On land many insect families became extinct, as did most mammal-like reptiles and large amphibians (though the extinction of these vertebrate groups does not show up well in Figure 3.5 as other reptile and amphibian families were originating at about the same time).

Late Cretaceous (K–T boundary)* Whole groups that became extinct near (and not necessarily *at*) the end of the Cretaceous included ammonites, large marine reptiles such as plesiosaurs, and, on land, dinosaurs and pterosaurs. Groups suffering major losses included microscopic marine plankton, brachiopods, bivalves and sea-urchins. Vertebrate groups *little* affected included fishes, amphibians, crocodiles, snakes, turtles and mammals. Flowering plants, including hardwood trees, suffered also, but mostly in the Northern Hemisphere.

*The abbreviation 'K–T' is often used when referring to this extinction at the Cretaceous–Tertiary boundary; 'K' is the international symbol for the Cretaceous.

None of the Big Five mass extinctions was instantaneous; each probably took from about 0.5 to 3 Ma. And mass extinctions are probably not discrete phenomena, completely different from other extinctions, any more than there are clear boundaries between large and medium earthquakes, or between hurricanes and severe storms. There seems to be a continuous spectrum of extinction severity from background rates at one end, through times of moderate extinction, to mass extinctions at the other. Some of the groups lost in mass extinctions were already far from flourishing. For example, the decline of trilobites was well underway before their eventual demise in the late Permian.

Can one make any generalizations about the victims of mass extinctions? Well, it seems that large-bodied species tend to be more vulnerable than smaller-bodied species, perhaps because they tend to be more specialized, have smaller population sizes, and slower rates of population increase. Tropical organisms, at least those in the sea, appear to be more vulnerable than those of higher latitudes.

- Imagine a species of marine snail that can live today only in the hot, shallow seas found immediately around the Equator. Would an increase or decrease in global temperature be more likely to threaten this tropical species with extinction, and why?

- If global temperature were reduced, the snails would have nowhere to go that was warm enough; they are already in the hottest environment. If, however, there were an *increase* in temperature, the snails might well, over generations, be able to migrate away from equatorial latitudes to where the water was cooler, or perhaps migrate into deeper, cooler water on the Equator. Other things being equal, tropical species may therefore be more susceptible to global cooling than to global warming.

The average duration of a marine invertebrate species in the fossil record (from origin to extinction) is about 5 Ma, though there is much variation about this mean. Interestingly, many of these fossil species, having made their first appearance, show very little change (in their hard parts at least) before becoming extinct several million years later. Continuous, gradual transitions from one species to another are rare in the fossil record. This may, however, be partly due to the lack of fossils from on land in the tropics (see Question 2.2iii) and from the deeper sea — relatively stable environments where evolution may tend to be more gradual and continuous than in shallow marine environments.

Estimating the rate at which species are becoming extinct today is very difficult, not least because we do not know how many species there are to start with (Block 4, Section 5.1).

- Mammals and birds probably provide the best data of any groups. Why do you think this is?

- They are particularly well-studied, being relatively large, conspicuous and mostly living on land, and in the past many have attracted attention as a human food source.

The average duration of mammal and bird species in the fossil record is much nearer 0.5–1 Ma than the 5 Ma for marine invertebrate species, partly perhaps because their complex social behaviour favours rapid evolution and speciation (Block 9, Section 14). Many large mammals and large flightless birds became extinct between 15 000 and 10 000 years ago, and there is evidence that human hunting activities, as well as climate changes, were responsible. Today, there are about 14 000 living species of birds and mammals, and at least 100 species have become extinct during the last 100 years alone through human activities. The rate of extinction is escalating, and in a few decades the average time remaining before a typical bird or mammal species becomes extinct is projected to be 200–400 years; this is approaching 4 orders of magnitude (i.e. a factor of 10^4) faster than the background rates seen in the fossil record. The loss among mammals and birds may also be broadly representative of other groups of animals, and plants. Conservative estimates of current total extinction rates are 5–50 species *per day*. Many biologists believe that this general time in Earth history could appear as another mass extinction in the geological record — 'the Sixth Extinction' to add to the previous Big Five. As a warning, the fossil record shows that recovery from earlier mass extinctions is extremely slow by human time-scales. The regeneration of biodiversity, and re-establishment of communities such as reefs, typically takes 5–10 Ma.

3.2.1 The Cretaceous-Tertiary (K–T) mass extinction

The mass extinction that ended the Cretaceous Period, 65 Ma ago, is the most famous of them all. Although the dinosaurs were its most notable victims, a wide range of animals and plants was affected, including many species of microscopic organisms.

A massive research programme was triggered in 1980 by the discovery of a clay layer containing an abnormally high concentration of the metallic element iridium at precisely the K–T boundary (Figure 3.6a). Because iridium (atomic number 77) is very rare in the Earth's crust but is relatively abundant in certain meteorites, this clay layer was interpreted as the fallout from material ejected into the atmosphere by the impact of a huge meteorite — one estimated to be roughly 10 km in diameter travelling at more than $10\,\text{km}\,\text{s}^{-1}$.

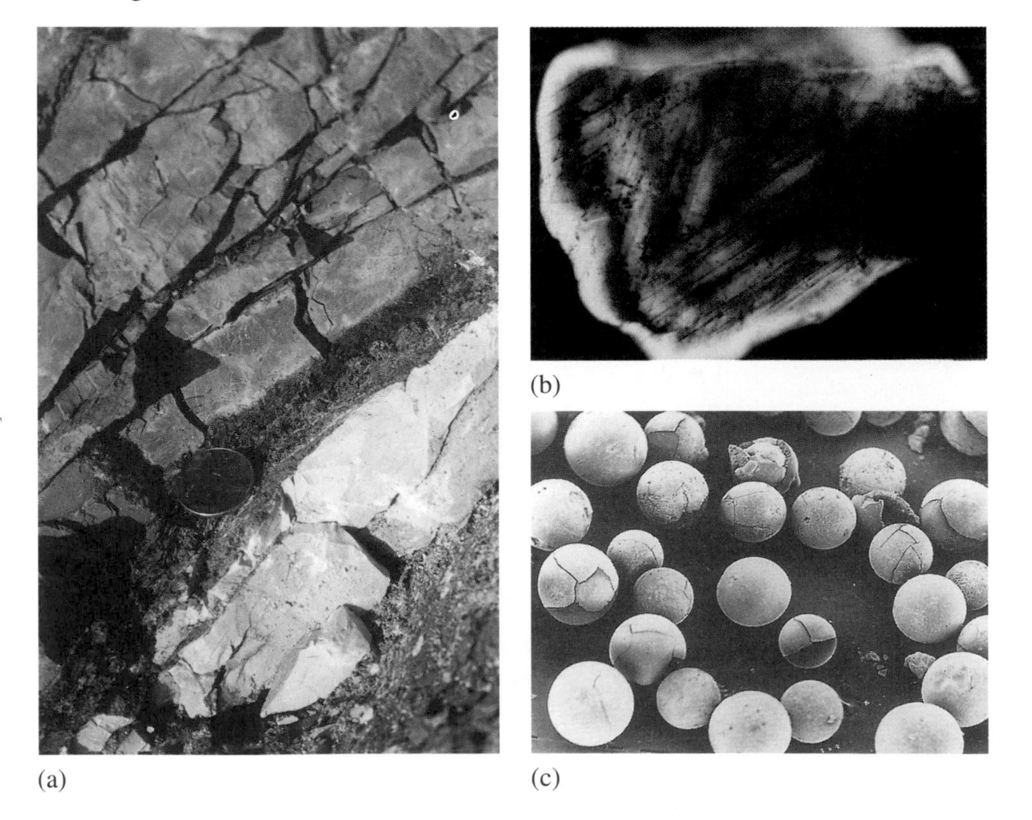

(a) (b) (c)

Figure 3.6 Aspects of the Cretaceous–Tertiary boundary. (a) The clay layer at the K–T boundary in Italy, where the anomalously high concentration of iridium at this level was first discovered. A rich variety of fossil plankton occurs below the boundary, but few forms survived into the layer above it. A coin for scale rests on the thin dark clay layer in these tilted beds. (b), (c) Tell-tale signs of impact at the K–T boundary:
(b) a quartz grain showing parallel lines known to result only from intense shock; (c) minute spheres (0.5–1 mm in diameter) that have cooled rapidly from droplets of molten rock.

Such an impact would certainly have ejected a variety of materials, including dust, into the atmosphere, and could have darkened the skies for months.

- What effect would this darkening have had on plants?

- It would have suppressed photosynthesis for a while, and inhibited the growth of plants both in the oceans and on land.

Plankton (Block 2, Section 8.4.4) suffered intense casualties. Coccolithophores (Block 2, Figure 8.5a), the minute phytoplankton whose calcite plates accumulated on the late Cretaceous sea-bed to form Chalk* deposits, and many species of zooplankton, such as planktonic foraminiferans (Block 2, Figure 8.5b), were reduced by at least 90%.

- If extinction of marine reptiles, zooplankton and phytoplankton occurred, which loss could be expected to have had the most detrimental effect on the biosphere generally?

- Phytoplankton are autotrophs, at the base of the oceanic food chain (Block 2, Section 8.4.4), so their loss would potentially have affected the largest number of species.

Zooplankton are mainly small heterotrophic organisms that provide food for larger organisms. The extinction of relatively large predators, such as marine reptiles, near the top end of the food chains and having fairly small numbers of individuals, would have affected the food source of relatively few species. A reduction in autotrophs, therefore, in addition to a wide range of physical and chemical effects resulting from the impact, could have led to a cascade of extinctions.

Since 1980 the evidence of an impact has strengthened. Unusually high levels of iridium have been found at over 100 K–T boundary sites throughout the world (Figure 3.7). The boundary layer contains tiny diamonds formed at very high pressure, and other minerals showing features indicating intense shock (Figure 3.6b). There are also splash-shaped droplets and tiny spheres resulting from rapid cooling of melted rock ejected into the atmosphere (Figure 3.6c). Many lines of evidence point to the impact site being a structure known as the Chicxulub Crater, over 200 km in diameter, centred on the coast of northern Yucatan, Mexico (Figure 3.7). The crater has since been filled with sediments and is now inconspicuous.

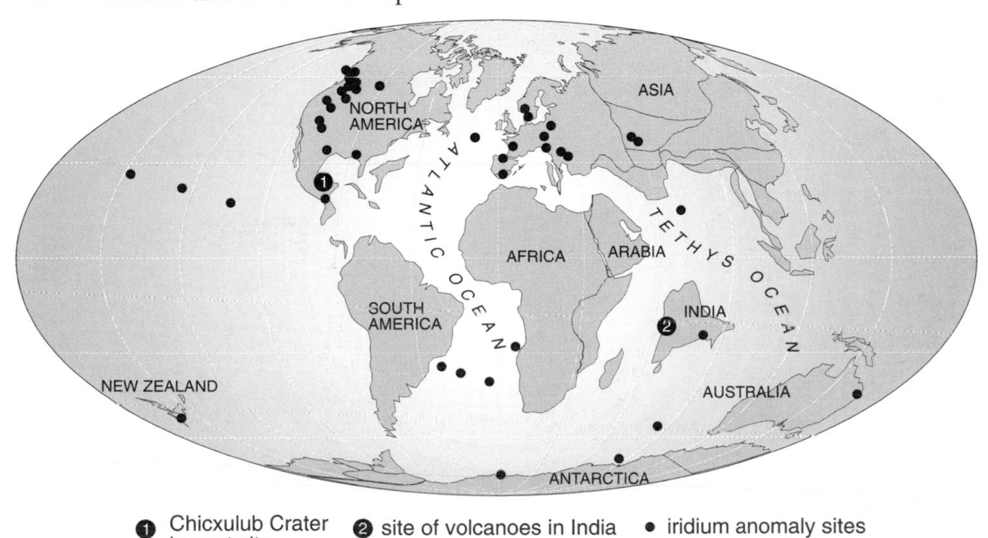

Figure 3.7 Location of iridium anomalies at the K–T boundary, the Chicxulub Crater, and the site of huge volcanic eruptions in India. The reconstruction shows plate positions at 65 Ma ago, but with present-day coastlines.

*The term 'Chalk' (with a capital C) refers specifically to late Cretaceous deposits of fine-grained, white limestone rich in fossil coccolithophores.

There is evidence of a brief initial spell of *cooling* due to darkening by dust clouds — similar to the 'nuclear winter' scenarios for the aftermath of all-out nuclear war — followed by *warming* for several hundred thousand years, which was possibly the key factor in the demise of some species. Global warming may have been promoted by various mechanisms, including the release of CO_2 from widespread fires, from impact with limestones, and from the dissolution of limestones and even shells of living organisms by acid rain. Acid rain (formed by solution of sulfur dioxide and nitrogen oxides in rainwater) was probably caused by heating of the atmosphere as the meteor passed through it, and by vaporization of rocks rich in sulfur at the impact site. Whatever the details, the K–T impact certainly initiated environmental disturbance, with more stable conditions resuming only a few hundred thousand years later. A huge thickness of basalt lava flows in India was also erupted around this time (Figure 3.7), and the gases emitted probably added to the atmospheric disturbance.

Although the impact at the end of the Cretaceous Period appears to have led particularly to the mass extinction of plankton, it seems to have had little or nothing to do with some, perhaps most, of the other extinctions occurring around this time. Some groups had already become extinct over a million years before the impact. The short-lived global events at the K–T boundary occurred within a context of much longer-term environmental change, including the lowering of sea-level and global cooling, and a sustained period of biological change. The diversity of ammonites, for example, had been slowly declining for some millions of years, though what was left of the group seems to have become abruptly extinct at the K–T boundary. The details of dinosaur extinction are much debated. Unfortunately, the precise extinction pattern of many animal groups remains ambiguous, due mainly to the limitations of the fossil record.

Given a long enough time interval, an 'exceedingly unlikely event' on a short time-scale, such as the impact of a huge meteorite, is very likely to happen at some time within that interval. If the impact at the end of the Cretaceous did cause many extinctions, then such catastrophes must play an important role in evolution. Conditions after the K–T impact may have been both drastically and *randomly* changed from conditions prevailing for millions of years before. The extinction of some species may therefore have been more a matter of bad luck than bad genes. New evolutionary opportunities then arose for some of the lucky survivors.

3.2.2 Establishing the causes of mass extinctions

Reasons invoked in the past for the extinction of the dinosaurs included constipation and stupidity.

- Apart from being untestable, why would such suggestions be inadequate as explanations for *mass* extinctions?

- Any proposed mechanism(s) for mass extinctions must embrace many groups, and operate over a wide area, both on land and in the sea.

- In what ways, other than extinction, might a species respond to severe environmental change affecting its habitat?

- A species may be able to migrate into more favourable areas, or, in the longer term, evolve adaptations to the new environment (Block 9, Section 14.2).

What kind of environmental changes, then, are so severe that large numbers of species prove unable to migrate away from, or evolve to avoid, extinction? The most plausible hypotheses are those such as rapid changes in global temperature or oxygen levels — as opposed to, say, disease or predation, which are unlikely to affect many thousands of species at the same time.

In addition to the possible influence of extraterrestrial events, the Earth-bound causes most often proposed for mass extinctions include: climate change, especially cooling and aridity; sea-level rise or fall; changes in oceanic circulation, leading to lower levels of dissolved oxygen in shallow waters; changes in atmospheric chemistry (especially lowered oxygen levels); and intense volcanic activity. Most of these causes are not mutually exclusive; for example, cooling and widespread glaciation lower sea-level because water is transferred from the oceans and locked up as ice on land; volcanic activity could promote climate change and also pollute the atmosphere.

The only mass extinction for which the influence of a meteorite is strongly implicated is that at the K–T boundary. Some mass extinctions, such as the one at the end of the Permian, may have occurred when several changes in the physical environment coincided accidentally; in this case there was probably a lowering of atmospheric oxygen levels linked to changes in sea-level and oceanic circulation patterns, combined with adverse effects from extensive volcanic eruptions in Siberia. The late Ordovician mass extinction of marine organisms was almost certainly linked to widespread glaciation and a large fall in sea-level. Climate change is also implicated in both the late Devonian and late Triassic mass extinctions.

The positive and negative feedback mechanisms (Block 2, Section 7.5) in the Earth's ocean–atmosphere system, and in its ecosystems, are immensely complex. Establishing the full chain of cause and effect during extinctions, and precisely which biological attributes — or lack of them — led to the demise of a particular species, is a difficult if not impossible task, even for most extinctions taking place in the 20th century.

3.3 Evolutionary radiations

Extinction is, as we have seen, forever. But, depending on one's perspective, mass extinctions aren't always bad news. For example, the mass extinction of dinosaurs at the end of the Cretaceous Period seems to have cleared the way for mammals to expand into vacated niches, and 65 Ma later it's even keeping some of their descendants employed trying to find out how it all happened.

The expansion of mammals in the early Cenozoic is an example of an **evolutionary radiation** — an episode of rapid and sustained increase in diversity, often involving the origin of many new groups above the species level such as orders and families. In Section 2.4 we considered the radiation of animals into many new phyla during the Cambrian explosion. Let's now look briefly at the radiation of mammals, a single class of vertebrates, during the Cenozoic Era.

3.3.1 The radiation of mammals

Mammals first appeared towards the end of the Triassic Period, about 210 Ma ago. For a long time they remained small, perhaps nocturnal, shrew-like creatures living in the nooks and crannies of the dinosaur world. Figure 3.8 (*overleaf*) shows the distribution in time of the major groups (mainly orders) of mammals from the start of the Jurassic Period, and their evolutionary relationships. Such an evolutionary tree shows the most likely pattern of branching from a common ancestor, and is based on evidence from fossils, and on the comparative anatomy and genetics of living mammals. The width of each group on the diagram gives a rough indication of its diversity. Notice that during the Jurassic and early Cretaceous a number of short-lived groups evolved, but left no descendants. The placentals, which nourish their embryos with a placenta, are much more dominant than the other two groups present today — the marsupials and monotremes. The marsupials, such as kangaroos, transfer their new-born young to pouches. The monotremes, which are mammals that lay eggs, include the platypus and the spiny ant-eater; they have a poor fossil record.

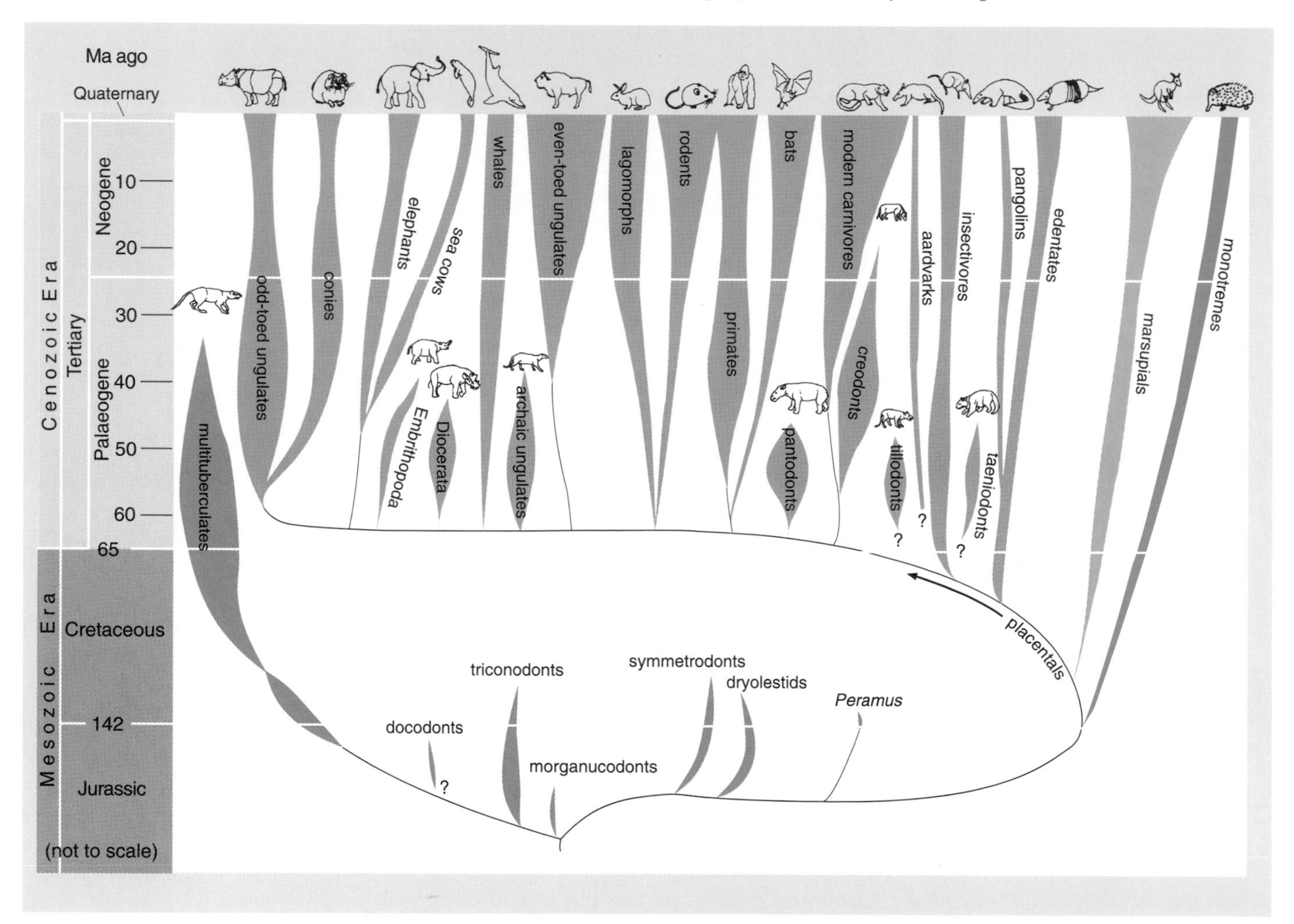

Figure 3.8 The pattern of radiation in mammals. See text for explanation.

- How long had mammals been in existence before their radiation in the early Cenozoic?

- About 150 Ma (from 210 Ma ago until about 60 Ma ago).

- According to Figure 3.8, has the diversity of the monotremes changed much since their origin in the Cretaceous Period, and how does it compare with that of the placentals?

- On the diagram, the width of the bar for monotremes remains thin, whereas the bars for many separate orders of placentals are wider than those for the monotremes. The diversity of monotremes has therefore changed little since their origin, and has remained much less than that of the placentals.

- How long after the extinction of the dinosaurs was it before almost all the orders of placentals had appeared?

- Most placentals had already appeared by 55–60 Ma ago, less than 10 Ma after the K–T mass extinction.

This extraordinary burst of evolution produced mammals adapted to a vast range of environments — think for a moment of today's flying bats, swimming dolphins, burrowing moles, running cheetahs, and so on. And ever since the early Tertiary, most of the world's largest animals have been mammals, as is true today — think of the African elephant and the blue whale, Earth's largest land and sea animals (see Box 3.2).

Box 3.2 The early evolution of whales

Whales have long been understood to be descended from four-legged land animals of the early Cenozoic Era. Modern whales lack hind limbs entirely, but many species retain within their bodies remnants of pelvic bones and of hindlegs, visible only internally (Figure 3.9). Occasionally, modern humpback whales and sperm whales are found with externally projecting rudimentary hindlimbs. Such quirks provide convincing evidence of evolution. In 1994, missing links between ocean-going whales and their land-dwelling ancestors were found in early Cenozoic rocks of Pakistan. These rather dog-like intermediates are believed to have been able both to walk on land *and* to swim with their hind legs 50 Ma ago (see Figure 3.10).

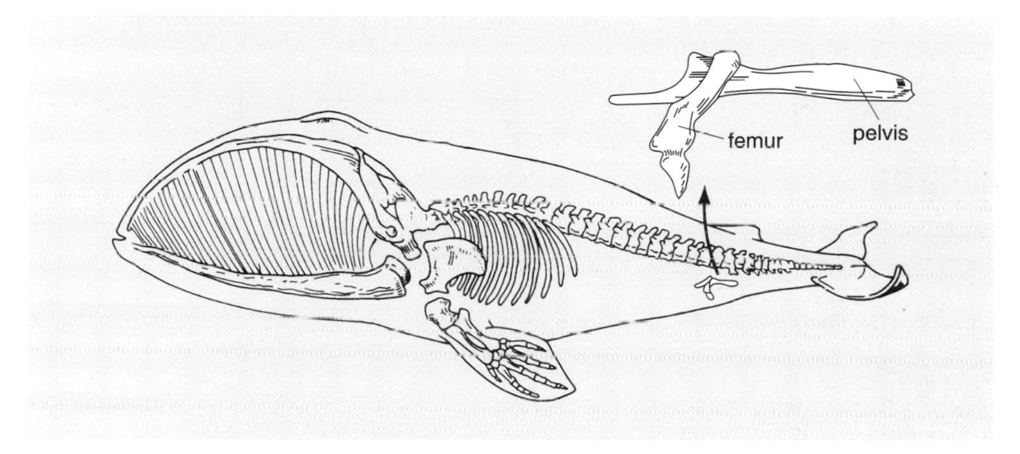

Figure 3.9 Skeleton and body outline of a whale, with internal rudimentary hindlimbs. (The long plates between the jaws are for filtering out crustaceans.)

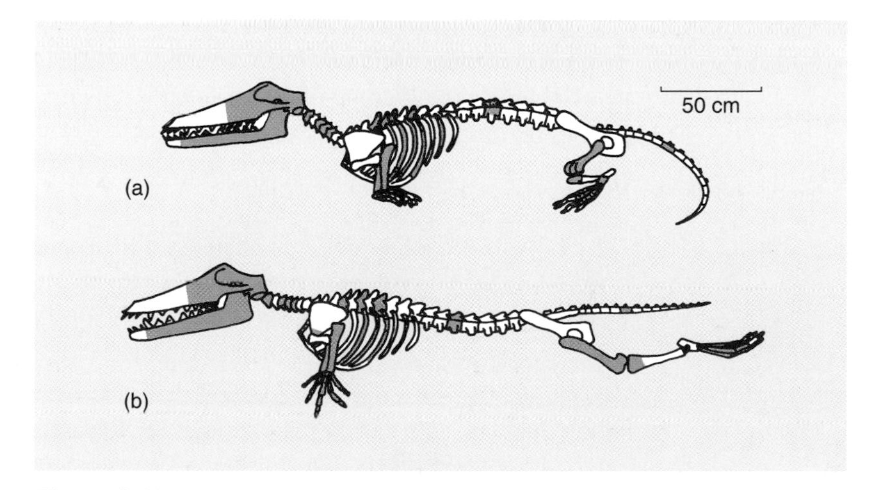

Figure 3.10 A missing link no longer missing: a fossil species about 50 Ma old from Pakistan that may have been the ancestor of whales. It could probably both (a) walk on land and (b) swim with its hind legs. The shaded regions indicate fossil parts found.

Humans, of course, are mammals, and apart from our exceptionally large brains, our anatomy and physiology are not much different from that of other primates, such as chimpanzees, to which we are closely related and with which, not long ago, geologically speaking, we shared a common ancestor. Our own species, *Homo sapiens*, appeared only 100 000–400 000 years ago (depending on how the origin of the species is defined). Like every other species on the planet, we are the unique product of a long string of biological events, none of which was an *inevitable* consequence of evolution. Although natural selection itself is the opposite of a chance process, it operates on what is already there, the details of which have a strong random component, such as the variation generated by sexual reproduction (Block 9, Section 13.2.2) and mutation (Block 9, Sections 9.6, 10.3 and 13.2.1). As we have seen, chance may also play a part on a much longer time-scale, such as in the ascendancy of mammals as opposed to reptiles.

3.4 Putting things in order

Establishing the *order* of geological events is essential for understanding just about anything we might like to know about the Earth and its history: Which of these volcanoes was the last to erupt? Was any oil formed before these rocks were folded? Which came first, reptiles or amphibians? In order to understand any complex situation, we need to unravel the *correct sequence of events* that led to it; imagine a detective trying to solve a complex 'whodunnit?' without piecing together events in the order in which they actually happened. And detailed knowledge of past events can help us make useful *predictions*: Where should we drill for oil or prospect for silver? When is this fault likely to move, causing an earthquake? How will global warming affect the melting of ice-caps?

During our brief glimpse at the history of life, we have seen that evolution produces new species, and that extinction can eliminate them, sometimes in geologically brief intervals of mass extinction. Suppose we already know from earlier work that a particular species of, say, ammonite appeared, and then died out after quite a short span of time. If we then discover this particular species in the strata (i.e. sedimentary rock layers, beds) of a new area, we can conclude that the strata must have been laid down during the lifetime of that ammonite species. We use this kind of logic in everyday life: for example, if you find a note written in, say, the handwriting of your great-grandmother, and you know her dates of birth and death, you can place the age of the note to within her lifetime.

But how do we know when an ancient fossil species actually lived in the first place? We don't have a reference book to look it up in — at least not until we've done the detective work. We have to work out its age using clues in the geological record.

There are two aspects of age: **relative age** and **absolute age**. To illustrate the difference between the two, consider the statement: 'this newspaper is more recent than that one'. It's a clear indication of relative age, but says nothing about the *actual age* of each newspaper, nor the *time difference* between them. The absolute date of a newspaper is the date it was printed, such as 28 April 1996; its absolute age is then the time that has elapsed between then and now.

Imagine a pile of old newspapers accumulating day by day at home in a recycling bin. Unless the order of the newspapers has been disturbed for some reason, the oldest newspaper will be at the bottom of the bin, and the youngest at the top. The same is also true of sediments as they accumulate; generally, the deeper you go in a sedimentary sequence, the older the layers of sediment. That's sufficiently important to be given a formal name: **the principle of superposition**. Older rocks are overlain by younger rocks. An individual layer is younger than the one beneath it and older than the one above it; the oldest layer lies at the bottom (Figure 3.11). Unless the rocks have been overturned (which may sometimes happen during plate collisions and mountain-building), the 'arrow of time' will be upwards through a set of strata. In fact, sedimentary rocks provide such an important key to the past that they are sometimes said to be the diaries of Earth's history. The principle of superposition was first explicitly stated by Nicolaus Steno (1638–1687), a Dane working in Italy. Steno also realized that sediments were normally laid down in a near-horizontal position, although later they may be folded or even overturned.

Figure 3.11 A spectacular sequence of Jurassic strata on the Dorset coast, England. According to the principle of superposition, the oldest strata lie at the bottom of the cliff.

The study of strata and their relationships in time and space is called **stratigraphy**. Sequences of strata have long been used to establish a generalized geological succession — the *stratigraphic column* — that we have already used several times in this block to show geological eras and periods. The boundaries between geological periods, and many of the subdivisions within them, have been assigned absolute dates (as in the geological time-scale of Figure 2.7) using methods outlined in Section 8.

Question 3.1 In two of the three major types of rocks, relative dating cannot be carried out by using fossils (except in very rare cases). Which two rock types are these, and why? ◀

To understand Earth history we need to know what happened at the same time *in different parts of the world*. For example, to get to grips with what occurred at the K–T boundary, we need to know which parts of the world were then mountains, which were deep sea, which were deserts and so on. The matching up of rocks of the same age from one area to another is called **correlation**.

William Smith (1769–1839), an English engineer and surveyor, was one of the first people to use the fact that different fossils occur in rocks of different ages, although he was not able to ascribe these differences to evolution as Darwin's key work had yet to be published. He worked on canals, roads and drainage schemes all over England, and found that he could recognize particular beds on the basis of their distinctive fossil content. For instance, he could match up certain beds of Chalk in the North Downs with others in the South Downs, because each contained a particular assemblage of fossils different from those in the similar-looking Chalk beds above and below.

William Smith then found he could correlate apparently *dissimilar* strata because they contained *similar* fossils. Widely separated limestone and sandstone beds, for instance, although quite different rocks, were sometimes found to contain certain fossils in common, so he concluded that they were laid down at the same time. Smith also found the same general succession of fossil assemblages from older to younger beds in different parts of the country. He proposed that each stage in this succession of fossils represented a particular span of geological history, and called this the **principle of faunal succession**. Using this principle, he was able to correlate widely separated outcrops of rock by the fossils they contained, and in 1815 Smith produced the first geological map of England, Wales and part of Scotland.

So, the main basis for the *relative* time-scale recognized by Earth scientists is the succession of strata, which is based on the principle of superposition, combined with the correlation of fossil assemblages from successions of strata in different areas (the principle of faunal succession).

The absence of strata from a particular time interval in a certain region may be due either to non-deposition or to erosion of any sediment that *was* deposited. Major breaks in the stratigraphic record occur quite often, and may be widespread across large geographic areas. They are called **unconformities**, and recognition of them, and the missing strata they represent, is crucial in working out the geological history of an area. Such breaks were recognized by the Frenchman, George Cuvier, born in the same year as William Smith. A highly skilled observer, Cuvier systematically described the succession of fossil animals and plants in the Cenozoic rocks of France, painstakingly reconstructing the living organisms. He also noticed that many forms of life seemed to have disappeared together in a sudden catastrophe at certain levels in the strata (*not* at unconformities). These levels were later identified in other areas and recognized as episodes of extinction.

Today, the stratigraphic column is divided into **zones** that are characterized by one or more particular fossils. The sequence of zones in the correct order makes up the **biostratigraphic column**. A *zone fossil* is a species used to characterize a zone in the biostratigraphic column. Ideally, such species should belong to rapidly evolving groups (with a short time range), have distinctive appearance, be wide-ranging geographically (like many free-swimming or floating marine creatures), and be abundant as fossils. Ammonites (such as fossil D in the Practical Kit) are an example of such a group; they are used extensively for establishing zones in the Jurassic and Cretaceous.

- Considering the criteria required of a good zone fossil, would you expect dinosaurs to be suitable zone fossils for the Jurassic Period?

- Dinosaurs are very rare as fossils, often found as incomplete remains, and restricted to land-based environments; they would therefore be unsuitable as zone fossils.

So, today, once we have correctly identified particular fossils from a rock of unknown age, we can then tell to which particular geological period — or part of it — the rock belongs, providing the succession of fossil species has already been well established.

The approximate absolute age (in Ma) can be obtained by referring to an up-to-date geological time-scale. The biostratigraphic column, and absolute dates, are continuously refined as new data emerge.

Activity 3.2 Matching up rocks — when it's age that matters

In this activity you can try a correlation exercise for yourself. ◀

There are many other ways of correlating rocks that are independent of the use of fossils, although many of these methods are specific to particular situations or times in Earth's history.

- What unusual geochemical feature of the K–T boundary can be used to correlate sediments deposited at that time around the world, and why is it present?
- The concentration of the rare element iridium is abnormally high in sediments at the K–T boundary, and derives from a meteorite impact. This iridium anomaly is a geochemical feature that can be identified around the world (Figure 3.7).

- Can you think of a potential problem in using this iridium anomaly *alone* to identify the K–T boundary?
- Meteorite impacts on the Earth have occurred at many other times, and some of these may have also introduced iridium, so that matching up iridium anomalies alone could lead to erroneous correlations.

We need to find other corroborating evidence, such as from fossils, and where possible obtain an absolute date too. The more independent lines of evidence that can be gathered, the less likely that mistakes will be made. Other means of correlating across a large area include matching up changes in global sea-level and in global temperature. Ice ages, for example, produce widespread glacial deposits that can be correlated across different continents (Block 3, Section 11.3).

We shall return later, in Section 8, to other ways of relative dating, and, in particular, to methods of absolute dating. But first, as the history of the Earth and its life is recorded in rocks, we need to know more about the origins of rocks — the subject of Sections 5–7 — and more about the minerals of which rocks are composed — the subject of Section 4.

Question 3.2 The following 12 items are mostly evolutionary events, here in random order. Write them in their appropriate positions on the right-hand side of the geological time-scale in Figure 2.7. (You should already have marked in the events listed in Question 2.5 and indicated each of the Big Five mass extinctions with an asterisk.)

- first birds
- first *Homo sapiens*
- radiation of mammals
- start of main diversification of fishes
- first amphibians
- first flowering plants
- Jurassic fossils in the Kit
- first fishes
- first mammals
- main invasion of the land by plants and invertebrates begins
- first dinosaurs
- first reptiles ◀

3.5 Summary of Section 3

When you have answered Question 3.2, your completed Figure 2.7 will provide you with a useful overview of important evolutionary events in many major groups, especially the vertebrates.

The invasion of the land required many new adaptations, and only got going about 3 500 Ma after the origin of life, when small plants (about 5 cm high) and tiny arthropods (a few mm long) first moved onto land. By the end of the Devonian Period, vertebrates capable of walking on land (amphibians) had evolved, and some plants had reached the size of trees.

The Big Five mass extinctions of the Phanerozoic were in the late Ordovician, late Devonian, late Permian, late Triassic, and late Cretaceous. The two most severe were at the end of the Palaeozoic and Mesozoic Eras. We may be living within another mass extinction now due to human activity.

There is strong evidence of the impact of a large meteorite at the Cretaceous–Tertiary (K–T) boundary, 65 Ma ago. Although its environmental effects may have led to the rapid extinction of much of the plankton, many other groups that disappeared in the K–T mass extinction were already in decline, and some had become extinct well before the boundary. Establishing the causes of mass extinctions is very difficult. The most likely mechanisms include those that would affect a great many species, such as a combination of global climate change and changes in oceanic and atmospheric chemistry.

The major evolutionary radiation of mammals occurred in the early Cenozoic Era, once the large reptiles that dominated the Mesozoic Era had become extinct.

The main basis for the relative geological time-scale is the succession of strata (which is based on the principle of superposition), and the pattern of succession of fossil assemblages. The resulting biostratigraphic column allows the matching up of strata deposited at the same time in different areas — an essential part of getting to grips with events in the Earth's history.

Minerals — the crystalline world

So far you have studied the development of life through geological time, as recorded by fossils preserved in rocks. Rocks are geological materials, formed over extended periods of *time*, by processes that operate over a range of *spatial* scales. For example, vast volumes of rocks form continents and planets, and each rock is made out of smaller particles: mineral grains. In turn, each mineral grain is built from huge numbers of atoms, arranged in nanometre-sized repeating units (1 nm = 10^{-9} m).

This section examines the internal, crystal structures of minerals, and relates them to external properties such as crystal shape, hardness and colour, which can be used to identify minerals in hand specimen. Identifying minerals is particularly useful because different rocks can be identified on the basis of their mineral contents. Sections 5–7 take a broader look at geological materials, especially rock types, the processes involved in their formation, and the various geological structures exhibited by rocks.

4.1 What are minerals?

You have already been introduced to some minerals in Block 3, Section 9.1. One of these was the quartz crystal in the Practical Kit, and you might like to re-examine this now. Its smooth, well-defined crystal faces are naturally formed (unlike the cut and polished faces of most gemstones seen in jewellers). The arrangement of the quartz crystal faces is very precise. If your crystal resembles the one shown in Figure 4.1, you could verify this by measuring the angles between each of the six large faces parallel to the crystal's length. You should find that although the faces are of different sizes, the angle between neighbouring faces is exactly 60° (Figure 4.1).

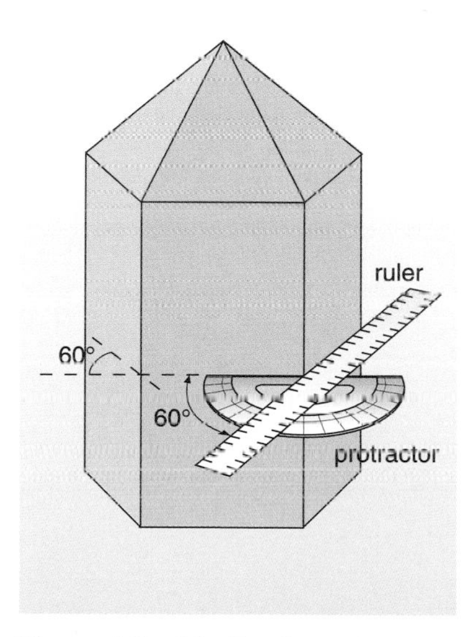

Figure 4.1 Idealized quartz crystal, showing three of the six faces, which, regardless of their relative size, are always 60° apart, as measured using a ruler and a protractor.

Having examined your naturally-formed quartz crystal, you should have concluded that it has certain well-defined properties, such as shape. What do you think causes these properties? It might seem reasonable to believe that they have something to do with the internal structure of the crystal. However, we cannot observe this structure directly — even with the highest-power light microscope — so the structure must be very fine scale. In fact, the technique of X-ray diffraction (discussed in the TV programme 'Hidden visions') is required to determine the internal structure of crystals. We now know that crystals are built from regular arrangements of atoms, in contrast to glasses, liquids and gases, which have irregular ('disordered') internal structures.

> Formally, a mineral is defined as:
>
> a solid body, formed by natural processes, that has a regular arrangement of atoms which sets limits to its range of chemical composition and gives it a characteristic crystal shape.

What does this regular internal structure look like at an atomic level? Consider first a sheet of patterned paper (Figure 4.2, overleaf). This type of design looks fairly complicated; however, if you look more closely, you should be able to see that actually the sheet consists of a basic pattern that is continually repeated in two dimensions. The basic pattern is like a 'building block' for the complete sheet.

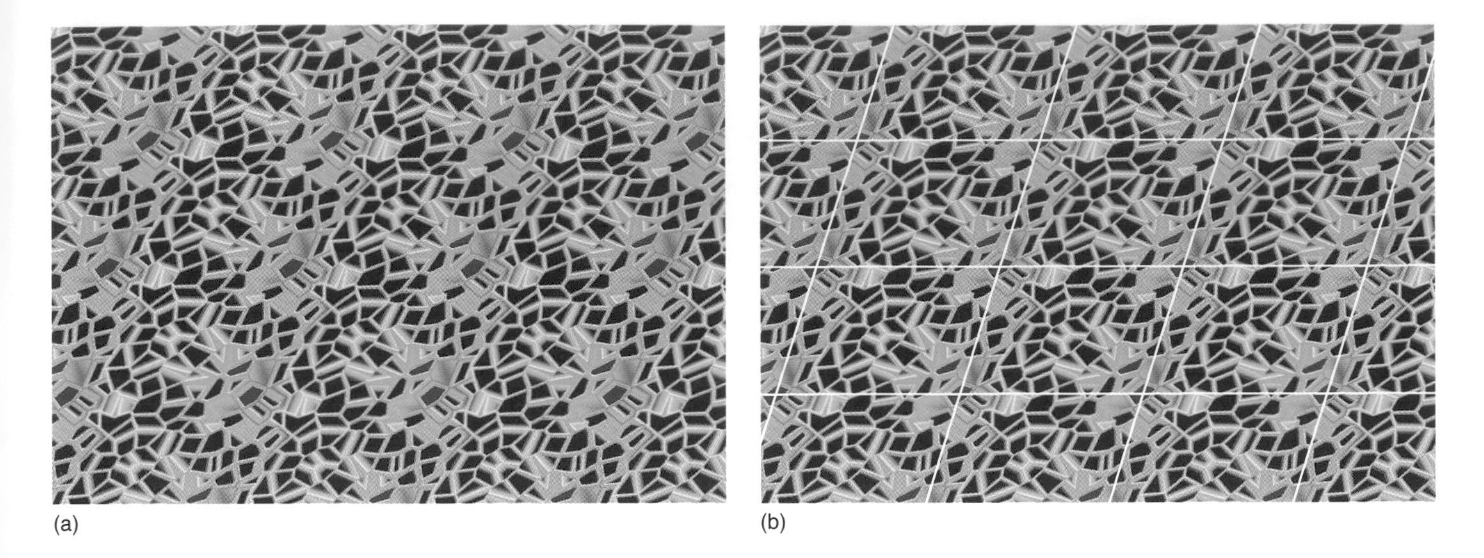

Figure 4.2 (a) Part of a sheet of patterned paper. (b) One of the many ways in which this pattern can be divided into identical, repeating blocks.

In a similar way, minerals are built out of *microscopic*, three-dimensional building blocks, repeated in three dimensions (Figure 4.3). The three-dimensional building block is called a **unit cell**. Each mineral has a unique unit cell which may contain one or more different kinds of atoms, joined to each other by chemical bonds. Shapes of unit cells vary from mineral to another; all have six sides (three sets of parallel faces, though not necessarily perpendicular to each other as in Figure 4.3).

The unit cell is very small — typically less than 1 nm wide. It is therefore a huge jump in scale from a single unit cell to a single crystal visible to the naked eye. Such a crystal contains very large numbers of unit cells stacked against each other in three dimensions (Figure 4.3).

- How many unit cells are needed to build a 1 mm^3 single crystal? Assume that each unit cell is a cube with edge length 1 nm.

- The number of unit cells is equal to the volume of the crystal divided by the volume of a single unit cell.

  Volume of crystal = $1\ mm^3 = (10^{-3}\ m)^3 = 10^{-9}\ m^3$

  Volume of unit cell = $(1\ nm)^3 = (10^{-9}\ m)^3 = 10^{-27}\ m^3$

  $$\text{Thus, number of unit cells required} = \frac{10^{-9}\ m^3}{10^{-27}\ m^3} = 10^{18}$$

The regular atomic arrangement (or *crystal structure*) of a mineral gives rise to well-defined physical properties such as *crystal shape*, *cleavage*, *hardness* and *lustre.* We can therefore distinguish between different minerals on the basis of the differences in these properties.

Activity 4.1 Properties of minerals

In this CD-ROM activity you will investigate the various properties of minerals and how they can be used to distinguish between different minerals. ◀

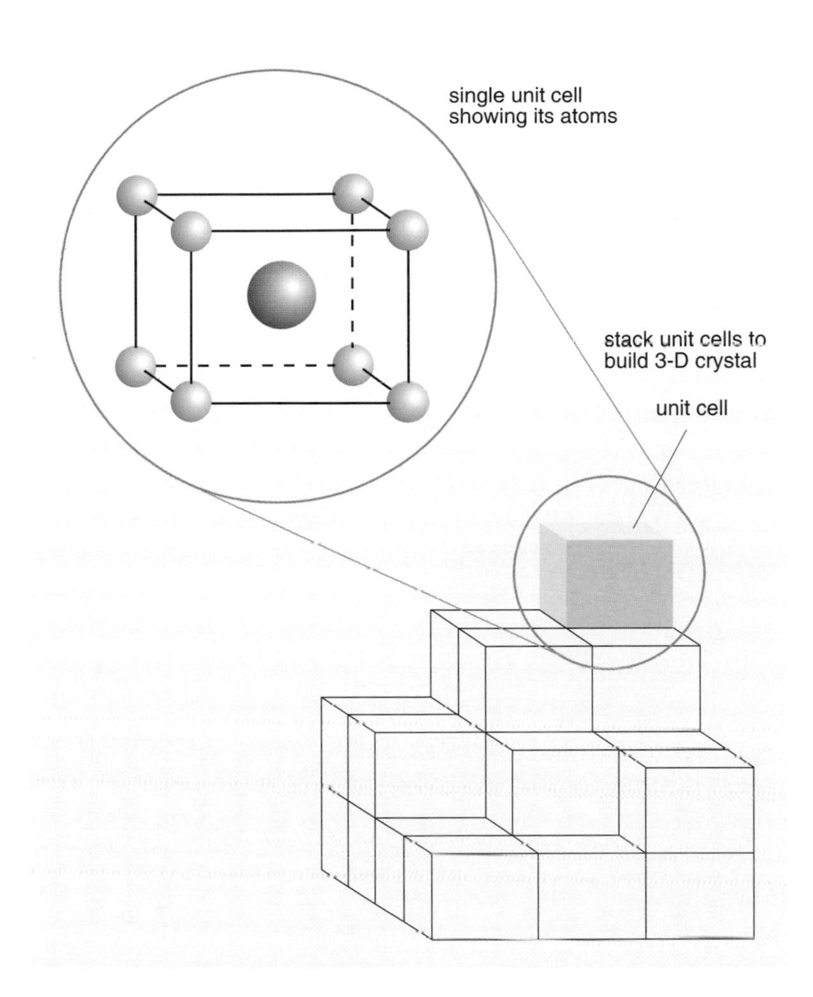

Figure 4.3 A three-dimensional crystal structure is built out of identical 'building bricks' called unit cells. Each unit cell contains a number of atoms, arranged in the same manner.

4.2 Mineral chemistry

More than 3 500 different kinds of minerals have been identified at the Earth's surface, and new types continue to be discovered — although many of these are very rare. We shall focus on the much smaller number of important, *rock-forming minerals* found at the Earth's surface.

What controls the formation of a particular mineral? First of all, we need the right raw materials to grow a mineral. The abundances of some important elements in the Earth's continental crust are listed in Table 4.1.

Table 4.1 The average composition of the Earth's continental crust. Only the most abundant elements are listed.

Element	Symbol	% by mass
oxygen	O	46.6
silicon	Si	27.7
aluminium	Al	8.3
iron	Fe	5.0
calcium	Ca	3.6
sodium	Na	2.8
potassium	K	2.6
magnesium	Mg	2.1
others		1.3
total		100.0

From Table 4.1 you can see that oxygen and silicon are by far the most abundant elements in the Earth's continental crust. Minerals containing silicon combined with oxygen are termed **silicates**, and these are the most common minerals at the Earth's surface. Other important minerals you will encounter include **carbonates** (containing the CO_3 group), such as the mineral *calcite*, and **oxides** (containing metal atoms combined with oxygen), e.g. the mineral *haematite*, a form of iron oxide.

Many crystal structures can readily accept small variations in chemical composition — and sometimes these subtle chemical changes have a disproportionate effect on mineral properties such as colour (Figure 4.4, *overleaf*). Many silicate minerals show

Figure 4.4 Crystals of the mineral quartz showing a range of coloration, caused by slight variations in chemical composition. Pure quartz (SiO_2) is colourless; minute quantities of iron induce a purple coloration, characteristic of the quartz variety popularly known as amethyst. Trace amounts of titanium present with iron cause yellow (citrine) to pink (rose quartz) colours. Small amounts of aluminium in otherwise-pure quartz cause a dark coloration (smoky quartz). The largest specimen is 7 cm across.

variations in the proportions of their constituent elements, with some elements able to substitute for others. We can indicate this chemical substitution when writing a mineral's formula: we group the substituting atoms inside brackets; thus for magnesium–iron substitution, we would write (Mg,Fe), instead of just Mg or Fe. The mineral *olivine* is one example of a silicate with this type of variable composition and its formula is written $(Mg,Fe)_2SiO_4$. This formula indicates that for every SiO_4 group in olivine there are two metal atoms, but the proportions of Mg and Fe can vary from specimen to specimen.

Clearly, the relative abundance of elements available will affect the chemical composition of the minerals formed. Sometimes, however, different minerals can have the same chemical composition.

- Suppose that two specimens have different mineral names, but share the same chemical formula. Using the definition of a mineral given earlier, suggest a possible difference between the two specimens.

- A mineral was defined in terms of a regular atomic arrangement, or crystal structure. Different minerals must therefore have different crystal structures even if they have similar, or identical, chemical compositions.

Minerals which have the same chemical composition but different crystal structures are called **polymorphs** (literally 'many forms'; you met polymorphism in a different context in Blocks 4 and 9, where it referred to different forms of organisms). Pressure and temperature conditions help to determine which crystal structure is more likely to form. Dense, closely-packed atomic arrangements tend to be formed at high pressures such as those deep within the Earth's interior, and more open structures tend to be formed at the low pressures of the Earth's surface. For example, diamond and graphite are two polymorphs of carbon. Deep in the Earth's mantle carbon crystallizes with the high-density, diamond structure; however, when carbon crystallizes naturally at the Earth's surface, it has the low-density, graphite structure.

- When describing a particular mineral, why might a name (such as 'quartz'), be more meaningful than a chemical formula (such as SiO_2)?

- There are several reasons:
  - Several different minerals can have the same chemical formula (polymorphs).
  - Some minerals have very complicated formulae; mineral names are usually easier to remember!
  - Most minerals show some slight variation in their chemical composition, so giving a specific chemical formula might be misleading.

4.3 Silicate minerals: variations on a tetrahedral theme

Silicates are the most abundant minerals at the Earth's surface. All silicate minerals share a common building unit: the SiO_4 group (Figure 4.5). A central silicon atom is bonded to four oxygen atoms, arranged at the corners of an imaginary *tetrahedron*. (A tetrahedron is a three-dimensional shape with four faces; the prefix *tetra* is Greek for 'four'.) We call this three-dimensional building unit the **silicate tetrahedron**.

Many minerals contain silicate tetrahedra separated by metal atoms. For example, Figure 4.6 shows part of the structure of the mineral olivine. The oxygen atoms are shared between silicon atoms (at the centres of the tetrahedra) and the metal atoms.

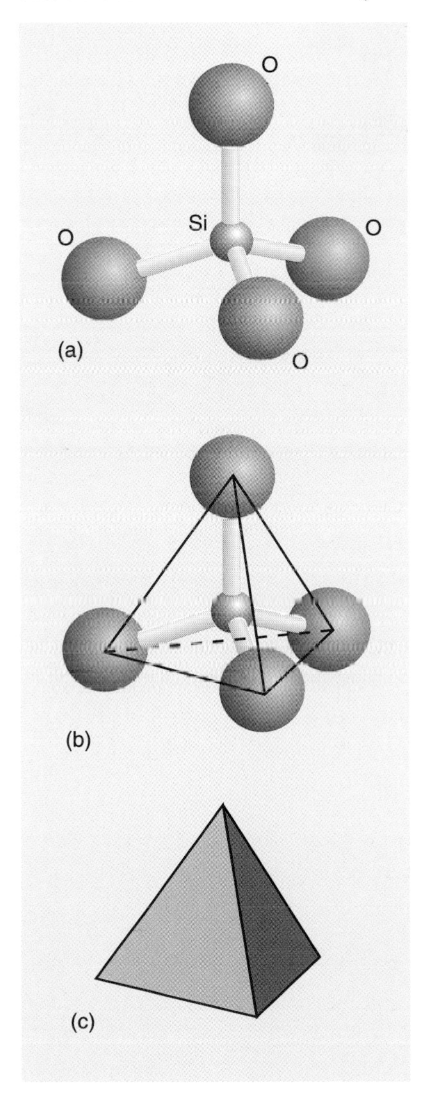

Figure 4.5 (a) Ball-and-stick model of the SiO_4 group. (b) Each oxygen atom is arranged at a corner of an imaginary tetrahedron, with the silicon atom at the centre. (c) A tetrahedron representing the SiO_4 group.

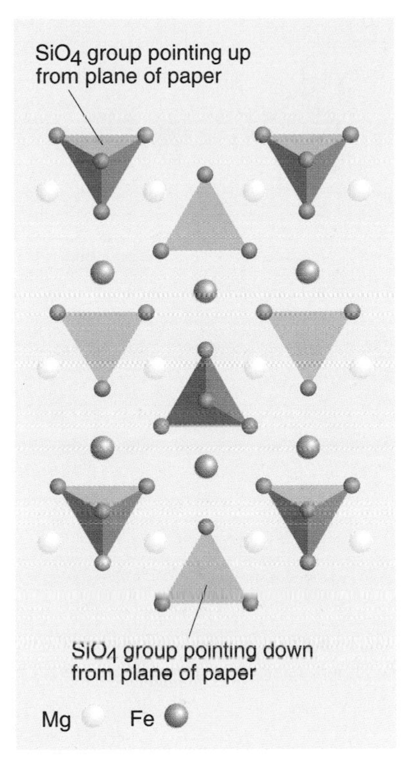

Figure 4.6 Part of the olivine $(Mg,Fe)_2SiO_4$ structure. The structure contains SiO_4 groups (half pointing up, and half pointing down), which are drawn as tetrahedra with oxygen atoms at their corners. Metal atoms (magnesium, Mg, and iron, Fe) are arranged between the SiO_4 tetrahedra, and help to bind the structure together.

Table 4.2 Structural classification of silicate minerals.

Description	Arrangement of tetrahedra	Mineral examples
isolated groups		olivine, garnet
1-D chain structures		pyroxene
		amphibole
2-D sheet structures		mica, clay minerals
		quartz, feldspar

If we were to replace some of the metal atoms by extra silicon atoms, then some oxygen atoms would become shared between adjacent tetrahedra (that is, we would get Si—O—Si bonds). This linking of silicon atoms by shared oxygen atoms is a form of polymerization (you saw something similar for CH_4 groups in organic molecules in Block 8). In the case of silicate minerals, we are concerned with SiO_4 groups; shared oxygen atoms correspond to the shared corners between two SiO_4 tetrahedra. Thus, as we consider mineral structures that contain more and more silicon, the trend is of *increasing polymerization* of SiO_4 groups.

We can classify silicate minerals according to the degree of connectivity of SiO_4 groups. Table 4.2 illustrates the sequence of structures formed with increasing silicon content: we pass from structures characterized by isolated tetrahedra (as found in the mineral olivine), through long chain structures (as found in pyroxene and amphibole), to sheet structures (characteristic of mica), and finally to three-dimensional framework structures (such as in quartz, which only contains silicon and oxygen atoms).

Activity 4.2 Minerals gallery

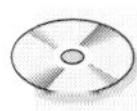

In this activity you will investigate the three-dimensional structures of a number of important minerals and compare their different properties. You will be able to observe how their internal crystal structures relate to their external crystal shapes and physical properties. ◀

In this brief section we have moved from the nanometre length-scale (atoms), to the length-scale of millimetres or centimetres (hand specimens). In the following sections we shall continue to expand our length-scales, exploring the ways in which different rocks form, and what they can tell us about the Earth and its history.

4.4 Summary of Section 4

Minerals are natural crystals. A crystal is built by the repetition — in three dimensions — of identical unit cells. The shape of the unit cell, and the arrangement of atoms inside it, uniquely define the crystal structure.

The precise arrangement of atoms in a crystal gives rise to specific physical and chemical properties. Cleavage is caused by planes of weak bonding, and density relates to how tightly atoms are packed together. Being able to recognize distinctive mineral properties is a crucial skill when identifying and distinguishing different minerals.

Single crystals may occur as well-formed specimens, but they tend to be quite rare. More usually, crystals occur packed together, as mineral grains, in rocks. Generally, different rocks can be identified on the basis of their mineral contents — and this is where a knowledge of mineral properties is especially useful.

5 Igneous rocks — out of the melting pot

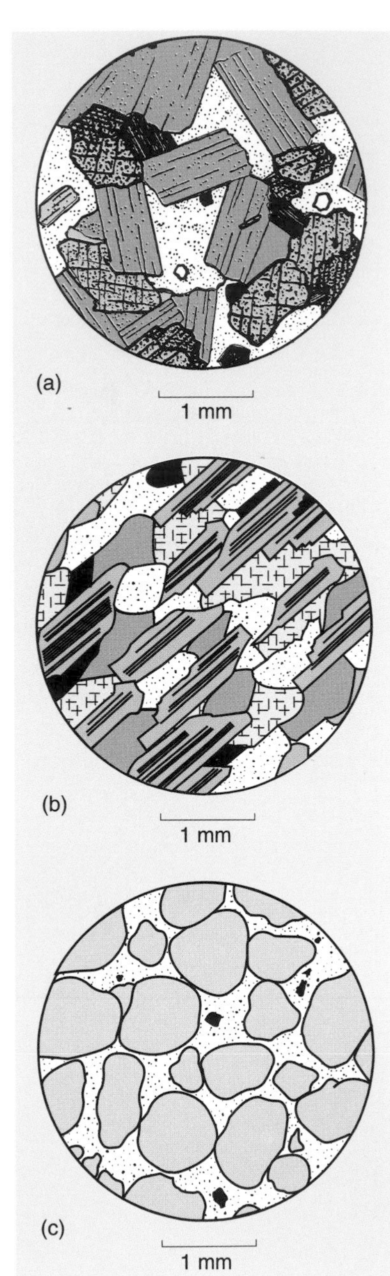

Figure 5.1 Typical textures of (a) igneous, (b) metamorphic, and (c) sedimentary rocks. The different forms of shading represent different types of mineral. Magnified images help geologists to establish the history of a rock (especially if it is fine-grained) from its texture and the minerals present.

We have seen how life has developed over the Earth's long history, but if we want to discover what else happened on Earth during geological time we need to know more than fossils can tell us. Indeed, many rocks don't contain fossils, and fossils are very rare in rocks over 600 Ma old (Section 2.3). So what else can we use? Well, Section 4 took us into the realm of minerals that make up the Earth's rocks (introduced in Block 3, Sections 9 and 17). Rocks of igneous, sedimentary and metamorphic origins can tell us about many different aspects of the Earth's past; in particular the geological events, environments and processes through which the Earth evolved into its present state. Our continuing voyage of discovery involves direct observation of these rocks, using scientific principles and knowledge of modern-day Earth processes to explain our observations.

Let's briefly recap some of what you learned about rocks in Block 3.

- Based on your observation of the Practical Kit samples in Block 3, Activity 9.1, how did you distinguish between the three main groups of rocks?

- By looking at their textures — the form and arrangement of their constituents — you could tell whether rocks were igneous, sedimentary or metamorphic.

Typically, igneous rocks (for example, the Kit granite and basalt) are made of randomly-oriented crystals that are interlocking and intergrown. Metamorphic rocks (for example, the Kit schist) also contain interlocking and intergrown crystals, but often the crystals are platy or elongate and are aligned in a common direction, and some minerals may form distinct bands. Sedimentary rocks (for example, the Kit sandstone and limestone) usually have a fragmental texture, with grains that can vary in shape from rounded to angular, but are not normally interlocking or intergrown. These textures, shown in Figure 5.1, provide more than a means of recognition; they also tell us about the ways these different rocks formed.

(a) The interlocking textures of igneous rocks (Figure 5.1a) indicate that mineral grains were competing for space as they grew from crystallizing magma; initially their growth was unimpeded and therefore they grew in random directions.

(b) The interlocking textures of metamorphic rocks (Figure 5.1b) also indicate growth of minerals occurring at the same time and in competition for space with adjacent minerals, but here the alignment of platy and elongate minerals reflects crystallization occurring in the solid state under the influence of external forces.

(c) The fragmentary textures of most sedimentary rocks (Figure 5.1c) indicate the accumulation of rock or mineral fragments as separate grains. The spaces between the grains often become occupied by a cement which binds them together.

A great number of rock types occur in nature. If you think for a minute, you can probably recall examples of different rocks that you've seen — at the coast, in mountains, in quarries or in road cuttings. Some rocks form hard, jagged cliffs; others soft, crumbly cliffs. Rocks also come in a variety of colours and may even be spotted or banded.

How can we start to sort out all these rocks and discover how they formed? In fact, you're already well on the way, having distinguished igneous, metamorphic and sedimentary rocks by their textures. Although this is only a crude classification, it is based on readily observable features and tells us a lot about a rock's origins. Next time you have a chance to look at a rock — perhaps the rough stone blocks sometimes used for buildings or for walls in rural areas, or the polished stone slabs used for monuments or facings of buildings in towns — try deciding for yourself whether its texture indicates an igneous, sedimentary or metamorphic origin.

In Sections 5–7 we shall look at a variety of different rocks and use both their textures and the minerals they contain to distinguish them and reveal how they formed. It's important to remember that rock samples come from larger bodies of rock, and that the form of those bodies, which can't be seen in small specimens but can be seen in field exposures, can also tell us a lot about the circumstances of their formation and the processes involved. The ability to interpret and understand how all kinds of rocks originate is essential for extending geological knowledge and piecing together the jigsaw puzzle of the Earth's history. We shall start by focusing on igneous rocks.

5.1 Diversity in igneous rocks

Block 3 provided an introduction to the nature and occurrence of igneous rocks (Section 9), and to volcanoes, the visible face of igneous activity (Section 8). It went on (Section 17) to consider the place of igneous rocks in the rock cycle and their formation by the melting of any rock type (Figure 5.2). In Activity 9.1 you examined the basalt and granite samples from your Practical Kit; not only are they the most common igneous rocks, but they illustrate many features common to other igneous rocks.

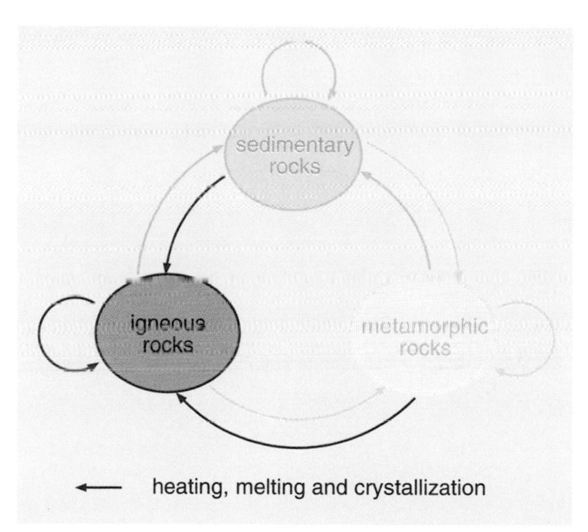

Figure 5.2 The formation of igneous rocks within the rock cycle. The three bold arrows indicate the routes through which igneous rocks can be formed by heating, melting and crystallization.

Activity 5.1 Revision: basalt and granite

This activity will refresh your memory about the basalt and granite samples in your Kit. ◀

Which of the features that you observed in the basalt and granite samples of the Kit could be used more generally to distinguish between different kinds of igneous rock — in other words, to act as a basis for classifying them? You discovered that *basalt* is mainly fine-grained — an *extrusive* igneous rock, formed by rapid cooling and crystallization; in contrast, *granite* is coarse-grained — an *intrusive* igneous rock formed by slow cooling and crystallization. Grain size is therefore an easily observable feature that provides a suitable way of classifying igneous rocks as it tells us how they crystallized. Let's now look at some of the ways in which igneous rocks occur and at relationships between grain size, occurrence and form of igneous rock bodies.

5.1.1 The occurrence of igneous rocks

Magmas erupted at the Earth's surface form **extrusive** igneous rocks, which can accumulate in many different ways, depending on the nature and circumstances of the eruption. A variety of eruptions are featured in the video 'Volcanoes' (Block 3, Activity 8.1), and a distinction was drawn between *lavas*, which are quietly effusive, and *pyroclasts*, which rain down or surge out after violent and explosive activity.

- Recalling the 'Volcanoes' video from Block 3, in what *form* do bodies of extrusive igneous rock tend to occur?

- They usually occur as sheets lying on top of existing rocks, either as lava flows or layers of volcanic ash.

Layers of pyroclastic material that fall to Earth from clouds of dust and ash are often extensive (covering many hundreds of square kilometres). Nearer to the centre of an eruption, deposits are thicker and coarser-grained: finer deposits extend further away. The influence of the wind is critical, and mapping out the spread and thickness of an ancient ash deposit can tell us the wind direction during the eruption.

Lava flows spread out over the surface, solidifying as they cool; their extent depends on the fluidity of the magma. One of the best known lava flows in the British Isles forms the Giant's Causeway, famous for its vertical columns of rock with polygonal sections (Figure 5.3). This regular pattern of cracks formed after the lava solidified and as it contracted on cooling.

Magma generally cools rapidly at the Earth's surface to produce fine-grained lava, like the basalt of the Giant's Causeway, but sometimes cooling is so rapid that constituents don't have a chance to sort themselves out into mineral structures; the liquid solidifies as a glassy rock without crystals. Such rapid cooling may occur during eruptions under water or onto cool land surfaces.

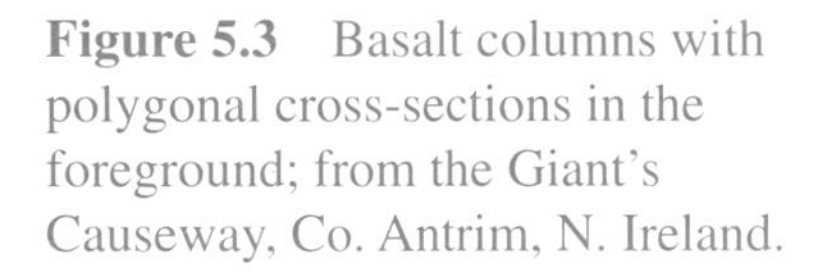

Figure 5.3 Basalt columns with polygonal cross-sections in the foreground; from the Giant's Causeway, Co. Antrim, N. Ireland.

- In Block 3 (Activity 12.1 and Section 14) you also came across a particularly distinctive form of igneous rock called pillow lava. What form of eruption does it signify?

- Pillow lavas form by effusive extrusion of magma *under water*. The surface of protruding magma is chilled by contact with water to form a skin which bulges like a balloon and then breaks to release another tongue of magma, building up an arrangement of bulbous structures or 'pillows'.

Volcanoes provide clear evidence of magmatic activity originating within the Earth today, but recording the formation of **intrusive** magma bodies, which crystallize below ground, is not easy. In the geological record, however, there is abundant evidence of intrusive igneous bodies because they are exposed by erosion. Among these igneous intrusions it is possible to recognize channels that may once have fed volcanoes, and magma chambers that stored magma.

Magma chambers that crystallized deep beneath the Earth's surface often form large bodies of igneous rock known as **plutons** (after Pluto, the Greek god of the underworld). The magma that cooled in them, deep down, crystallized very slowly to form coarse-grained *plutonic* rocks. Some plutons are many tens, even thousands, of cubic kilometres in volume, and are exposed only after many kilometres of overlying rocks have been removed by erosion. Plutons generally cut across bodies of older rock and often have no visible base. In southwest England, several granite plutons are exposed, forming tors on Dartmoor and cliffs at Land's End; in fact, they are parts of an even bigger plutonic body (see Figure 5.4), extending down for 10–20 km beneath the surface.

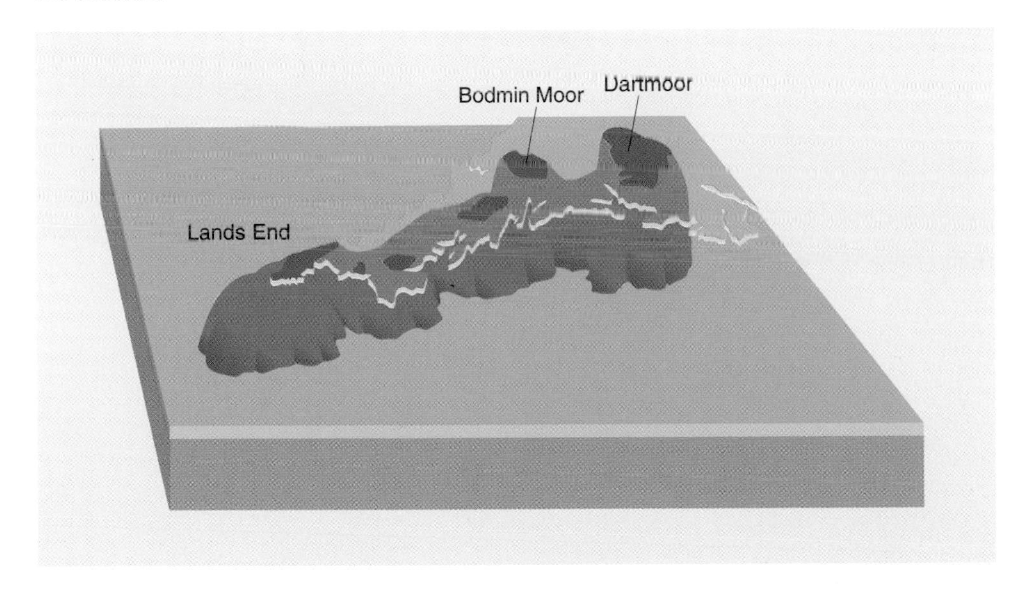

Figure 5.4 The form of the granite plutons extending below ground in southwest England.

Off-shoots from magma chambers and feeders to volcanoes tend to form much smaller bodies of igneous rock, and crystallize at shallower (hence cooler) depths than plutons. As a result, they cool more rapidly and are finer-grained. They usually form sheet-like bodies because magma tends to penetrate along planes of weakness, such as along fractures or the boundaries between rock layers. When these sheets *cut across* rock layers, they are generally known as **dykes** (Figures 5.5a and 5.5b); and when they *lie between* rock layers, they are generally known as **sills** (Figures 5.5a and 5.5c). In Block 3, Section 14.1, you came across sheeted dykes — a series of vertical, parallel dykes, making up part of the oceanic crust.

like a pack of cards on end – each card representing a dyke.

Igneous sheets forming dykes and sills may be tens of centimetres to hundreds of metres thick, and from a few hundred metres to several hundred kilometres in extent. The Whin Sill of northern England (Figure 5.5c) is intruded between Carboniferous rock strata, and underlies an area of 5 000 km^2.

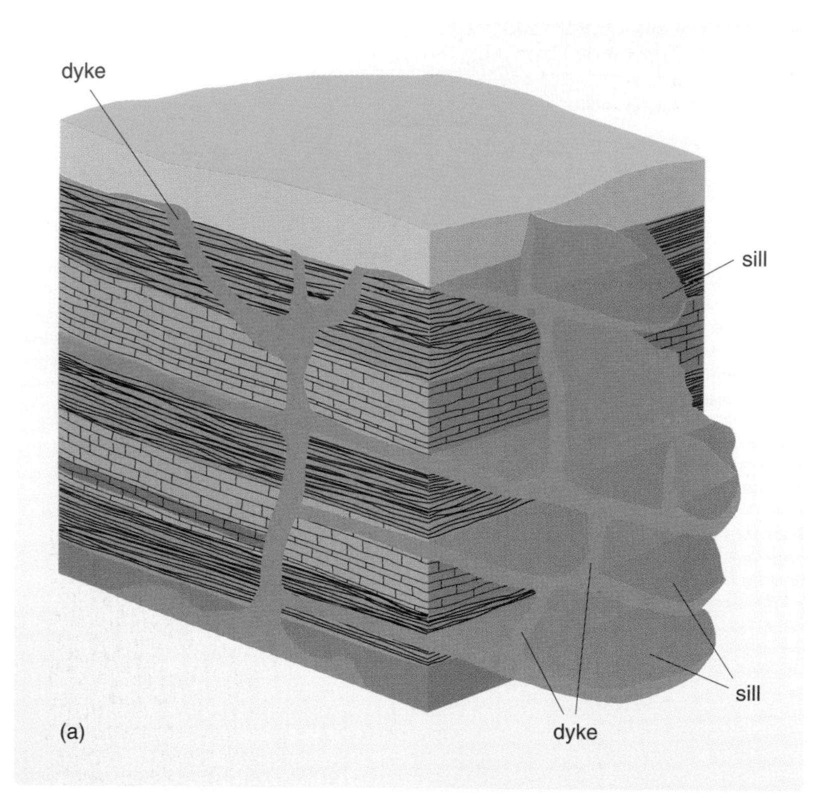

Figure 5.5 Minor intrusive bodies: (a) the form of igneous dykes and sills in two and three dimensions, (b) a dark basaltic dyke cutting jointed granite; from Lundy, southwest England, (c) the Whin Sill of northern England. The cliff forming the upstanding ridge on which part of Hadrian's Wall was built represents approximately the vertical height of the sill. The sloping land surface in the middle distance represents the top surface of the sill, which tilts down to the right.

Question 5.1 (a) What can you tell about the circumstances of formation of an igneous rock from its grain size?

(b) What kind of intrusion might be mistaken for a lava flow? Explain why, and suggest how they might be distinguished. ◀

Sometimes minerals start to crystallize and grow to a large size while still residing in a magma chamber. If the magma is then injected as a dyke or a sill, or erupted as lava, the rock formed contains these large individual crystals of one or two types of mineral, set in a mass of fine-grained crystals. This distinctive texture is known as *porphyritic* (pronounced 'porf-ir-itic') and the fine-grained material is called the *groundmass*.

- You have already seen porphyritic texture in a rock from the Kit. Which rock was it?

- The basalt. It contains some large crystals set in a fine-grained groundmass. Its texture can therefore be described as porphyritic.

With your knowledge of igneous textures you should now be able to examine a variety of igneous rock types in Figure 5.6 and attempt Question 5.2.

Figure 5.6 A variety of igneous rocks with different textures and grain sizes (note the different widths of the fields of view): (a) granite (80 mm), (b) feldspar porphyry (containing distinctive crystals of feldspar) (90 mm), (c) rhyolite (70 mm), (d) pumice (100 mm), (e) obsidian (50 mm).

Question 5.2 Figure 5.6 shows a variety of igneous rocks that formed in different circumstances. Some may be new to you (e.g. porphyry, pronounced 'porf-i-ri', and rhyolite, pronounced 'rye-o-lite'); others were mentioned in Block 3. Briefly describe the texture of each of them. Suggest how and under what circumstances you think each may have been formed. ◀

5.1.2 The compositions of igneous rocks

The rocks shown in Figure 5.6 can be distinguished on the basis of their *grain size*, and that's one way of classifying them. If we know what minerals they contain, we can also distinguish them according to their *mineral content*. In fact, three of these rocks (a, b, c) contain crystals — mainly of quartz, alkali feldspar and plagioclase feldspar; the other two, the pumice (d) and the obsidian (e), are glassy and don't contain crystals. The obsidian is solid glass, very rapidly chilled magma: the pumice is solidified magma froth, glass that's full of gas bubbles.

Remarkably, although the rocks in Figure 5.6 look very different, they all have essentially the *same* chemical composition. This means that they each contain the same percentages of different chemical elements, and each of them could have originated from the same type of magma. However, that's not true of all igneous rocks. For example, the basalt and granite from the Kit, which have quite different grain sizes, must have crystallized in quite different circumstances — but is that the only difference between them?

Activity 5.2 Exploring the mineral content and composition of igneous rocks — basalt and granite revisited

This activity allows you to use your knowledge of minerals from Section 4 to investigate the basalt and granite samples in the Kit in more detail. ◀

Your deductions in Activity 5.2, from the minerals contained in the basalt and granite samples, and the compositions of those minerals, tell you about the chemical compositions of the two rocks. You knew that they crystallized under quite different circumstances; now you know that they differ for another very fundamental reason — their chemical compositions, like those of the magmas from which they crystallized, are quite different. Such chemical differences are reflected in their mineral content, and therefore minerals can be used to classify and distinguish different types of igneous rocks. In fact, we shall soon see that the chemical compositions of basalt and granite are about as different as you can get among common igneous rocks.

Basalt contains the minerals pyroxene, plagioclase feldspar, and sometimes olivine (see Activity 4.2). Of these, those that are generally dark in colour contain magnesium and iron, and are called **mafic** minerals* (from *ma*gnesium and iron (*Fe*) and '*ic*'). Consequently, dark igneous rocks containing a high proportion of such minerals are called *mafic rocks*. Most mafic rocks, like the basalt considered in Activity 5.2, contain relatively high levels of magnesium, iron and calcium.

In contrast, **granite** contains the minerals quartz, alkali feldspar and plagioclase feldspar, and usually some mica (see Activity 4.2). These pale-coloured minerals, especially the feldspars and quartz, are known as **felsic** minerals (from *fel*dspar and *s*ilicon and '*ic*'). Igneous rocks that contain them in abundance (such as those illustrated in Figure 5.6), and glassy rocks that have a similar chemical composition, are known as *felsic rocks*. Few felsic rocks are very dark in colour — obsidian is an exception. As you discovered for granite in Activity 5.2, felsic rocks contain much more silicon, sodium and potassium than mafic rocks.

*Mafic minerals are also known as ferromagnesian minerals (Activity 4.1).

- Which of the felsic igneous rocks in Figure 5.6 is best described as fine-grained?
- The rhyolite, in which crystals are visible but not distinguishable.

Rhyolite contains the same minerals as granite, but is a fine-grained extrusive rock, like basalt. In Block 3 (Section 14.1) you were introduced to gabbro, a mafic rock that has essentially the same composition as basalt, but is coarse-grained.

In nature there is a range of igneous rock compositions — from granites and rhyolites, which are rich in silicon and contain mainly felsic minerals, to gabbros and basalts, which are poorer in silicon and contain significant amounts of mafic minerals. The variation in mineral content of these rocks is revealed in Figure 5.7. Here, percentages of minerals are represented on the vertical scale, and the range of rock types is given on the horizontal scale. Since mafic rocks are on the left and felsic rocks are on the right, the silicon, sodium and potassium contents increase from left to right. There is a complementary decrease in magnesium, iron and calcium contents. The percentages of different minerals change across the diagram, reflecting the typical variation in mineral content of the common igneous rocks.

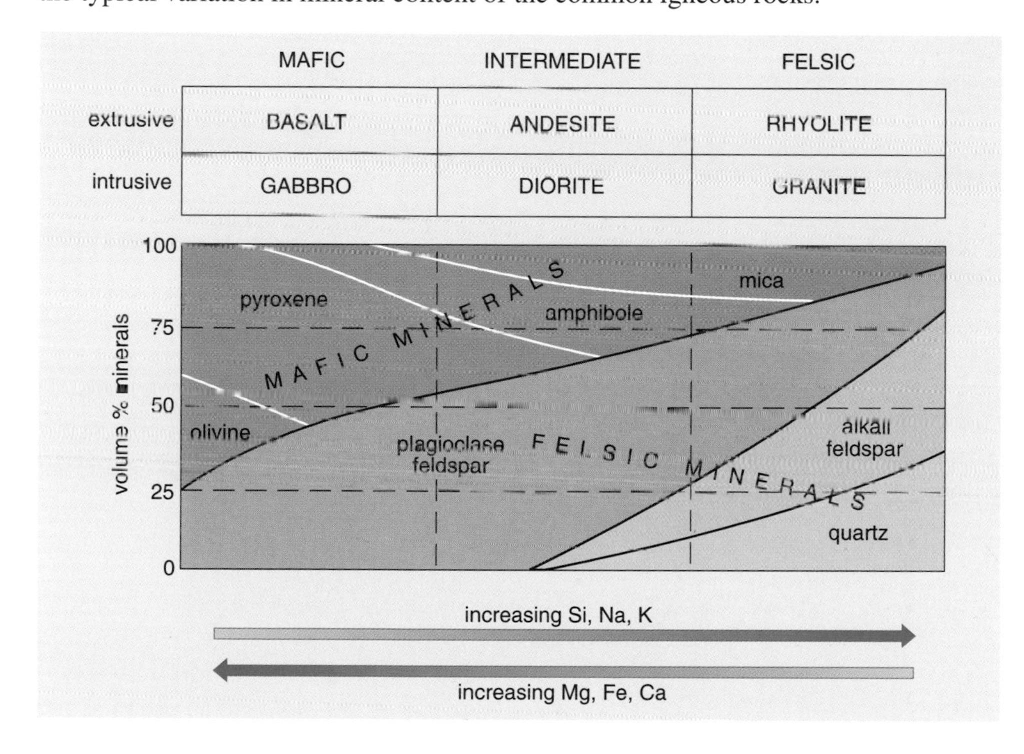

Figure 5.7 The variation of mineral contents for the range of common igneous rocks. The mineral contents shown are more appropriate for intrusive rocks than extrusive rocks. In intrusive rocks, hydrous minerals (hydrous means containing water), such as amphibole and mica, are more abundant than in equivalent extrusive rocks (because water tends to escape on eruption, before crystallization occurs). The arrows beneath the diagram show how the contents of certain elements vary across the compositional range of common igneous rocks.

- In Figure 5.7 how much do the percentages of (a) plagioclase feldspar in gabbro, (b) quartz in granite, and (c) pyroxene in diorite, vary?
- (a) Plagioclase feldspar in gabbro varies from about 25% to 55%.
  (b) Quartz in granite varies from about 10% to nearly 40%.
  (c) Pyroxene in diorite varies from about 25% to 0%.

There is a third group of rocks in the middle of Figure 5.7 with compositions between the felsic and mafic rocks; these are the *intermediate rocks*. Fine-grained lavas of this kind are **andesites** and the equivalent coarse-grained plutonic rocks are **diorites**. The dominant felsic mineral in these intermediate rocks is plagioclase feldspar. The dominant mafic mineral is usually pyroxene or amphibole, a hydrous chain silicate mineral (Table 4.2).

Question 5.3 Use Figure 5.7 to answer the following questions:

(a) Which common igneous rocks contain the highest proportion of quartz?

(b) Which common igneous rocks contain the highest proportion of mafic minerals?

(c) Which common igneous rocks contain no alkali feldspar?

(d) How does the mineral content of diorite differ from that of granite?

(e) How do the proportions of chemical elements in diorite differ from those in gabbro? ◀

Figure 5.7 shows there is a marked diversity of mineral, and therefore chemical, compositions among igneous rocks. How can we account for this diversity of igneous rock types? What geological processes might be responsible? Explaining how different types of igneous rock are formed has long been a major preoccupation of geologists. It will help you to understand the origins of different igneous rocks if we consider first the plate-tectonic settings in which they occur.

5.1.3 The global framework of igneous activity

In Block 3, Section 14, you saw how the global distribution of volcanic activity is related to plate boundaries. Figure 5.8 makes this link directly by combining Figures 8.3 and 13.4 of Block 3.

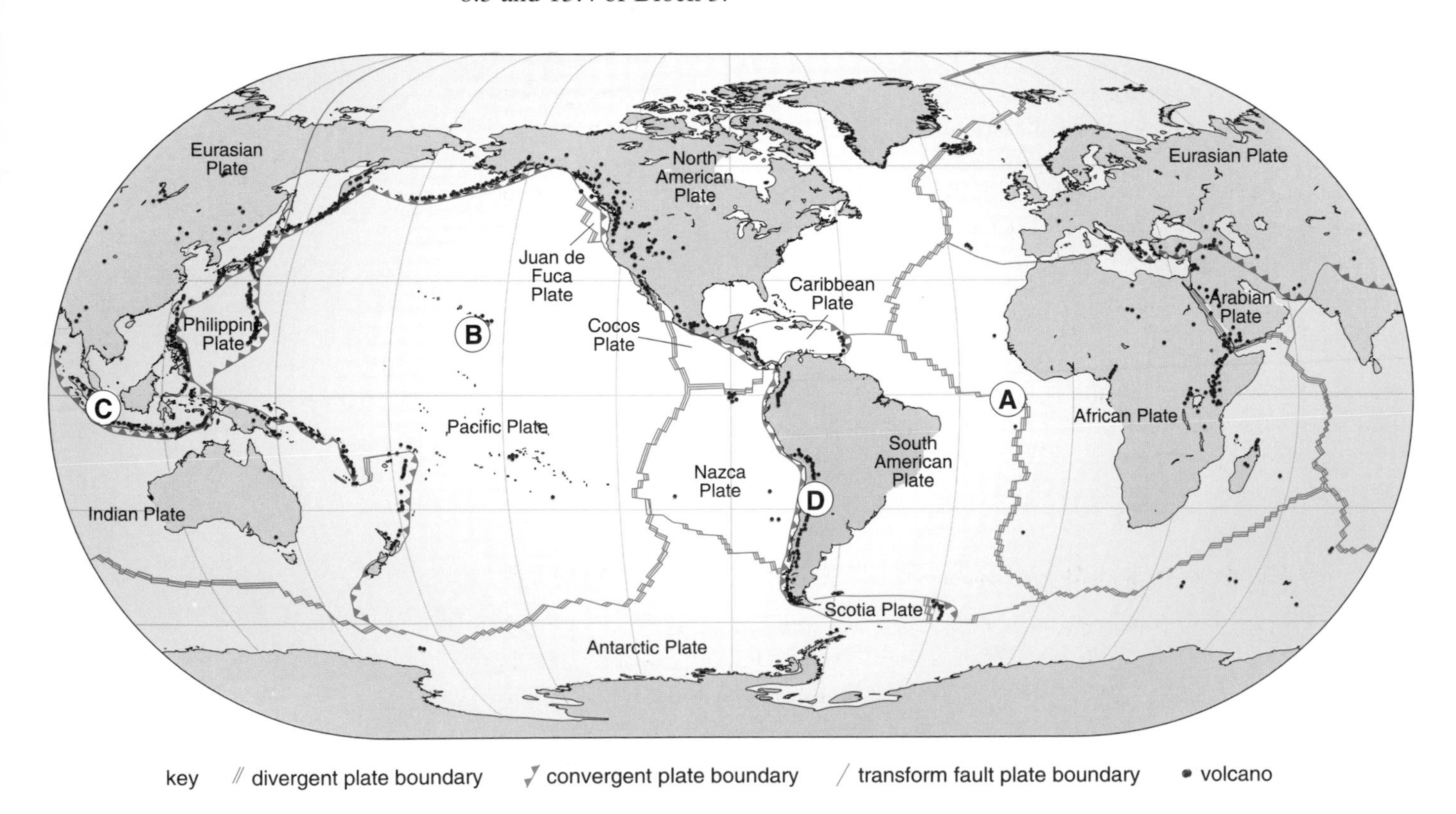

Figure 5.8 The world distribution of modern-day volcanoes and lithospheric plate boundaries.

- Describe the three main types of occurrence of active volcanism — for example at locations A, B, C and D in Figure 5.8 — in relation to particular types of plate boundaries.

- The main occurrences are at:

  A: divergent plate boundaries, where submarine volcanism (not represented in Figure 5.8) is centred on mid-ocean ridges and forms new oceanic crust (Block 3, Sections 12 and 14).

  B: localized centres, often remote from plate boundaries, where volcanic activity occurs above hot spots in the Earth's mantle (Block 3, Section 15).

  C and D: convergent plate boundaries where volcanic arcs occur either on oceanic crust (C) or on continental crust (D) that overlies oceanic lithosphere that is being subducted (Block 3, Section 14).

Magmatism at these sites can be characterized by the main kinds of igneous rock to be found there. In Block 3 we found that magmas erupted at divergent plate margins (A), and hot spots (B), such as Hawaii, are both mainly basaltic. In each case the source of the magma is the underlying mantle (Block 3, Sections 14 and 15). The implication is that the peridotite mantle melts to produce magma of basaltic composition. **Peridotite** generally contains much more Mg-rich olivine (Mg_2SiO_4) and much less of the other minerals normally found in basalt. It is therefore much richer in magnesium and poorer in calcium, aluminium and silicon than the magma it produces. We shall see why this is the case in Section 5.2.

The compositions of magmas erupted at volcanic arcs at convergent plate boundaries (locations C and D) are much more variable than those at divergent boundaries (A) or at hot spots (B). They range from basaltic to andesitic to rhyolitic. In *oceanic* volcanic arcs (C) the dominant compositions tend to be basaltic to andesitic; and in *continental* volcanic arcs, like the Andes (D), they are andesitic to rhyolitic.

- In which of these types of arc would you be more likely to find granite plutons?

- In continental volcanic arcs, where rhyolitic magmas are more important.

To explain how different magmas are produced and to account for the diversity of igneous rocks, particularly those of volcanic arcs, we need to examine more closely the ways in which igneous rocks form. We shall look first at the melting processes that generate magma and then at the crystallization processes that form igneous rocks.

5.2 From rock to magma: melting processes

All igneous rocks are formed from magma, but, as we discovered in Block 3, Section 13, the lithosphere is essentially solid, and not even the asthenosphere beneath it is liquid, although it *is* less rigid. So how do magmas arise in the first place? Considering the global distribution of volcanism (Figure 5.8), magma formation must be something that happens locally and regionally, but not everywhere, and must involve melting of either mantle or crustal rocks.

5.2.1 Partial melting of rocks

If the molten material or magma produced when a rock melts had the same composition as the rock itself, rather like ice (solid water) melting to form (liquid) water, we would hardly need to consider melting any further. However, this is not the

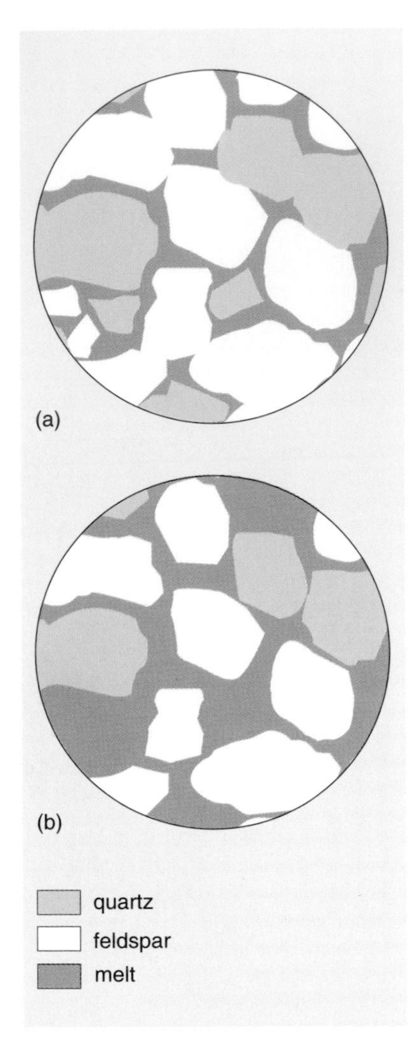

Figure 5.9 Progressive melting in rocks starts at grain boundaries where minerals are in contact: (a) 10% melting; (b) 30% melting.

case; we have already seen that basaltic magma comes from mantle that has a different composition — that of peridotite (Section 5.1.3). So what happens when rocks melt to produce magma?

When ice melts to form water it does so at a fixed temperature, 0 °C (at normal atmospheric pressure). But pure water (H_2O) behaves this way because it's a single chemical compound. Rocks, on the other hand, are usually made up of several minerals, each of which melts at a different temperature. Of course, the melting temperatures of silicate minerals are all very high compared with water; most are well in excess of 1 000 °C. However, when an assemblage of minerals is heated up and melts, the minerals don't melt individually as you might expect. Instead, several minerals melt at the same time and at much *lower* temperatures than any of them would on their own. This kind of effect may be more familiar in a different context.

- What is the effect of spreading rock salt on icy roads in winter?
- It causes the ice to melt.

When ice and rock salt are in contact, the mixture of solids melts at a much lower temperature than ice itself. Together they make a salt solution which remains liquid at temperatures well below the freezing temperature of pure water. Likewise, an assemblage of minerals in a silicate rock starts to melt at lower temperatures than the melting temperatures of the individual minerals. Consequently, melting starts at grain boundaries where minerals are in contact with one another, as can be seen in Figure 5.9a. Unlike pure water, a mineral assemblage melts over a range of temperature (several hundred degrees Celsius), and the amount of melt produced increases progressively with increasing temperature (Figure 5.9b).

The actual temperature at which melting begins depends on the particular minerals present *and* on the amount of water present, as water reduces the melting temperature of most mineral assemblages. Experimental studies show that rocks containing felsic minerals (including quartz and feldspars) along with water or hydrous minerals (e.g. mica), start melting at between 650 and 800 °C, whereas rocks containing mafic, mainly anhydrous minerals (minerals such as pyroxene or olivine that do not contain water) start to melt only at much higher temperatures of 1 050 to 1 300 °C.

The order in which common minerals tend to melt is shown in Figure 5.10. As a rock is heated up, depending on the minerals it contains, assemblages of mainly felsic minerals (i.e. quartz, feldspar and pale mica*) melt first. At higher temperatures, mafic minerals (i.e. dark mica, amphibole, pyroxene and olivine) start to melt.

Question 5.4 Referring to Activity 4.2 and Figure 5.10, describe how in general the composition and internal structure of felsic minerals that melt at lower temperatures differ from those of mafic minerals that melt at higher temperatures. ◄

When peridotite mantle rich in olivine starts to melt, pyroxene and other minerals melt along with some olivine. The proportion of olivine that melts, however, is much less than its proportion in the rock (because of its high melting temperature), hence the composition of the first drops of magma is very different from the mantle — it is basaltic. With continued melting, the magma would consume proportionately more

*Pale mica (muscovite), which contains very little magnesium and iron, melts at lower temperatures than dark mica (biotite), which contains much magnesium and iron.

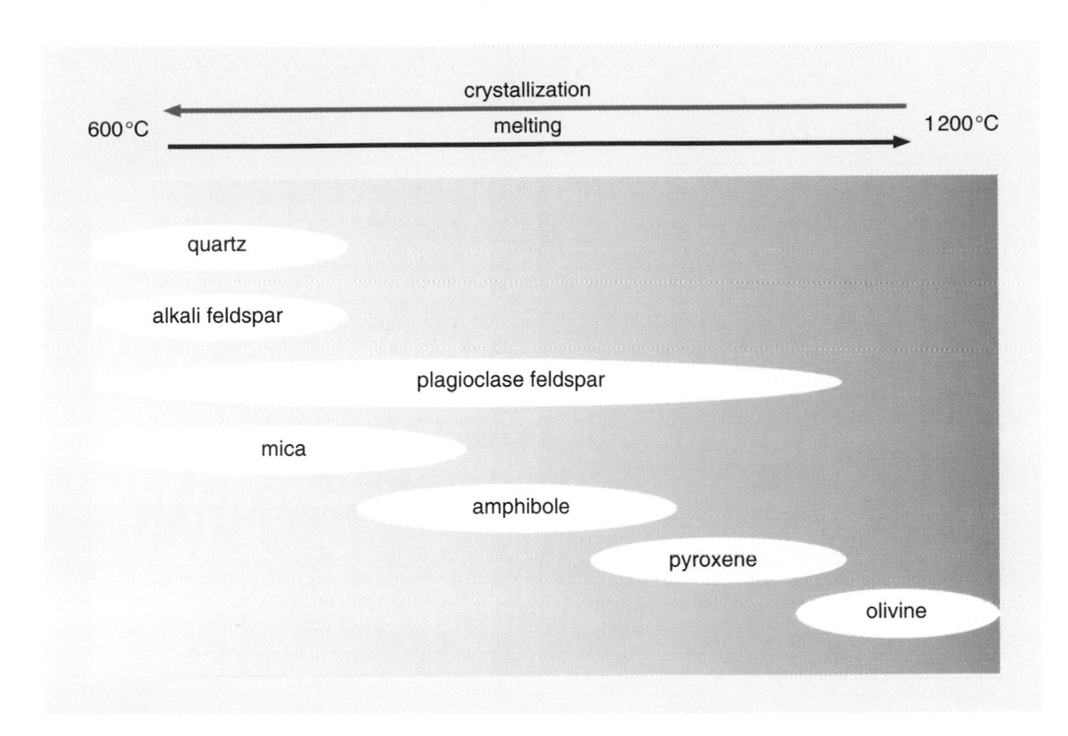

Figure 5.10 Generalized sequence of melting (and crystallization) of common rock-forming minerals with changing temperature.

olivine. If melting continued to completion, melting peridotite mantle would produce a magma of peridotite composition — but that doesn't happen because temperatures high enough for peridotite to melt completely are never reached in the mantle. In addition, once melting is under way, pockets of magma can join up and coalesce. The rock structure is weakened and the magma can migrate away from its source, usually in an upwards direction, because it is less dense than the minerals remaining. As a result, an unmelted *residue*, mainly of olivine, is left behind.

Magmas, therefore, are generally produced, not by complete melting, but by **partial melting** of their source rock. This explains how basaltic magma containing higher levels of silicon and calcium, but much lower levels of magnesium, comes to be produced from peridotite. To put it another way, because felsic minerals generally melt more readily and at lower temperatures than mafic ones, partial melting tends to create magmas that have more felsic compositions than their sources.

- Considering the order in which minerals melt during partial melting, how might you expect the chemical composition of a magma formed when a dioritic rock starts melting to differ from the initial rock composition?

- The felsic minerals of the diorite will tend to melt first, so the magma produced initially, at least, will be more felsic. By reference to Figure 5.7, you can see that it will be a granitic (rhyolitic) magma which is *richer* in silicon and alkali metals than the diorite.

In a simplified way, the melting of any rocks containing both felsic and mafic minerals may be represented as follows:

$$\text{felsic minerals} + \text{mafic minerals} \xrightarrow{\text{partial melting}} \text{dominantly felsic magma} + \text{dominantly mafic mineral residue} \quad (5.1)$$

Thus, a dioritic (andesitic) magma can be produced by partial melting of gabbro – in composition the same as average oceanic crust; and a granitic (rhyolitic) magma can be produced by partial melting of diorite – in composition the same as average continental crust. (We called continental crust granitic in Block 3, for simplicity, but now we can say, more accurately, that it is dioritic.) Partial melting therefore provides a means to produce magmas, and hence igneous rocks, with compositions that differ from their source rocks, as indicated in Figure 5.11.

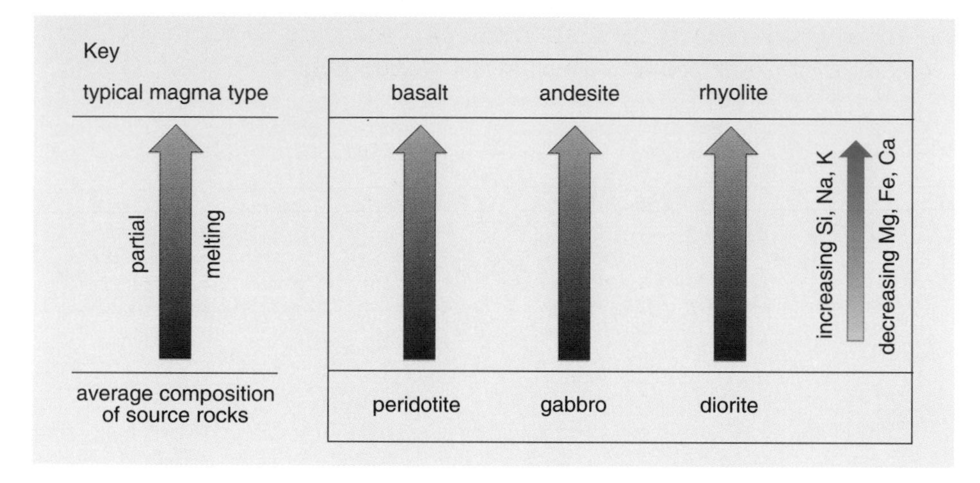

Figure 5.11 Typical relationships between source rocks and types of magma produced by partial melting. Named sources represent average rock compositions. Magmas are referred to by extrusive terms; intrusive terms are equally acceptable. Changes in chemical composition due to partial melting are also summarized.

Melting to produce balsatic magma occurs mainly in the mantle, and usually at considerable depth, because mantle peridotite (containing mainly mafic minerals) requires high temperatures to melt. Only in exceptional circumstances are melting temperatures attained in the continental crust sufficient to produce granitic magma, and then only at the base of very thick crust such as that formed during plate collisions (Block 3, Section 16, and Section 7.3 of this block).

5.3 From magma to igneous rock: crystallization processes

Just as a rock melts progressively over a range of temperatures, when a magma cools, it crystallizes progressively over a range of temperatures. If cooling is rapid, however, crystallization is also rapid and forms a network of randomly-oriented, fine-grained crystals. This is what happens when magma solidifies at the Earth's surface to form volcanic rocks. If cooling is slow, as in a large magma chamber deep within the Earth, crystallization is gradual and crystals can grow much larger. Minerals with high melting temperatures are the first to crystallize (Figure 5.10); they get an early start, and often grow large. If the magma erupts before crystallization is complete, and cools quickly, a porphyritic texture results (Figure 5.6b), very like that of the basalt in your Kit. The large pyroxene and plagioclase feldspar crystals that you observed in Activity 5.1 were probably formed early, before eruption.

5.3.1 Fractional crystallization of magma

- When basaltic magma cools gradually, what minerals are likely to crystallize first?

- They are likely to be minerals with high melting temperatures: olivine first, and then pyroxene and plagioclase feldspar (Figure 5.10).

These early-forming minerals, both individually and combined in the proportions in which they crystallize together, have a different chemical composition from that of the magma itself, and so the composition of the magma that remains must change continually during crystallization. While crystals and liquid remain together, complete solidification will produce a rock with the same overall composition as that of the original magma. However, if a crystal-rich portion and a liquid-rich portion of the magma become separated (Figure 5.12), each will have a different composition from the original magma. This process is known as **fractional crystallization** because the magma separates into different *fractions*: one is rich in crystals of early-formed mafic minerals, the other is a more felsic magma with few of those crystals.

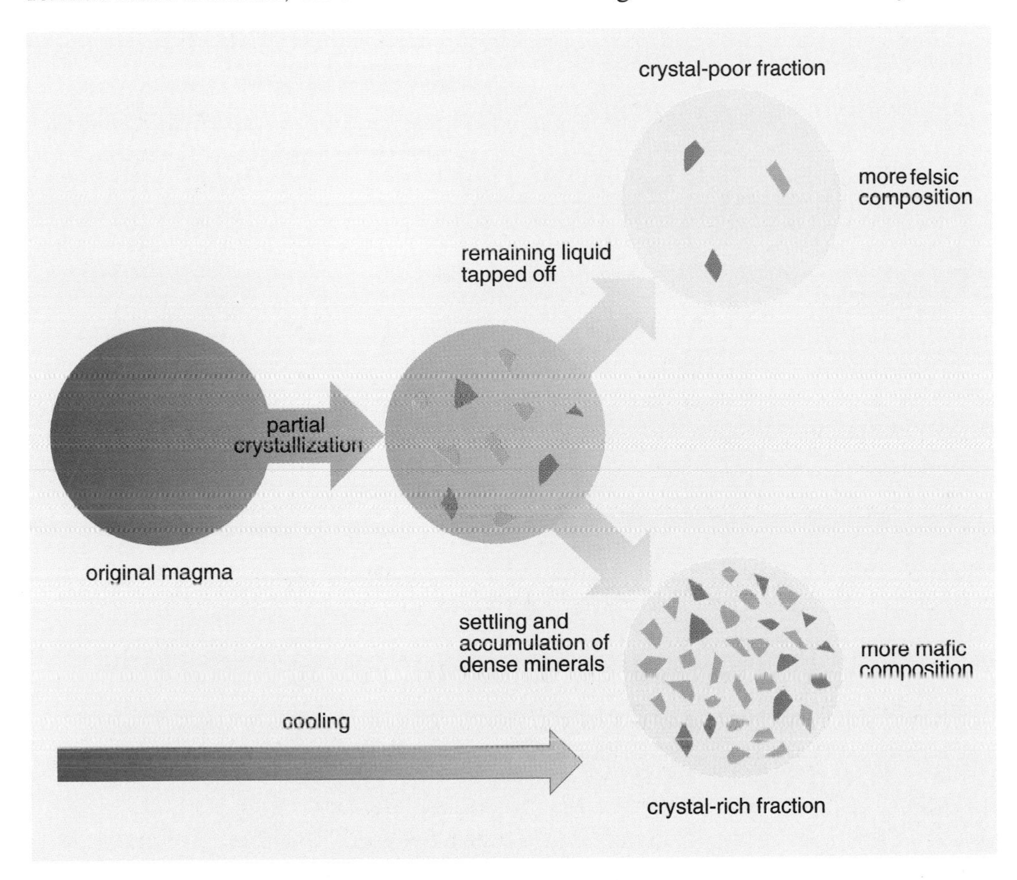

Figure 5.12 The production of different igneous rocks by fractional crystallization. One fraction is rich in accumulated crystals of mafic minerals, the other is mainly a more felsic liquid.

- If the minerals forming at high temperatures in a basaltic magma were dominated by olivine, how would the chemical composition of the remaining liquid change?

- Because olivine is rich in magnesium and iron, the magma remaining must become depleted in these constituents, and become correspondingly richer in its other constituents, especially silicon, sodium and potassium. (Calcium is depleted too because plagioclase feldspar and pyroxene also crystallize at high temperatures and are rich in calcium.)

How might separation of crystals and magma occur? Crystals of early-formed mafic minerals are denser than basaltic magma and tend to settle under gravity. If the liquid-rich portion of magma were separated from the crystal-rich portion, as indicated in Figure 5.12, it would be more felsic than the original magma. If this process occurred repeatedly, fractional crystallization of a basaltic magma could produce a series of intermediate (andesitic) and felsic (rhyolitic) magmas, as indicated in Figure 5.13.

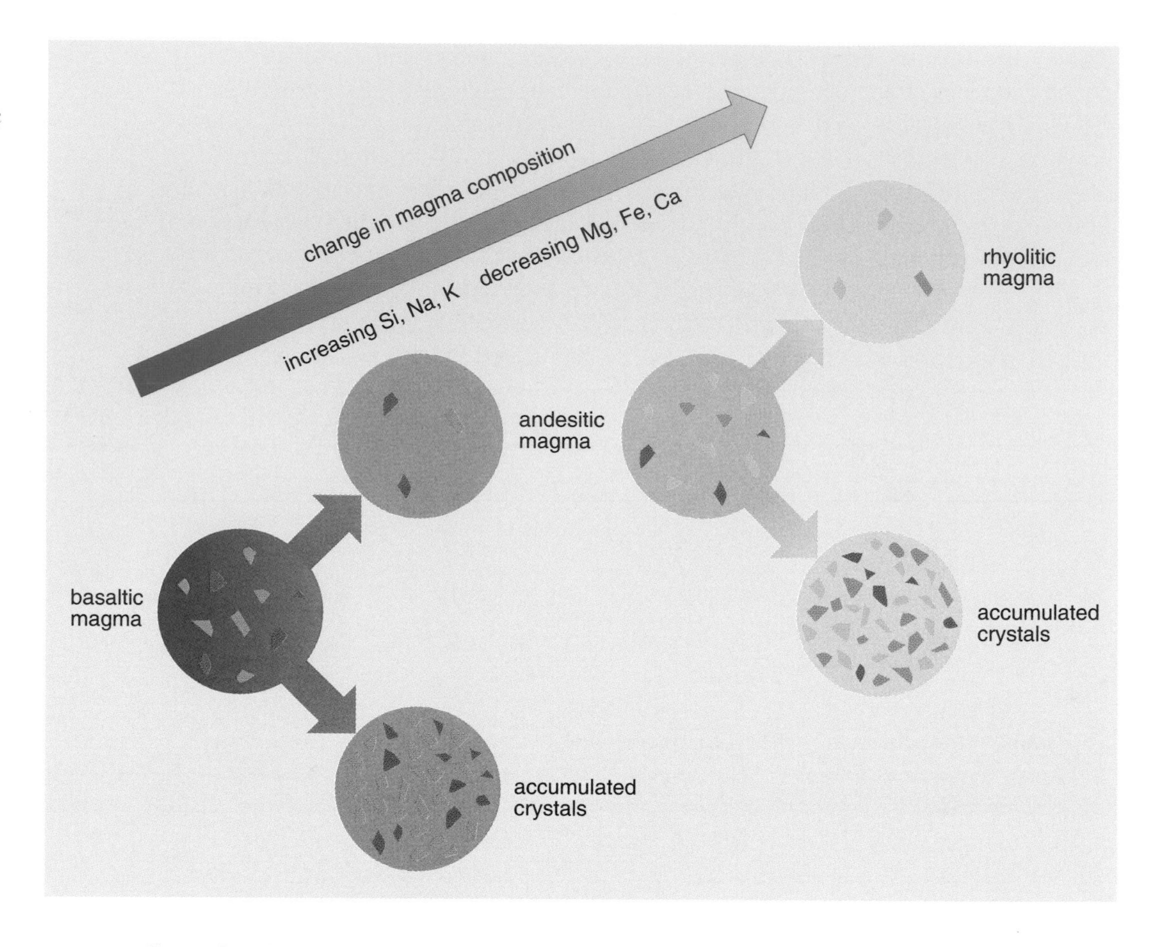

Figure 5.13 The production of progressively more felsic magmas as a result of repeated fractional crystallization. The process may be continuous or occur in stages, as shown.

So, rather like partial melting, fractional crystallization also provides a mechanism that can produce a range of increasingly felsic magmas (Figure 5.13). This process starts from a magma derived by partial melting and already more felsic than its source.

5.4 Magmas, processes and plate-tectonic settings

Having investigated the main processes involved in the formation of magmas and igneous rocks, we can look again at the igneous rocks produced in different tectonic settings (Section 5.1.3) and see how these processes may account for the presence of different magma types. Magma types produced by partial melting depend on the composition of the rocks available for melting, as indicated in Figure 5.11, as well as the *extent* of melting. Likewise, fractional crystallization may produce different magma compositions depending on the extent of crystallization and the starting composition of the magma (Figure 5.13).

The character of magmatic activity arising in the different global settings featured in Figure 5.8 is summarized in Figure 5.14. At mid-ocean ridges, magma is mainly basaltic, produced by partial melting of mantle peridotite at relatively shallow depths. At hot spots, magma is produced by partial melting of mantle peridotite at greater depths. Although basaltic compositions again dominate, other compositions can be produced by fractional crystallization in shallow magma chambers.

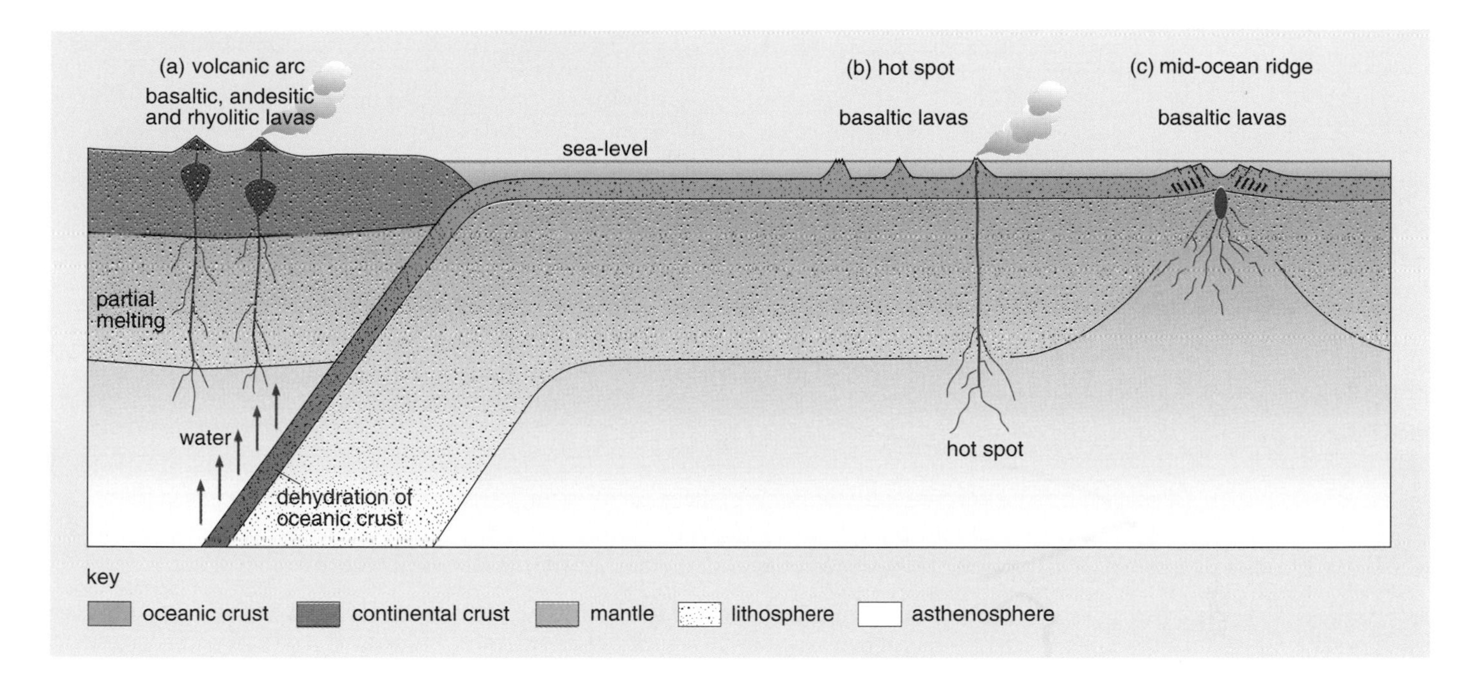

Figure 5.14 Composite diagram showing the typical nature of magmatism in various plate-tectonic settings: (a) basaltic, andesitic and rhyolitic magmas generated by melting of mantle (and crust) at a convergent plate margin to form a volcanic arc (shown here, on continental crust); (b) basaltic magma generated by partial melting of the mantle at hot spots to form oceanic volcanic islands; (c) basaltic magma generated by partial melting of the mantle at a divergent plate margin.

Magmatism in volcanic arcs is more complicated: the volcanic rocks have a variety of compositions ranging from basalt to andesite to rhyolite (Figure 5.14). Not surprisingly, intrusions of gabbro, diorite and granite (of equivalent compositions) are exposed in older, eroded arcs. However, as noted in Section 5.1.3, basaltic to andesitic magma compositions tend to dominate in oceanic arcs (underlain by thin oceanic crust), whereas andesitic to rhyolitic compositions tend to dominate in continental arcs (underlain by thick continental crust; Figure 5.14a). How might we explain this?

In oceanic arcs, partial melting of the peridotite mantle, assisted by water released from dehydrating minerals in the subducting oceanic crust (Block 3, Section 14.2 and Figure 5.14 of this book), is responsible for basaltic magma formation, and andesitic magmas are produced by fractional crystallization of this magma. In continental arcs, it's not quite as simple. From Figures 5.11 and 5.13, you can see that andesitic to rhyolitic magma compositions could be produced either by partial melting of gabbroic to dioritic source compositions or by fractional crystallization of basaltic to andesitic magmas (or by a combination of both). However, we know that hot basaltic magmas can be produced in the mantle beneath continental arcs, and we know that continental crust is of dioritic composition and therefore more felsic than the gabbroic crust of oceanic arcs.

- What do you think might happen if hot basaltic magma intrudes dioritic crustal rocks containing a high proportion of felsic minerals?

- If the temperature of the dioritic rocks were raised sufficiently, felsic minerals could start to melt, producing a granitic magma.

Therefore, when crust of dioritic composition at continental arcs is intruded by basaltic magma from the mantle, melting could form granitic magma. Mixing of the basaltic and granitic magmas could produce magmas of intermediate compositions, and, with fractional crystallization, this would account for the prevalence of andesitic and rhyolitic magmas in continental arcs.

5.4.1 Keys to the past

Clearly, distinctive types of igneous rocks are produced in particular tectonic settings today, and the presence of the same rock types can be used to indicate equivalent settings in the geological past. However, the geological record, as seen on land, may be biased.

- Which are more likely to be preserved in the geological record on land — igneous rocks of volcanic arcs or those of the ocean floor?

- The rocks of volcanic arcs are more likely to be preserved, as they are less likely to be subducted than those of the ocean floor (Block 3, Section 16.2 and Figure 16.4).

Volcanic arcs are preserved in the geological record either because they formed along a continental margin (e.g. the Andes), or in the case of oceanic arcs because they were accreted in tectonic events during collisions with continents. Some ocean floor rocks are also accreted onto continents (Block 3, Section 16.2).

Rocks of the Lizard Peninsula in Cornwall, England, were formed as oceanic crust. They include basaltic submarine volcanic rocks (pillow lavas) in association with typical oceanic rocks or *ophiolites* (gabbro, peridotite and serpentinite), as described in Block 3, Section 14.1. The volcanic rocks of either oceanic or continental arcs are distinguished by the presence of a range of igneous rock compositions, often dominated by andesitic volcanic rocks or dioritic intrusive rocks. The Lake District of northern England is considered to have been a volcanic arc about 470 Ma ago, because thick sequences of basaltic and andesitic rocks of that age are found there (Section 9.1).

Question 5.5 Which is more diagnostic of a particular type of former plate boundary, a large quantity of basaltic lava or a large quantity of andesitic lava? Explain your answer. ◀

You've now seen how melting can transform rocks into magma and how magma can crystallize to produce an igneous rock. Igneous processes operate rather like melting down scrap metal to create a sparkling new product on solidification. Natural recycling by igneous processes (melting and solidification) is an important part of the rock cycle (Figure 5.2). Extrusive igneous rocks are erupted directly onto the Earth's surface: intrusive igneous rocks become exposed only as a result of crustal uplift due to earth movements and subsequent erosion. Once at the surface, igneous rocks are attacked by weathering and erosion to embark on yet another stage of the rock cycle, which is the subject of Section 6.

5.5 Summary of Section 5

Igneous rocks are distinguished by their textures, which feature randomly-oriented, interlocking and intergrown crystals.

A diversity of igneous rocks exists because of different magma compositions and different crystallization histories. Usually, large bodies of intrusive rock are coarse-grained; layers of extrusive rocks are fine-grained. Magma chambers form plutons; and their offshoots form sheet-like dykes and sills.

Fundamental differences in magma composition are often reflected by the presence of different minerals in igneous rocks. Mafic rocks (e.g. gabbro, basalt) are rich in mafic minerals (especially pyroxene). Felsic rocks (e.g. granite, rhyolite) are dominated by felsic minerals (especially quartz and feldspar). Amounts of mafic and felsic minerals are more equally balanced in intermediate rocks (e.g. diorite and andesite).

Magmatic activity today is concentrated at mid-ocean ridges, at hot spots in oceanic areas, and along volcanic arcs, both in oceanic settings and along continental margins.

Partial melting produces magmas more felsic in composition than their source rock. Fractional crystallization produces magmas more felsic in composition than the original magma.

Partial melting and fractional crystallization processes operating in different circumstances account for the production of different types of igneous rocks in different tectonic settings. Peridotite mantle partially melts to produce basaltic magma beneath mid-ocean ridges, ocean island hot spots and oceanic volcanic arcs. Partial melting of peridotite mantle and dioritic crust beneath continental arcs, with subsequent mixing of magmas and fractional crystallization together produce a range of igneous rocks, including andesites and rhyolites.

Particular associations of igneous rock types in the geological record can help to reveal past tectonic settings.

Activity 5.3 Revision and consolidation

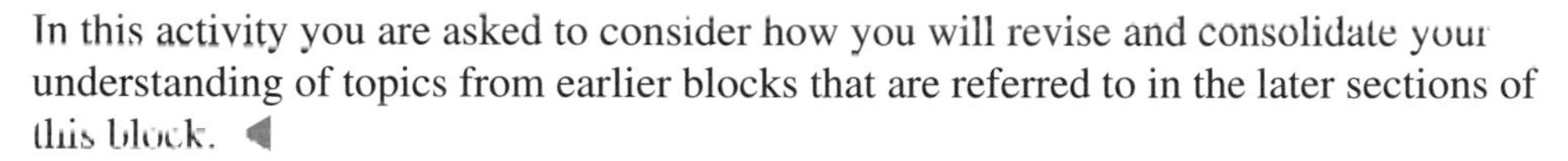

In this activity you are asked to consider how you will revise and consolidate your understanding of topics from earlier blocks that are referred to in the later sections of this block. ◀

6 Sedimentary rocks — recording surface environments

We saw in Block 3 (Section 9 and Activity 9.1) that most sedimentary rocks are formed by the accumulation of fragmentary material at the Earth's surface. Consequently, sedimentary processes are more visible than most igneous processes, which operate largely within the Earth where they are hidden from view. We don't have to go far to see sediments accumulating: they might be sands or pebbles on beaches, muds in river estuaries, pebbles or boulders in upland streams, or just sand and gravel at the roadside after heavy rain.

(a)

(b)

(c)

In contrast, most sedimentary *rocks*, as often seen exposed in quarries, road cuttings, mountains and cliffs, are not made of loose materials. How then, would you recognize their sedimentary origin? In Block 3, Section 9 (and subsequently in Figure 5.1c of this block) we distinguished sedimentary rocks by their fragmentary texture, but in rock exposures it's possible to recognize another important feature of most sedimentary deposits — the presence of layering. Changes in the type of sediment deposited over time, and breaks in deposition, give rise to individually distinguishable sedimentary layers. Layering occurs on a variety of scales from millimetres to metres in thickness. Marked changes or breaks in deposition define *beds* (e.g. the strata of Figure 3.11), each of which may contain a series of layers. Figure 6.1 shows examples of bedded sedimentary rocks in field exposures. When formed, beds are usually horizontal (Figure 6.1a and c), but layers within them can be deposited at an angle to the horizontal (Figure 6.1b).

From these examples (and others you may have seen), you will be aware that a wide diversity of sedimentary rocks exists, just as there is a wide diversity of igneous rocks. Our main task is to discover what these rocks can tell us about the way they formed, but first we need to see what they are made of and how we can classify them.

6.1 The stuff of sediments

The fragmentary materials of which most sedimentary deposits are made come in a vast range of grain sizes, from the finest of wind-blown dusts, measured in micrometres, to blocks of rock as big as buses that may be moved by floods, by glaciers, or by landslides. Familiar names are used for grains of different sizes (Figure 6.2). In categories of increasing grain size, there are **muds** (including clay and silt), which are very fine-grained and feel smooth when squeezed between fingers; **sands**, which are granular and feel gritty; pebbles, which are grains larger than peppercorns; cobbles, larger than a tennis ball; and boulders, which are larger than a football.

Figure 6.1 A range of sedimentary rocks in field exposures (with scales given as vertical extent): (a) beds of rounded pebbles and cobbles (2 m), (b) sloping layers of sand (2 m), and (c) beds of fine-grained mud (40 cm).

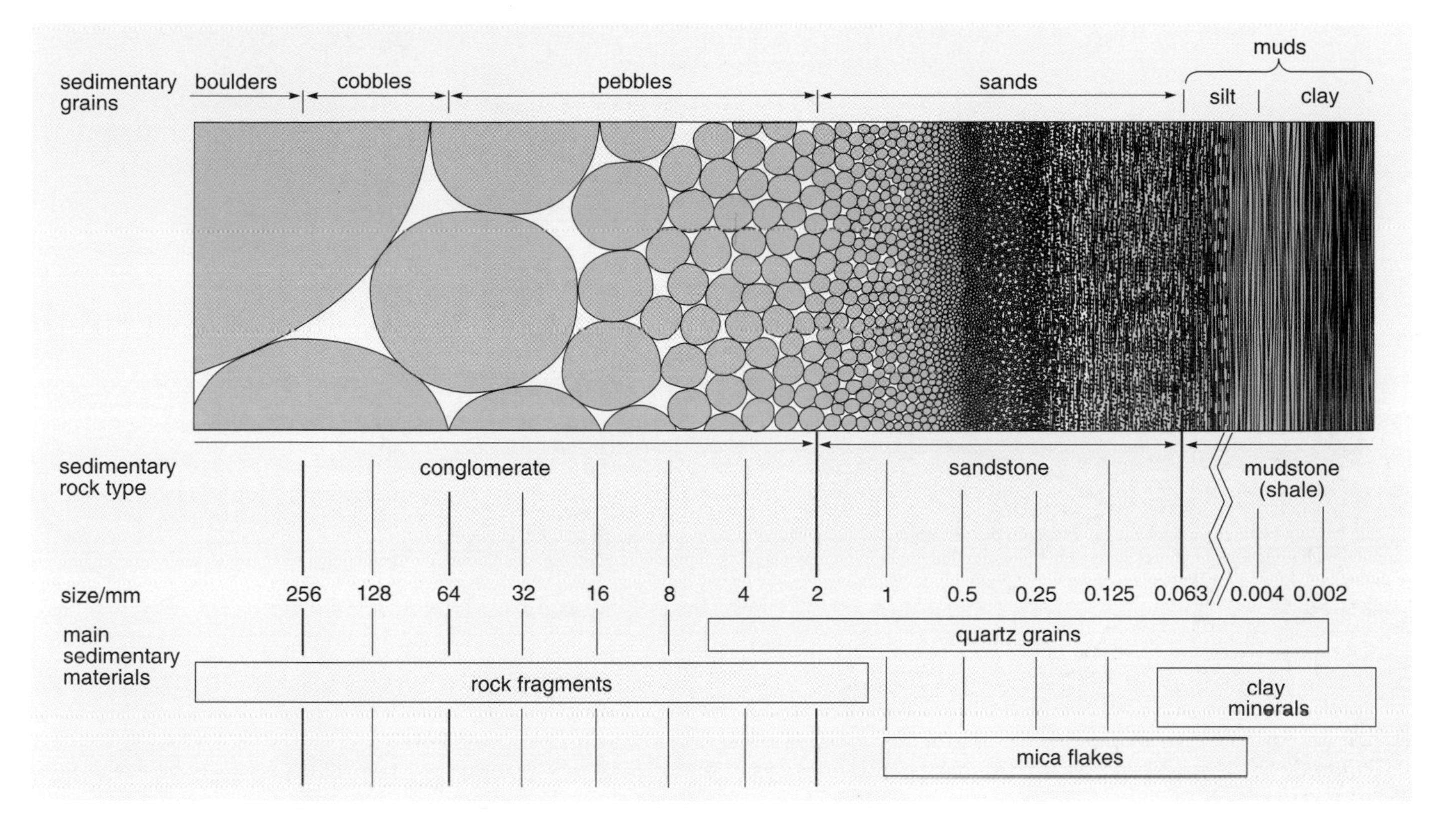

Figure 6.2 Classification of sedimentary materials and corresponding rock types according to grain size. Typical materials found in sediments are also indicated. Note that the scale is not linear; successive divisions represent halving of grain size, with a break between 0.063 and 0.004 mm.

Activity 6.1 A look at sedimentary materials in soil

In this activity you will investigate the sedimentary materials in a sample of soil. ◀

You discovered in Activity 6.1 that individual grains of sediment can be distinguished by a variety of features, such as their size, their shape and their mineral composition. In fact, many sedimentary rocks are classified according to the nature of the fragments they contain, especially their grain size and composition.

Grain size: **Mudstones** and **sandstones** are named according to their grain sizes (Figure 6.2). A rock with larger grain sizes is usually called a **conglomerate** if the grains are well-rounded, and a *breccia* if the grains are angular.

Composition: Sediments can be made of any material at the Earth's surface that can survive transport and accumulation. Fragmentary grains are derived mainly from rocks, minerals, and the skeletons or shells of organisms (Section 2). Pebbles and larger grains are usually made of rock fragments. Sands are mostly composed of mineral grains (especially quartz), or the broken shells of organisms. The shelly material usually consists of calcium carbonate (mostly the mineral calcite) and forms limestone deposits (Block 2, Section 8). Muds contain very fine mineral grains, especially clay minerals, but also silt (mostly fine quartz) and organic matter. Curiously perhaps, many minerals found in igneous rocks, such as olivine, pyroxene and feldspars, are rare in sediments; we shall see why in Section 6.2.1.

Recognizing the grain size, grain shape, and composition of sedimentary materials can help us to classify sediments and sedimentary rocks (e.g. Figure 6.2). But what does the character of these materials tell us about the formation of sedimentary rocks? To discover that, we need to know more about the processes by which sedimentary grains are formed and shaped. Fortunately, these processes occur at the Earth's surface, and we can observe many of them directly.

6.2 Sedimentary processes

The processes involved in forming sedimentary rocks operate in the 'surface' part of the rock cycle (Figure 6.3 and Block 3, Section 17). This is where all kinds of existing rocks are *broken down* by weathering and erosion to form fragmentary material that is *transported* until it settles out under gravity to *accumulate* as layers or beds of sediment.

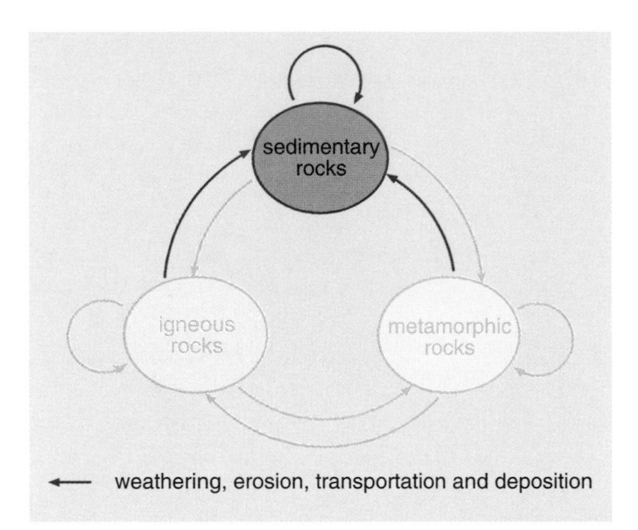

Figure 6.3 The formation of sedimentary rocks within the rock cycle. The three bold arrows indicate the routes through which sedimentary rocks can be formed by weathering, erosion, transportation and deposition.

- What are the main ways in which sedimentary material can be transported?
- By flowing water, by wind, and by glaciers (Block 3, Section 9.3).

These forms of transport account for most kinds of sediments, but some sedimentary rocks are made of accumulations of material that have not been transported far. For example, on land, dead plants such as trees collapse and decay, and may be buried where they fall, eventually to form deposits of peat and coal; in the seas, many organisms such as reef corals die, yet remain where they lived, and may become buried intact to form limestones. These are all sedimentary deposits. We shall also see (in Section 6.3.2) that some sedimentary rocks are not fragmentary.

6.2.1 Breaking down surface rocks

Most sedimentary materials are produced by the break-up of existing rocks — that's why they are fragmentary. Rocks exposed at the Earth's surface can be broken down in several ways. The processes that cause the disintegration and decomposition of rocks, during exposure to rain and surface waters, to sunshine and cold, to plants and atmospheric gases, are known as weathering (Block 3, Section 18.4). We recognize two main forms.

Figure 6.4 Slabs of broken rock on a mountain top.

Physical weathering breaks rocks apart by fragmentation. Cracks may be opened up by penetrating tree roots, but slabs of rock are commonly found broken apart on mountain tops where there have been no trees (see Figure 6.4). Percolating rainwater, however, can get into cracks in the rock.

- How could water open up cracks and split apart the rocks shown in Figure 6.4?

- Water can freeze, and, unlike most substances, water increases its volume on freezing (the density of ice is less than that of water: Block 1, Section 4.2) — that's why ice floats. As ice forms, it expands by about 9%, and in confined spaces it creates huge pressures which can open up cracks in rocks. This is also why frozen water pipes burst, and road surfaces break up in frosty weather.

On mountain tops where temperatures drop below the freezing temperature of water on many days of the year, repeated freezing and thawing of water in cracks and fissures enlarges them and causes rocks to split apart. This is frost shattering, the dominant form of physical weathering in cold, mountainous areas (Figure 6.4). Breakage tends to occur along existing lines of weakness in the rock, especially along boundaries between grains, but mineral grains themselves may also break apart.

- Some minerals break apart more easily than others. What mineral property is likely to assist breakage?

- Some minerals have one or more cleavage planes, the planes of weakness within their crystal structure that allow them to break apart more easily (Activity 4.1).

Thus, easily cleaved minerals, such as mica, feldspar and calcite, are more susceptible to breakage by physical weathering processes than is quartz, which has no cleavage planes.

Chemical weathering breaks down rocks and minerals through the chemical action of acidic waters. These waters are acidic because they contain dissolved atmospheric gases or organic acids from soils. Atmospheric carbon dioxide is soluble in rainwater and forms a weakly acidic solution according to the following reaction:

$$\underset{\text{rainwater}}{H_2O(l) + CO_2(aq)} \longrightarrow \underset{\text{acidic solution}}{H^+(aq) + HCO_3^-(aq)} \qquad (6.1)$$

The natural acidity of rainwater (pH about 5.6) can cause minerals to decompose, but in industrial areas especially, pollution of the atmosphere by sulfur and nitrogen oxides gives rise to *acid rain* (pH = 3–5), which intensifies chemical weathering.

Some minerals are more prone to attack by chemical weathering than others. Quartz is extremely resistant to chemical attack because of its framework structure made entirely of silicate tetrahedra with strong Si–O bonds (Table 4.2). Feldspars and micas are less stable than quartz because they have a variety of metal ions connecting the layers of silicate tetrahedra that form their framework and sheet structures respectively, and these metal ions can be removed during chemical weathering. As a result, their mineral structures collapse during weathering to form clay minerals that are more stable under such conditions because their sheet structures have fewer connecting metal ions. For example, the breakdown of alkali feldspar by acidic waters forms kaolinite, a hydrous clay mineral, along with soluble metal ions and silica, which are taken into solution. This is represented by the following reaction:

$$\text{alkali feldspar(s)} + \underbrace{H_2O(l) + H^+(aq)}_{\text{acidic rainwater}}$$

$$\longrightarrow \underbrace{\text{kaolinite(s)}}_{\text{clay}} + \underbrace{Na^+(aq) + K^+(aq)}_{\text{soluble ions}} + \underbrace{SiO_2(aq)}_{\text{silica}} \qquad (6.2)$$

Minerals with structures containing many metal atoms connected to silicate tetrahedra, such as olivine and pyroxene (Table 4.2), are particularly susceptible to chemical weathering. Many of these minerals form at, and are stable at, high temperatures when igneous rocks crystallize (Section 5), but under low-temperature conditions in which weathering takes place they are unstable and break down readily to produce new minerals that are more stable under the new conditions.

- How might high rainfall and high temperatures influence chemical weathering reactions, like that of Equation 6.2?

- High rainfall provides copious amounts of acidic water, an essential participant in most weathering reactions. High temperatures speed up chemical reactions (Block 8, Section 10.4).

Chemical weathering is rapid, therefore, in warm, wet, tropical climates. High temperatures and high rainfall also promote high levels of plant growth and organic activity in the soil. On the death and decay of such organisms, organic acids are produced and they increase the rate of chemical weathering. Indeed, underlying rock can be weathered to depths of tens of metres in tropical climates. In cold climates, chemical reactions are much slower, organic activity is minimal, and physical weathering dominates.

Rocks almost always break down by a *combination* of chemical and physical weathering processes. Cracks produced by physical weathering allow chemical weathering to penetrate more deeply, and the decomposition of minerals by chemical weathering makes rocks more susceptible to physical weathering. In addition, the smaller the grains produced by physical weathering, the greater the surface area for chemical weathering to attack. Thus well-cleaved minerals can be particularly susceptible to both kinds of weathering.

The products of combined physical and chemical weathering include: (i) new, stable minerals, such as clays; (ii) liberated grains of resistant minerals, such as quartz; and

(iii) soluble ions. Although it is not very soluble, small amounts of silica (SiO_2) can be carried away in solution along with the soluble metal ions (see Equation 6.2).

Once mineral grains and rock fragments are released by weathering, they can be picked up and removed more easily by a *transporting medium*, which could be flowing water, wind, or even a glacier. These are processes of **erosion** — the *mechanical removal* of rock materials. Erosion can also operate directly on solid, unweathered rock, particularly when the transporting medium is already loaded with rock debris. Moving debris, such as pebbles carried along in a turbulent river, sand blown by the wind, or boulders embedded in ice, is abrasive — it can scrape, pluck and wear away at rock surfaces and, at the same time, gets worn away itself.

Rates of erosion vary immensely. Erosion can be a gradual process, slowly wearing away rocks over long periods of time, or it may be associated with sudden, catastrophic events. You may have witnessed the scouring of a river bank during a flood; the collapse of a sea cliff by wave action during a storm; or the slippage of rock debris on a slope after heavy rain.

Question 6.1 How does weathering in hot, humid climates differ from that in cold, wet climates? What kind of weathering would you expect on the Moon? ◀

Question 6.2 How does weathering affect granite? Explain the effects of physical and chemical weathering on the main minerals of granite (as in the specimen in the Practical Kit), and state the main products of weathering. ◀

6.2.2 Transporting grains

Whether or not sedimentary material can be transported depends in part on the energy available to move it, and that energy comes from the transporting medium.

- What form of energy is this and on what properties of the transporting medium does it depend?

- It is energy due to movement, or kinetic energy (E_k), given (in Block 5, Section 3.2.1) as:

$$E_k = \frac{1}{2}mv^2 \tag{6.3}$$

This form of energy depends on the speed of movement (v) and the mass (m), and therefore on the density of the medium (i.e. its mass per unit volume).

Whether transport occurs also depends on the material itself, especially its resistance to motion, which is related to the shape, size and density of the grains. The video 'A story in sand' (Activity 6.2) shows what happens when sediment, containing a range of grain sizes, is dropped into a stream of flowing water. The larger grains settle to the bottom, as the inertia due to their mass (Block 3, Section 4.2) is too great for them to be transported. Under the influence of the water current, smaller grains roll or bounce along the stream bed, and very small grains are carried along in suspension.

Activity 6.2 Sedimentary grains, transport and sorting

This activity is based on the video 'A story in sand', which investigates what we can learn about the origins of a sediment from the grains it contains. The activity also looks at the graphical representation of grain-size distributions and at what variations in grain size can tell us about environments of sediment deposition. ◀

Activity 6.2 shows that the ability of wind or flowing water to pick up, transport and deposit sediment grains depends to a large extent on the speed of the flowing medium and the grain size of the material. The behaviour of different grain sizes with varying speed of flow is described in Figure 6.5. This graph is explained in some detail in the video 'A story in sand'.

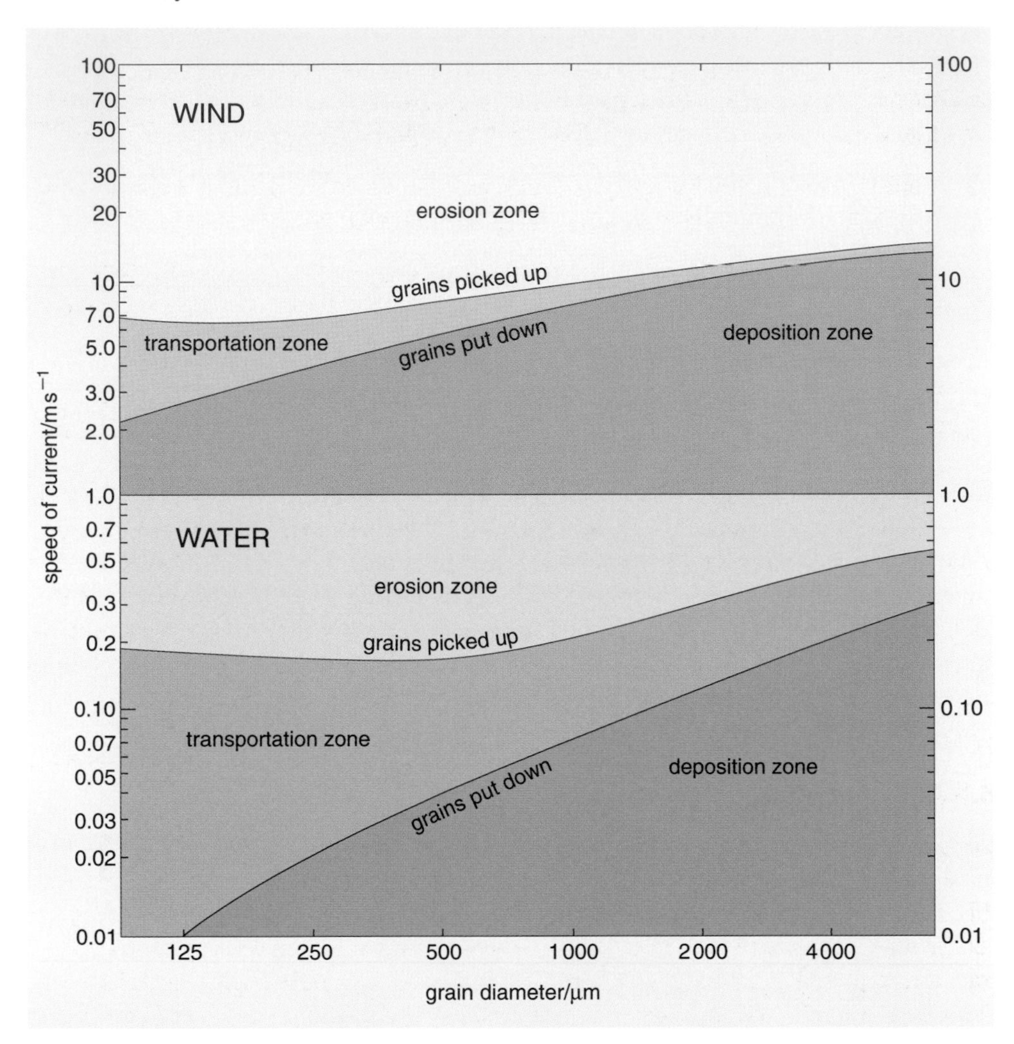

Figure 6.5 The behaviour of different-sized sediment grains at varying speeds of flow for wind and water. In each case, the boundaries of the erosion zone, the transportation zone and the deposition zone (explained in the text) were derived experimentally under controlled conditions of flow using sediment grains of uniform density. Note that the scales on the axes of the graph are not linear: on the horizontal axis, each division corresponds to a doubling of grain size; on the vertical axis, each major division corresponds to a factor of ten increase in the speed of current. These forms of scaling allow a wide range of flow rates and grain sizes to be shown.

The main points to appreciate from the blue part of Figure 6.5 relating to *water* transportation are as follows:

(i) Grains of a particular size can be *picked up* only if the speed of flowing water exceeds that of the upper curve. The slope of the curve for grain diameters above 500 micrometres means that the speed of the water current (and therefore its energy, Equation 6.3) must be increased to pick up larger grains. The region of the diagram above this curve, the *erosion zone*, therefore describes conditions under which static material of a particular size can be picked up and moved.

(ii) Grains that have already been picked up can continue to be transported at speeds of flow lower than those required for pick-up (the upper curve), until the speed of flow drops to the lower curve at the particular grain size, and then movement of the grains stops altogether. Between these two curves is the *transportation zone*.

(iii) Grains do not move at all at flow speeds below the lower curve. Material of a particular grain size, transported at higher speeds of flow, is deposited when the flow speed drops to the lower curve — this defines the *deposition zone*.

From Figure 6.5, at what speed of water current would 1 mm diameter sand grains be picked up and at what speed would they be deposited?

A flow of more than 0.2 m s^{-1} would be required to pick up 1 mm (i.e. 1 000 μm) sand grains; but they would not be deposited until the flow speed had dropped to about 0.07 m s^{-1}.

What happens to sedimentary grains while they are being transported? They are exposed both to physical abrasion and, in moist or wet conditions, to chemical attack. Sedimentary material affected by *chemical* decomposition during transport breaks down to form stable products of chemical weathering, such as clay minerals: resistant minerals, such as quartz, are liberated (Section 6.2.1). Sediments formed largely by *physical* processes of weathering and erosion tend to contain rock fragments and mineral grains derived from their source rocks. In water, impacts are cushioned, so rock fragments tend to become rounded by abrasion, rather than broken by impact. The physical nature of a rock often influences the eventual shape of the fragments produced. A thinly-layered rock tends to wear away to form disc-shaped pebbles, whereas a uniformly hard rock tends to form more spherical pebbles.

6.2.3 Dumping the load

You know from your study of Figure 6.5, and from Activity 6.1, that sedimentary material is deposited when transporting currents slow down sufficiently. Where does this usually occur? In the case of water, gravity acting on both water and its sedimentary load causes their downhill movement as gravitational energy is transformed into kinetic energy. Where flow rates are high, only coarse material is deposited; we call this a *high-energy environment*. On reaching relatively low-lying areas where slopes flatten out, the flow becomes much slower, and fine-grained sediments are deposited; this is a *low-energy environment*. Areas of lowland or sea floor where thick sequences of sediments accumulate are known as *sedimentary basins*.

The lower curve of Figure 6.5 gives the size of grains deposited at a particular speed of water flow. Because the curve rises steadily, there is a direct link between the speed of the current and the size of grains deposited: this is the basis of sediment **sorting**. The 'degree of sorting' can be used to describe and characterize certain types of sediment, as in the video, 'A story in sand'. It describes the extent to which the grains deposited are of a similar size. Thus a *well-sorted* deposit (Figure 6.6a(i), *overleaf*) contains a narrow range of grain sizes (as do packs of granulated sugar or frozen peas), whereas a *poorly-sorted* deposit (Figure 6.6a(ii)) contains a wide range of grain sizes (rather like muesli). The video also shows how the variation in grain size of a sediment (i.e. the degree of sorting) can be measured and represented as a histogram showing the proportions of material in different size ranges. Typical histograms of contrasting grain-size distributions are shown in Figure 6.6b.

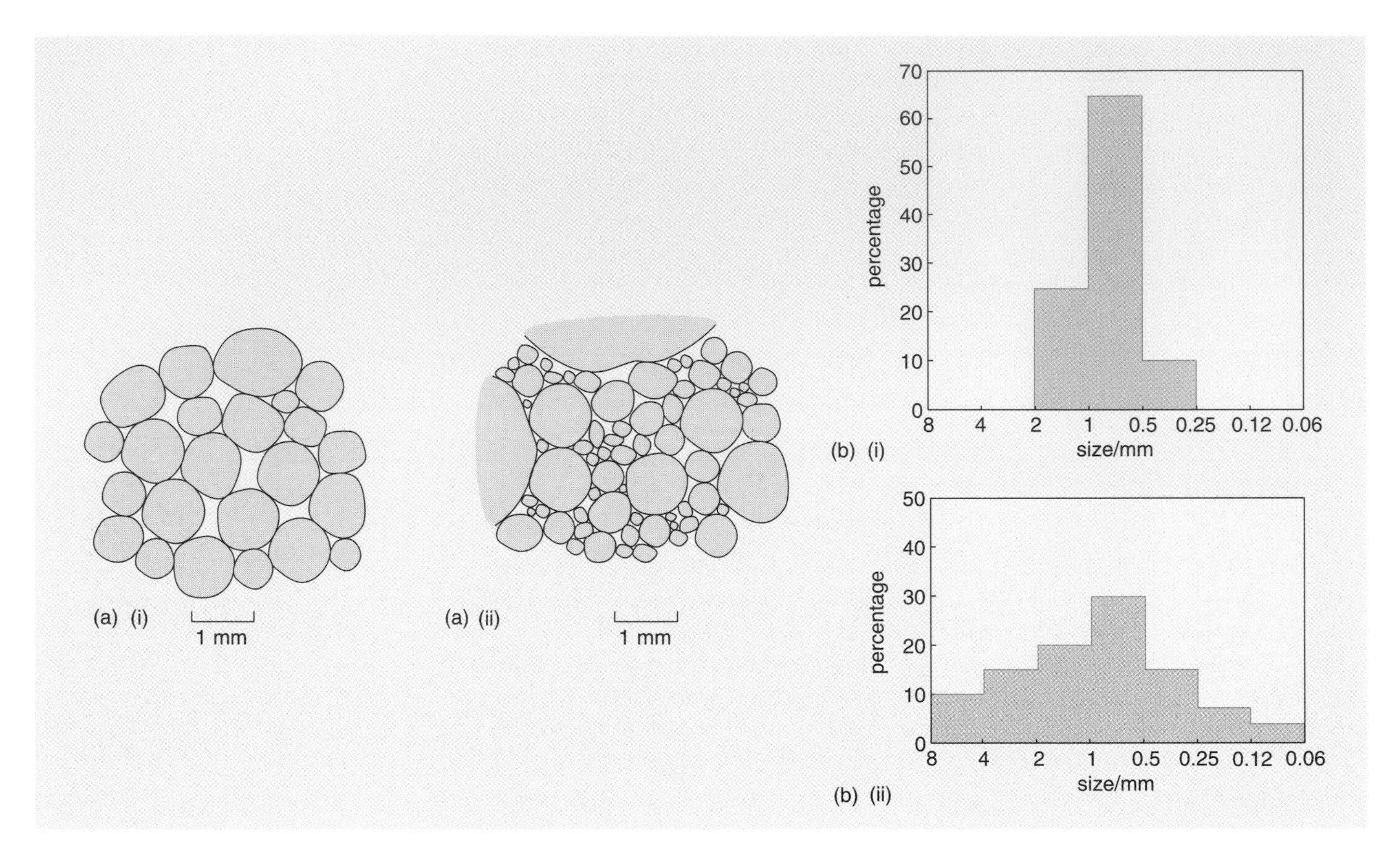

Figure 6.6 (a) Schematic representation of (i) well-sorted, and (ii) poorly-sorted sediment grains. (b) Histograms (i) and (ii) of grain-size distributions (percentages by mass) for sediments similar to those shown in (a). Note that grain sizes in the histograms decrease from left to right.

- Which of the histograms, (i) or (ii), in Figure 6.6b, corresponds more closely to the well-sorted sediment in Figure 6.6a?

- (i) is the well-sorted sediment because it records a narrow range of grain sizes.

How might sorting occur? According to Figure 6.5, a rapidly-flowing current can pick up and carry a range of grain sizes. If the current slows gradually, all the grains picked up continue to be transported until a point is reached when the coarsest material is deposited. Finer material is still carried onward. So, when speeds of flow drop slightly — either because gradients flatten, or there is a reduction in volume of flow — a narrow range of grain sizes is deposited. If the speed of flow continues to decrease steadily, grains of successively smaller size are deposited, but grains deposited at *one place* at a *particular time* will have a narrow size range and be *well-sorted*. In contrast, if a rapid flow were to subside abruptly, a wide range of grain sizes would be deposited all at once, making a *poorly-sorted* sediment. Thus, measuring the degree of sorting of a sediment can tell us about the way it formed, especially about the conditions of flow that transported and deposited it.

- In Activity 6.2 you looked at grains from the Kit sandstone and their variation in size. Is it a well-sorted or a poorly-sorted sandstone? What does that indicate about the conditions of deposition?

- In most samples, 0.5–1 mm grains are common, but grain size ranges from less than 0.1 mm to about 2 mm in diameter, so the sandstone is only moderately well-sorted and must have been deposited under somewhat variable flow conditions.

- A rapidly flowing river carries a range of sediment grain sizes. What happens to the sediment at a certain point in the channel as the current gradually slows?
- The coarse-grained material settles out first, and then as the current slows further, progressively finer material builds up on top.

A bed produced in this way is rather like the sediment that accumulated after you stopped shaking the jar during your experiment with soil in Activity 6.1. The grain size varied with height, but at a particular level in the jar the sediment was fairly well-sorted. The gradual change in grain size from the bottom to the top of the bed is known as **graded bedding** (Figure 6.7).

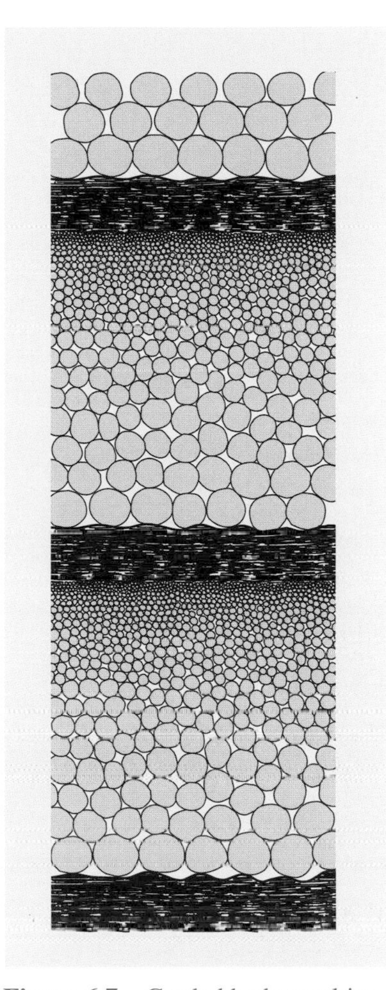

Figure 6.7 Graded beds resulting from deposition as flow speeds repeatedly decline. Successive graded beds are often separated by an eroded surface reflecting the increase in flow that precedes deposition of the next graded bed.

- Which do you think is more common, and why — to find a bed that gets finer upwards or one that coarsens upwards?
- Graded beds normally get finer upwards, as seen in the jam jar (Activity 6.1), because deposition occurs when speeds of flow decline, thus depositing progressively finer material. Increasing flow rates tend to pick up any fine material previously deposited.

Graded bedding that gets finer upwards can be useful to the field geologist, as it indicates the order in which beds were deposited. The importance of this becomes clear in Section 7.2, where you will see that rock strata can be overturned by tectonic activity.

6.3 Sedimentary deposits as environmental indicators

We have already seen how sedimentary deposits and their grains can reveal much about their origins and their conditions of deposition. All sorts of influences, such as climate, biological activity and the Earth's surface elevation create a huge diversity of depositional environments. Quite distinct types of sedimentary deposit form in environments dominated by water, by wind and by ice. The greatest variety of sedimentary environments is associated with deposition from water and includes rivers and lakes on land; beaches and deltas at coasts; shallow marine waters and deep oceanic waters. By studying the deposits of specific sedimentary environments today we can learn to recognize and make deductions about their ancient equivalents in the rock record — thus providing keys to understanding the environments of long ago.

There are many different sedimentary environments which produce distinctive rock types; far too many to cover in this course. We shall look briefly at three diverse sedimentary environments involving the transportation of fragmentary material by wind; the crystallization of salts from water; and the extraction of soluble material from seawater by marine organisms.

6.3.1 Desert sands

Imagine a hot, dry desert — a barren wilderness with sand dunes and winds that create storms of sand and dust.

- What implications does the lack of water have for weathering and for soil formation in such a desert?
- Lack of water inhibits chemical weathering, which means a lack of both soluble ions (nutrients) and clay minerals which are important components of fertile

soils. The lack of water and the poor soils severely restrict the ability of plant and animal life to survive, and without vegetation there is nothing to bind together fragments of rocks and minerals so as to resist erosion.

The main cause of physical weathering in hot deserts is associated with the expansion and contraction of rock surfaces due to extreme temperature changes. By day the Sun may raise rock surfaces to over 80 °C, and lack of cloud cover at night allows temperatures to plummet, often to well below 0 °C. Layers of rock flake off, but experiments have shown that it is only when moisture, as dew perhaps, is available to penetrate grain boundaries that this type of fragmentation is important.

The lack of water to support vegetation, and to bind together grains liberated by physical weathering, means that rock and mineral fragments in deserts are readily eroded and transported. Only rarely do heavy rains fall, but when they do, the water runs off the land surface rapidly with intense erosive power, causing flash floods. Strong winds are a frequent occurrence; and, although air is 1 000 times less dense than water, winds can move loose, dry sand grains.

- A water current of over $0.2\,\mathrm{m\,s^{-1}}$ can pick up 1 mm quartz grains (Figure 6.5). How much faster must the wind travel to pick up the same grains?

- A wind travelling at more than $10\,\mathrm{m\,s^{-1}}$ (i.e. $36\,\mathrm{km\,h^{-1}}$ or 22 miles per hour), at least 50 times as fast as the minimum water current, would be required. A similar factor is applicable across a wide range of grain sizes (Figure 6.5).

Once picked up, dust grains (<0.01 mm in diameter) can be carried by a light wind, but it takes a brisk wind to carry sand grains, and pebbles are rarely moved even by very high winds. Dust picked up and transported in suspension may be brought down by rainfall many thousands of kilometres away — sometimes airborne dusts from the Sahara are brought to Earth in the UK by falling rain.

Rock and mineral grains released by weathering are transported by the wind in various ways: (i) in suspension (held in the air); (ii) by rolling, causing surface grains to ‘creep’ along; or (iii) by *saltation*, a bouncing action in which sand grains, lifted and propelled by the wind, fall and hit other grains, triggering them to bounce too. Saltation of sand grains, illustrated in Figure 6.8, is similar to the way in which grains were shown bouncing along the river bed in an animation in the video ‘A story in sand’. By this mechanism, wind may lift sand grains above the ground to 50 cm, exceptionally to 2 m, producing a sand blast that abrades both other grains and rock surfaces. If you’ve ever walked with bare legs across a dry sandy beach or dunes on a very windy day you will know how much wind-blown sand can sting.

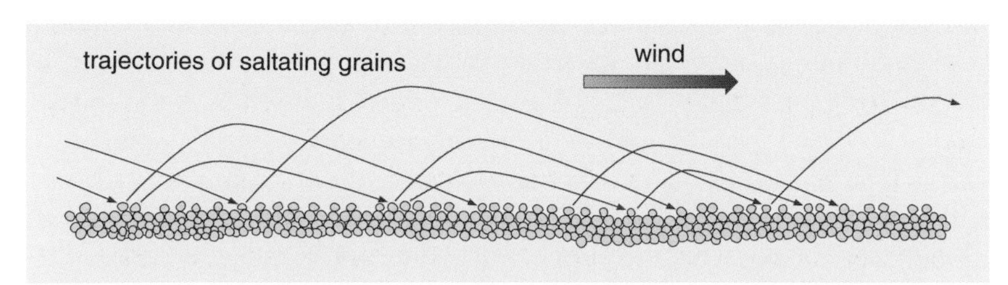

Figure 6.8 Sand movement by saltation (bouncing action). Grains propelled by the wind knock other grains into the air as they fall.

The repeated impacts between sand grains blown by the wind produces well-rounded grains with finely pitted surfaces — often described as a 'frosted' appearance — a particular characteristic of desert sands (as shown in the video 'A story in sand'). In contrast, sand grains worn down in water are never as well-rounded and they look more glassy; they do not become finely pitted because their collisions are cushioned by the water around them. Desert sands consist mainly of quartz, its lack of cleavage making it the most resistant of the common minerals to fragmentation. Sand grains in deserts are generally too large to be carried away in suspension but are small enough to be transported by high winds through saltation or surface creep.

- If you took a handful of sand from a desert dune, would you expect it to be well- or poorly-sorted?

- It's likely to have a fairly narrow range of grain sizes — the grains are small enough to be moved around by high winds but not small enough to be carried far away at diminishing wind speeds — and so it will be well-sorted.

Sedimentary deposits in the geological record that contain well-sorted, well-rounded and frosted grains of quartz sand are most likely to have formed under desert conditions. However, these characteristics are not sufficient to *prove* deposition by wind, because desert sand grains can be picked up by flowing water and redeposited. Consequently, it is important to use additional indicators to confirm arid conditions and deposition by wind.

Deposition of wind-blown desert sands typically forms a series of sloping layers, like those within the beds shown in Figure 6.9a (*overleaf*). These layers form by the movement of sand dunes as illustrated in Figure 6.9b. Wind blows grains up to the crest of a dune, and they collect at the top of the steep slope that faces 'forward' in the lee of the wind; eventually the top of the slope collapses, and the grains slide and roll down the slope, forming an extensive inclined layer (Figure 6.9b(i)). As the dune moves forward, a series of layers is formed, together making a bed that is partially eroded as the dune passes. As more dunes pass, further beds are formed, lying on the remnants of earlier ones (Figure 6.9b(ii)). The series of layers that is inclined to the upper and lower margins of a bed is known as **cross-bedding** (Figure 6.9a). Desert sand dunes generally produce steeply-inclined, large-scale cross-bedding. Water currents also produce cross-bedding, but mostly on a smaller scale, with shallower cross-beds.

Another feature of ancient desert deposits is reddening. The lack of vegetation and decaying organic material in deserts, combined with hot, dry conditions and rare rainfall, means that air fills the spaces between sand grains. This makes the environment of sediment accumulation in deserts very oxidizing (Block 8, Section 14.2.2). Although chemical weathering is very slow in deserts, when grains of ferromagnesian minerals (Activity 4.2) do break down, their iron, which usually has a valency of two (designated iron(II)), and can be transported in solution, becomes oxidized to iron with a valency of three (designated iron(III)), which forms insoluble compounds. In deserts, iron(III) forms fine-grained haematite (Fe_2O_3), and this accounts for the red colouring on the surfaces of sand grains. Ancient desert deposits are often coloured red or orange–red for this reason, forming 'red beds', which are important indicators of arid conditions and past climates, as in Block 3, Section 11.3. Examples of red beds from the UK are discussed in Section 9.3 and Activity 9.2. Other areas of the UK in which red beds occur include Cheshire, the East Midlands and the Vale of Eden, Cumbria.

Question 6.3 What are the main indicators of arid desert conditions in ancient sandstones? ◀

Figure 6.9 (a) An exposure of cross-bedded dune sandstone about 5 m high. Note that the main beds are horizontal. The inclination of the layers between them does not result from tilting but from deposition on a slope. (b) Movement of sand dunes and the formation of (i) sloping layers of sand, and (ii) a series of cross-bedded layers as in (a), with the passage of dunes.

(a)

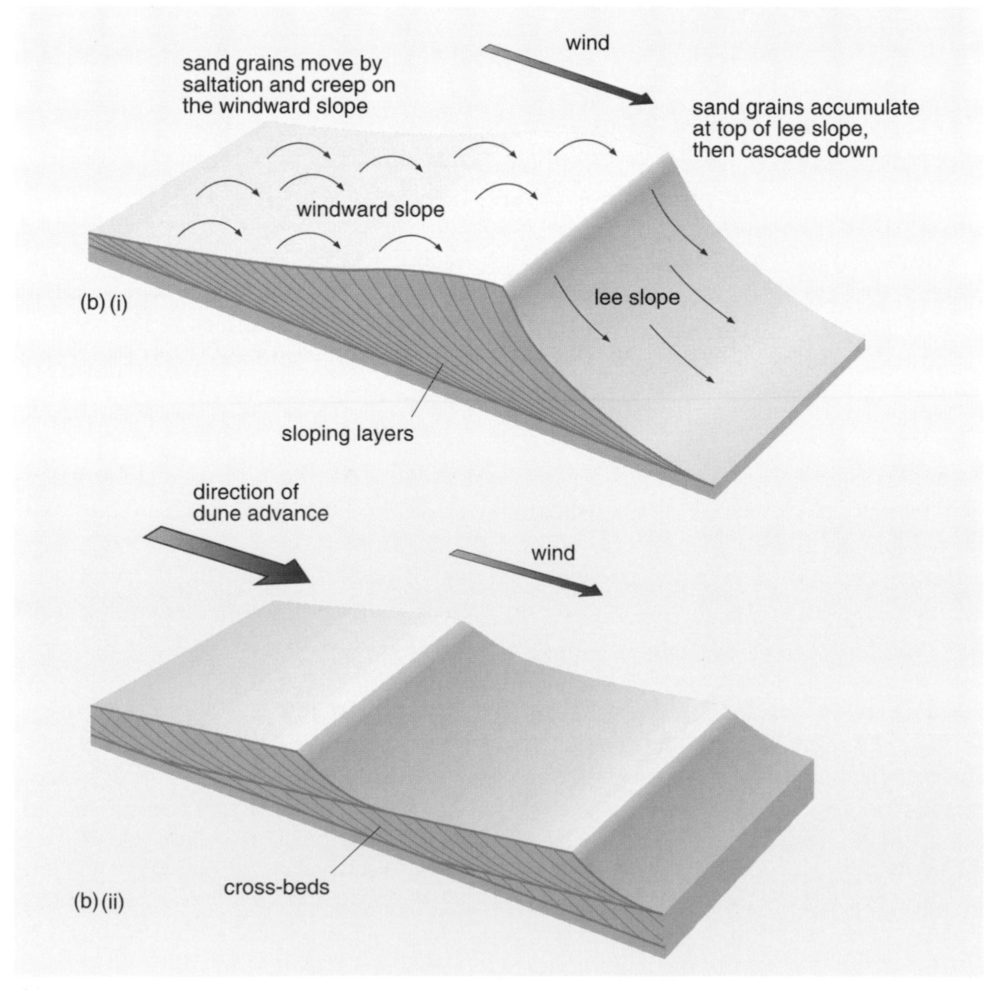

(b)

6.3.2 Evaporites — salts of the Earth

Soluble ions released by chemical weathering of rocks, including Na^+, K^+, Ca^{2+}, Mg^{2+} and HCO_3^- (as in Equation 6.1), are transported at low concentrations in rivers (freshwater) (Table 6.1) to lakes or onwards to the sea. In seawater, dissolved materials originating from these and other sources amount to 3.5% by mass, forming a salty solution in which Na^+, Mg^{2+}, SO_4^{2-} and Cl^- ions are the most important (Table 6.1). You might expect that continuous addition of soluble material to the oceans would lead to a steady increase in the concentrations of salts in seawater over time, but this is not the case. As in so many complex natural systems, a more-or-less steady state is maintained, and concentrations are constrained by natural processes, as you will see shortly.

Table 6.1 Typical concentrations of dissolved material in natural waters. Note that concentrations of most dissolved materials in river water are extremely variable. (You are not expected to memorize these figures!)

Dissolved ion	Concentration in river water/mg litre^{-1}	Concentration in sea water/mg litre^{-1}
Na^+	7	10 770
K^+	2	380
Ca^{2+}	15	410
Mg^{2+}	4	1 290
HCO_3^-	56	140
SO_4^{2-}	11	2 650
Cl^-	18	19 500

In hot climates, rates of evaporation are high, especially from bodies of shallow water (which heat up quickly). The concentration of salts in such bodies of water is increased by evaporation until the water becomes *saturated* (Block 8, Section 7.1.1); the salty water can then hold no more dissolved salts in solution. Further evaporation causes dissolved salts to crystallize out of solution, forming **evaporite** deposits. These salts include halite, NaCl (better known as rock salt), and the less soluble salt, gypsum, $CaSO_4.2H_2O$* (used to make plaster). Such deposits may form in several different environments, including:

- Enclosed inland basins in arid regions into which rivers flow intermittently, carrying dissolved salts, such as the Great Salt Lake, Utah, USA. The trapped water evaporates and salts eventually crystallize to form salt flats.
- Shallow water basins along the edges of seas, such as the eastern edge of the Caspian Sea (central Asia), where evaporation is high, bringing about crystallization of salts. Restricted access to the open sea allows the intermittent inflow of seawater to replenish the supply of salts.
- Coastal mudflats along arid shorelines, such as the Persian Gulf, where water evaporates from the exposed mud, and salts crystallize within the mud as it dries out. Seawater replenishes the supply both of water and of salts by seepage and by flooding at high tide.

*The formula signifies that gypsum contains water in its structure.

Curiously, in evaporites, we have now encountered a type of sedimentary rock that is not fragmentary, but is made of intergrown crystals rather like those of igneous rocks. It is an exception to our generalization, at the beginning of Section 5, that sedimentary textures are fragmental. However, evaporites are usually distinguishable as layered sedimentary deposits, and are often associated with 'red beds'.

- What properties of evaporite minerals could be used to distinguish them from the minerals of igneous rocks?

- Most evaporite minerals are soluble (some only slightly) in water, whereas silicate minerals are not. Also, most evaporite minerals, like halite (Activity 4.2), are much softer than those of igneous rocks.

Rock salt and gypsum are economically important evaporite deposits and are key indicators of arid climatic conditions in the geological record. In the UK, deposits of salt in Cheshire and gypsum in the East Midlands are mined: they indicate arid conditions in parts of the UK about 250 Ma ago (Section 9.3).

6.3.3 Limestones

Some of the components dissolved in seawater, especially calcium (Ca^{2+}) and hydrogen carbonate (HCO_3^-) ions (Table 6.1), are taken up by many groups of marine organisms to produce shells or skeletons composed of calcium carbonate, mainly as calcite (Activity 4.2). When these organisms die, their remains accumulate on the sea floor and, if in sufficient abundance, eventually form limestones. Fragments of calcite shells from animal groups such as bivalves, brachiopods, trilobites, echinoids and crinoids (Activities 2.1 and 3.1) are often found in ancient limestones. Some marine plants produce calcium carbonate too: for example, the Cretaceous Chalk deposits of southeast England and elsewhere are made mainly of the calcite plates of tiny phytoplankton called coccolithophores, along with some foraminiferans (zooplankton, Block 2, Figure 8.5).

An influx of clay and silt in seawater inhibits the growth of many carbonate-producing organisms, so limestones tend to indicate deposition in clear water, away from land-derived supplies of sediment (i.e. silicate minerals and rock fragments). The great majority of limestones are of marine origin, and most are composed of calcite.

The majority of ancient and modern carbonate sediments formed in shallow seas of the tropical–subtropical belt, between about 30° N and 30° S of the Equator. Here, reef-building organisms such as corals are common. As you learnt when studying the Wenlock Limestone fossils in Activity 2.1, corals forming reefs today, such as the Great Barrier Reef off eastern Australia (Block 3, Figure 18.2), are restricted in their distribution, thriving only in warm, clear, shallow, tropical seas, and many reefs that developed in similar circumstances can be recognized in ancient deposits.

- Among the many components of limestones, there is fine carbonate mud, which can form in various ways. Imagine you have found a bed of limestone formed almost completely of calcium carbonate mud, which is now a hard rock. What inference can you make about the strength of currents active when the bed was deposited, and about the proximity at that time to sources of land-derived sediment?

- The limestone must have accumulated in very quiet, low-energy conditions where currents were not strong enough to remove the carbonate mud. There was probably no nearby source of land-derived sediment, because this would have introduced material such as clay minerals and quartz.

- Look again at the crinoidal limestone in your Kit. What evidence is there that currents involved in its deposition were stronger than those depositing the muddy bed just discussed?

- The limestone contains small fragments of broken and haphazardly arranged crinoid stems and plates, some of which exceed 5 mm in length. The currents required to break up and move these sizeable crinoid fragments were certainly stronger than those that deposited only fine carbonate muds.

Some limestones contain calcium carbonate directly precipitated from seawater. For example, many well-known British limestones used for building, such as Portland Stone and Cotswold Stone, contain near-spherical grains about 1 mm across (resembling fish roe), in addition to shell fragments. Similar round grains form today by the precipitation of calcium carbonate around some kind of nucleus (such as a tiny shell fragment); they grow as they are rolled around in warm, wave-agitated, current-swept, shallow seas such as those at present around the Bahamas.

Question 6.4 Which sedimentary processes are important in maintaining the natural balance of salts in seawater? ◀

6.4 From sediments to sedimentary rocks

How do sedimentary deposits that start out as loose sands or sludgy muds end up as hard rocks? Recall your observations of the sandstone from your Kit (Activity 6.2).

- How well did this sandstone hold together? Was it easy to dislodge fragments with a fingernail? Did it need something harder? What happened to a drop of water placed on its surface?

- The sandstone probably held together quite well. Fragments could be dislodged easily with a steel knife but not easily with a fingernail. The rock absorbed water readily.

The sand grains of the Kit specimen are held together quite well by the material between them. This material coats the grains, but does not fill the spaces completely, allowing water to be absorbed. Some sedimentary rocks are held together even better than the Kit specimen: others crumble apart much more easily.

Several processes can harden sediments, resulting in **lithification** (from the Greek *lithos*, 'stone'), which can start soon after deposition. Most sediments are laid down underwater, and in any case, when sediments become buried, underground water usually occupies the spaces between the grains.

- What happens to the water filling the spaces between sediment grains when more and more sediment is loaded on top?

- The weight of overlying sediment tends to press the sediment grains closer together, driving out water from between them.

This process is **compaction**, and is especially important for muddy sediments, which may contain up to 60% water when they are deposited. Water is squeezed out during compaction, and if platy minerals (clays) are present, they are flattened (as shown in Figure 6.10a), making a rock that is *fissile*, i.e. easily split into thin layers. **Shale** is a fine-grained rock made of clay or silt that is fissile for this reason. Coarser sediments, such as sands, do not compact much during burial, because their grains pack together quite tightly when first deposited, whether in air or under water.

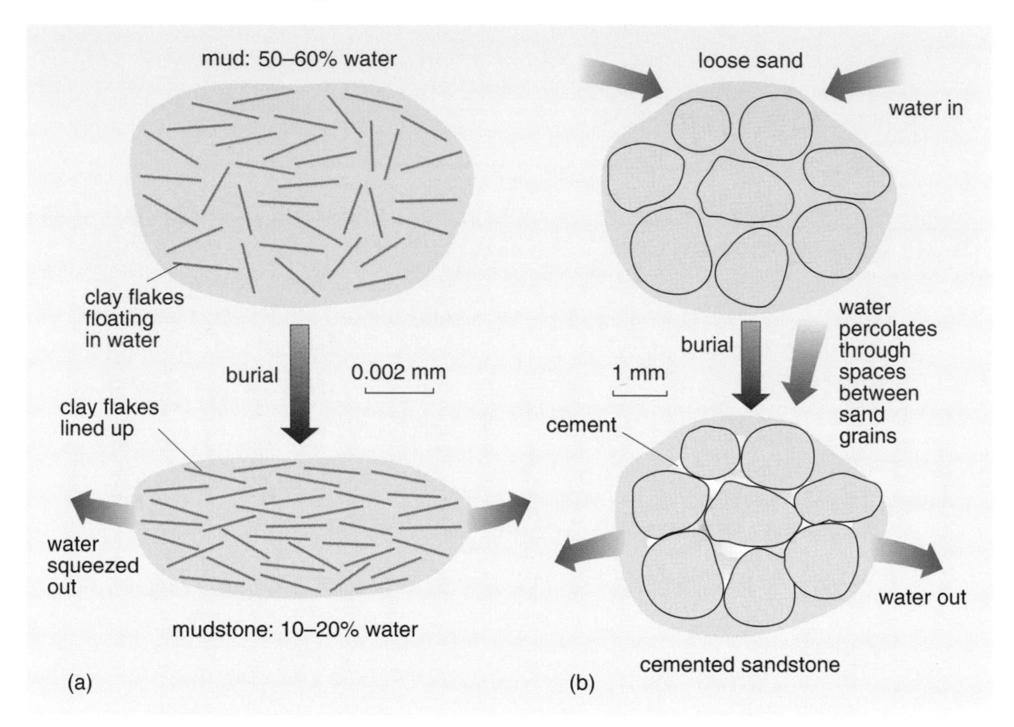

Figure 6.10 Lithification of sediments: (a) burial compacts muds, and (b) percolating water precipitates cement between sand grains.

Water between the grains in buried sediments may dissolve material from the surrounding mineral grains, especially where the grains are touching and under pressure. Minerals may then crystallize in those spaces, in spaces nearby, or in spaces elsewhere, from the resulting solution (Figure 6.10b). This process is known as **cementation**, and is the main way that sandstones become lithified. Calcium carbonate in sediments (e.g. shells) is particularly liable to dissolution and it often recrystallizes in the spaces between grains.

A simple experiment with sugar demonstrates how a loose sand can be cemented to form a sedimentary rock. Dry sugar behaves rather like loose sand. But if you add a few drops of water to a bowl of sugar and let it dry thoroughly over several hours, solid lumps will form. What has happened? Water seeps into the spaces between the grains and dissolves some sugar from the surfaces of the grains. As the water evaporates, the sugar in the solution crystallizes onto the remaining grains, sticking (i.e. cementing) them together. In a similar way, sands can be cemented to form sandstone, and shell fragments cemented to form limestone. The whole process takes much longer in rocks, and the cement that crystallizes in the space between grains is usually composed of either quartz or calcite.

In the analogy between sugar and sand grains, what would sugar cubes represent and to what use might that material be put?

The sugar cubes are analogous to well-cemented blocks of sandstone that could be used as building stone.

Fine-grained sediments are more often affected by compaction because their fine clay minerals become aligned and water is expelled. Coarse-grained sediments more often undergo cementation because they compact very little and water can pass through the space between the grains. Compaction may sometimes be accompanied by cementation, but once grains have been well-cemented, compaction ceases.

6.4.1 And from sedimentary rocks...

The key processes of the rock cycle involved in forming sediments at the Earth's surface are weathering and erosion, transport and deposition. Sediments usually require burial to become sedimentary rocks, and these rocks are normally exposed only when they return to the surface through earth movements. Sedimentary rocks can be buried to great depths (many km) in the Earth. There they are subjected to high temperatures and pressures, and change their form by recrystallization to become metamorphic rocks. This part of the rock cycle is the subject of Section 7.

Question 6.5 Match the following rock types to an appropriate description from the items (a)–(g) below: mudstone, conglomerate, limestone, evaporite, breccia.

(a) contains rounded grains of quartz sand

(b) contains a high proportion of clay minerals

(c) contains large angular rock fragments

(d) contains interlocking crystals of soft, water-soluble minerals

(e) contains layers of sandy and muddy sediment

(f) contains rounded pebbles cemented by quartz

(g) contains remains of shelly organisms in fine-grained carbonate mud ◀

6.5 Summary of Section 6

Sedimentary deposits are formed by the processes of weathering, erosion, transport and deposition at the Earth's surface. Sedimentary rocks are usually distinguished from other rocks by their fragmental texture and by their layering. Sedimentary materials can be classified according to their grain size into muds, sands, pebbles, cobbles and boulders.

Weathering involves the disintegration and decomposition of rocks by exposure to the weather, surface waters and organisms. Physical weathering opens up cracks, breaking rock into smaller fragments. Chemical weathering involves the breakdown of unstable minerals (e.g. feldspars) by acidic waters to form new, more stable minerals (e.g. clays) and soluble products (e.g. metal ions and silica): resistant minerals (e.g. quartz) are liberated. Erosion is the physical removal of rocks and minerals and the wearing away of rock by debris carried by flowing water, wind and ice.

The size of sedimentary grains picked up and transported by water or wind depends on the energy of the flowing medium (its density and speed of flow). Wind speeds need to be about 50 times greater than water speeds to pick up grains of similar size. Whether or not sediment is eroded, transported or deposited is mainly determined by its grain size and the speed of flow. Materials deposited under a narrow range of flow conditions have a narrow range of grain sizes and are well-sorted. Wind-blown sands are particularly well-sorted. A gradual change in grain size through a bed is known as graded bedding; fining upwards of grains reflects a declining speed of flow.

Desert sandstones typically contain well-sorted, well-rounded, finely-pitted and reddened grains in steeply sloping layers which indicate formation as a result of wind action in an arid environment. Evaporite deposits such as rock salt and gypsum also indicate arid environments where salts have crystallized by evaporation of shallow or enclosed waters. Accumulation of calcium carbonate shells or skeletons of organisms produce limestone, which is often indicative of warm, clear, marine waters. The observation of deposits formed in modern sedimentary environments provides us with a key to understanding ancient environments.

During burial, sediments become lithified by compaction and/or by cementation to form sedimentary rocks such as mudstones, shales, sandstones, conglomerates and limestones.

Metamorphic rocks — taking the heat and the pressure

7

You have seen that deep in the Earth (mainly in the mantle, but also in deeper parts of the crust), rocks may melt to form magmas which give rise to igneous rocks (Section 5). And, at fairly shallow depths, sediments deposited at the Earth's surface become compacted and lithified after burial, to produce sedimentary rocks (Section 6). But what happens in the rest of the Earth's crust? What rocks are found there? This brings us to the third category of rocks introduced in Block 3, Section 9, the *metamorphic* rocks. You may like to look again at the igneous, sedimentary and metamorphic rocks of your Practical Kit to remind yourself of the differences.

Metamorphic rocks can be distinguished from igneous and sedimentary rocks because of their intergrown, interlocking textures in which crystals usually have a strong alignment (e.g. Figure 5.1b) and minerals are often arranged in bands. Such metamorphic textures indicate that crystallization has taken place in the solid state (as we noted early in Section 5), a process that doesn't involve either the melting or the breakdown and reassembly of rocks (unlike the formation of igneous or sedimentary rocks). Metamorphic changes involve the growth of new minerals or the recrystallization of old ones and occur when atoms reorganize themselves in response to changes in their physical environment (i.e. changes in pressure and temperature); the overall chemical composition of the rock remains unchanged. Metamorphic reactions contrast markedly with chemical reactions that are carried out in the laboratory using test-tubes and aqueous solutions. They involve minerals in the solid state, usually deep under ground, at far higher temperatures and pressures than we are used to at the Earth's surface, and they take place very slowly in comparison to laboratory experiments. We consider the conditions of metamorphism in Box 7.1, *Conditions underground*.

Box 7.1 Conditions underground

Deep beneath us, the rocks are hotter than at the surface, and their temperature generally increases with depth, because the Earth is heated internally (mainly by radioactivity) and cools from its surface. Deep down, rocks also have to support the weight of overlying rocks, and that means they are under great pressure. In South Africa, for example, where gold mines extend beyond 4 km in depth, rock-face temperatures can exceed 100 °C and rock 'walls' are under such high pressure that they can explode. On average, there is a pressure increase of about 1 kilobar (kb)* for every 3.5 km depth. Therefore, at a depth of about 4 km, the pressure on the rocks is about 1.2 kb, which is about 1 200 times the atmospheric pressure at the Earth's surface (approximately 1 bar).

The increase in pressure and temperature with depth in the Earth can be shown on a graph of temperature versus pressure (Figure 7.1, *overleaf*). The vertical axis of Figure 7.1 is unusual in that it shows pressure *increasing* downwards, as it does beneath the Earth's surface. The rate at which rock temperatures increase with depth — the **geothermal gradient** — is commonly about 25 °C km^{-1}, a gradient similar to the 'typical geothermal gradient' of Figure 7.1.

*Pressure is measured in bars, abbreviated b (Block 2, Section 6.2).

However, geothermal gradients vary from place to place. For example, near sites of active volcanism, gradients can reach hundreds of °C per kilometre, whereas gradients around 20–30 °C km^{-1} are typical of stable continental regions that lack magmatic activity, as in Britain today. Consequently there is a wide range of pressure and temperature conditions within the Earth under which metamorphism can occur (see Figure 7.1).

The conditions under which metamorphism occurs, and the rocks formed as a result, are often described in terms of **metamorphic grade**. Thus, both the metamorphic conditions of high temperature and high pressure, *and* the metamorphic rocks produced by them, are called *high grade*; correspondingly, both the conditions of low temperature and low pressure, and the resulting rocks, are called *low grade* (Figure 7.1).

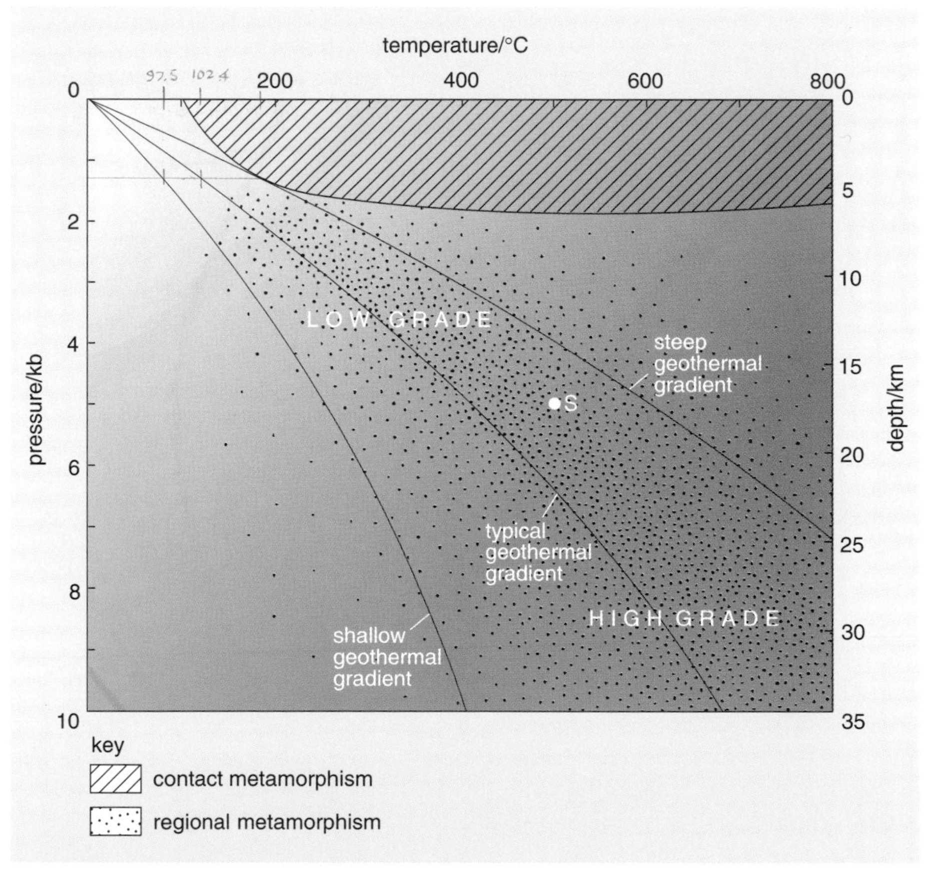

Figure 7.1 Pressure and temperature conditions under which metamorphic rocks may be formed. The two types of metamorphic conditions shown, i.e. contact and regional, are discussed in Section 7.1. Regional metamorphic conditions are more commonly developed in the stippled regions close to the line representing a typical geothermal gradient, but vary according to crustal setting. Note that pressure *increases* downwards in this graph. A depth scale is shown on the right. The point labelled S is referred to in Section 7.1.2.

7.1 New rocks for old

How can we find out how metamorphism affects rocks deep in the crust? We cannot sample many of the rocks directly, for the deepest mine takes us only to 5 km, and deep drilling to only about 10 km depth. That's not deep enough, because continental crust usually extends to about 35 km, and sometimes to 60 or 70 km. Fortunately, many metamorphic rocks have been raised to the Earth's surface from great depth by tectonic activity. Even more remarkable is that some of these metamorphic rocks were once sediments at the Earth's surface: they must have been buried beneath great thicknesses of rock before they were brought back up to the surface again.

Earth movements giving rise to burial and uplift are responsible for moving rocks around parts of the rock cycle (Figure 7.2 and Block 3, Section 17). Such events arise through **mountain-building**, when lithospheric plates converge and squash together to form mountain belts, such as the Alps or the Himalayas (Block 3, Section 14.2). Most mountain belts contain vast areas of rocks affected by metamorphism, and because it is developed on a regional scale we call it **regional metamorphism**. The more commonly encountered conditions of regional metamorphism are shown by stippling on Figure 7.1; but there are other circumstances in which metamorphism can occur.

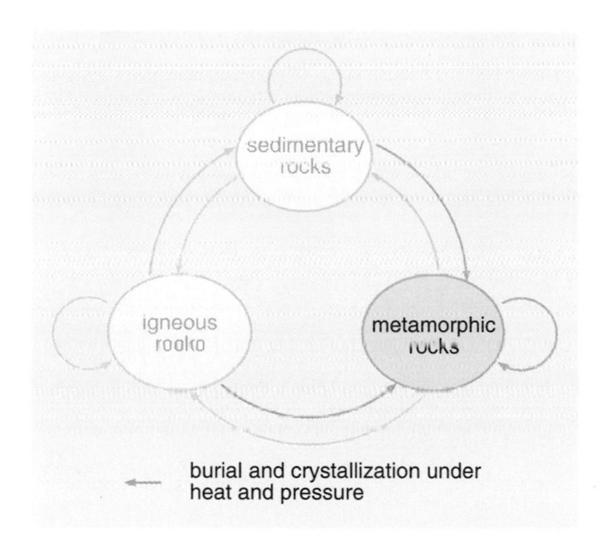

Figure 7.2 The formation of metamorphic rocks within the rock cycle. The three bold arrows indicate the routes through which metamorphic rocks can be formed by burial and crystallization under heat and pressure.

- How could rocks near to the Earth's surface get very hot?

- They could come into contact with very hot magma (at about 800–1 300 °C).

Rocks in contact with magma can be baked sufficiently for metamorphic changes to occur on a scale of centimetres to metres around sills or dykes, and on a scale of hundreds of metres to kilometres around plutons (Section 5.1.1). Metamorphism of this kind is called **contact metamorphism**; it involves high temperatures but low pressures (Figure 7.1).

- Why should contact metamorphism be more extensive around plutons than around sills and dykes?

- Plutons contain much larger volumes of magma and therefore provide much greater quantities of heat to be dissipated as cooling takes place. The heat spreads farther and the source stays hot for longer.

Sedimentary rocks containing clay minerals (i.e. mudstones and shales) are particularly susceptible to contact metamorphism. Although their clay minerals are stable at the Earth's surface temperatures, they are unstable at higher temperatures. Baking drives off water from the hydrous clay minerals to produce new anhydrous minerals (which lack combined water). At shallow depth, where plutons cool more rapidly, temperature rises are usually short-lived. Shallow contact metamorphic rocks therefore don't have long to crystallize and are usually fairly fine-grained, finer than most regional metamorphic rocks. Contact metamorphic rocks are not so commonly encountered, so we shall focus on regional metamorphic rocks.

7.1.1 Metamorphic 'cookery'

The way in which metamorphic rocks change their form under the influence of heat and pressure deep beneath the Earth's surface is rather like what happens when a cake is baked. A cake comes out of an oven after cooking with a constitution and texture quite different from the gooey mixture that went in. Similarly, metamorphic rocks end up with different textures (and usually different minerals) as a result of recrystallization.

When a cake comes out of the oven, its constitution and texture may tell us about the conditions in the oven (and how long it was there). A charred lump means the temperature was very high for some time: a soggy blob means it was never high enough for the ingredients to react. Like cakes, metamorphic rocks have a variety of mineral constituents and textures which can tell us about the conditions they have experienced in the Earth's metamorphic cooker. However, the results of cooking also depend on the ingredients used (e.g. whether the mix was for fruit cake or chocolate sponge), not just the oven temperature. Likewise, even under exactly the same metamorphic conditions, the type of metamorphic rock produced varies according to the original rock type. For example, the metamorphism of limestone (mainly calcite) produces marble; sandstones (mainly quartz) transform to quartzites; and basalts often change to amphibolites (mainly amphibole and plagioclase feldspar). You can look at some examples of other metamorphic rocks in Activity 7.1.

Activity 7.1 Comparing metamorphic rocks

In this activity you will make observations of the schist from the Practical Kit and compare it with the slate and gneiss (pronounced *nice*) of Figure 7.3. ◀

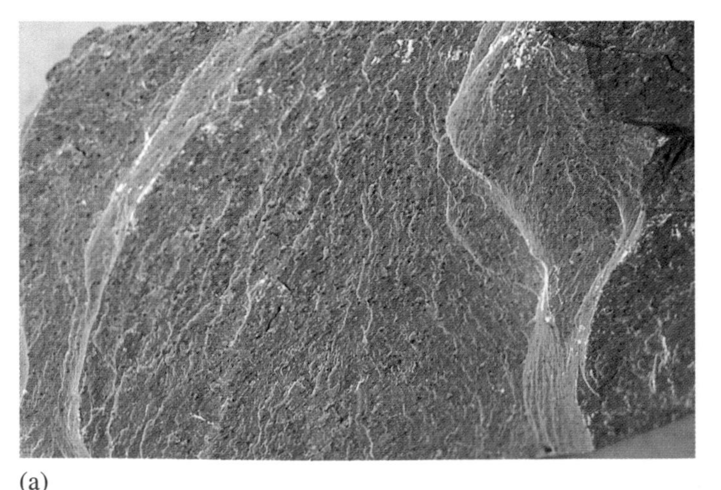

(a)

(b)

Figure 7.3 Examples of metamorphic rocks (with width of field of view): (a) slate (60 mm), and (b) gneiss (70 mm).

7.1.2 Changes with metamorphic grade

Your descriptions of slate, schist and gneiss in Activity 7.1 should enable you to recognize differences in the make-up of typical metamorphic rocks. The differences here are not due to differences in the original rock composition (as they are for marble and quartzite), but are due instead to their formation under different *grades* of metamorphism. Surprisingly perhaps, slate, schist and gneiss could all have started out as soft muds. They each contain essentially the same overall proportions of chemical elements, but they have developed distinctive mineral and textural characteristics under different metamorphic conditions.

The **slate** has the finest grain size, is the lowest grade metamorphic rock in the group, and was formed typically at 200–350 °C and 5–10 km depth. The **gneiss** has the coarsest grain size and was formed under high-grade conditions, typically at temperatures of 550–700 °C and depths of 20–35 km. The **schist** has an intermediate grain size and could well have formed under the conditions represented by point S on Figure 7.1.

- What temperature and pressure conditions does point S on Figure 7.1 represent?

- A temperature of 500 °C and a pressure of 5 kb.

Schists typically form at temperatures of 350–550 °C and depths of 10–20 km (3–6 kb pressure). The textures of all these rocks differ according to the way their minerals are arranged and their grain size, both of which vary with metamorphic grade.

Slate (Figure 7.3a) can be split, or cleaved, into thin parallel slices with smooth surfaces. The capacity of rocks to split in this way is called *cleavage* — a property exploited in making roofing slates. Cleavage in rocks originates for a different reason from cleavage in minerals (Activity 4.1). Slate can be cleaved because it contains very fine-grained flakes of mica, which are arranged in parallel alignment, but are usually too fine to be seen individually, even with a hand lens. These platy minerals grew when the rock was under tectonic compression, their parallel alignment being in response to compressive forces (Figure 7.4). Tectonic compression generally operates in a roughly horizontal direction as a result of lithospheric plate movements. It is distinct from the pressure due to the weight of overlying rocks, which acts in all directions (like atmospheric pressure or water pressure).

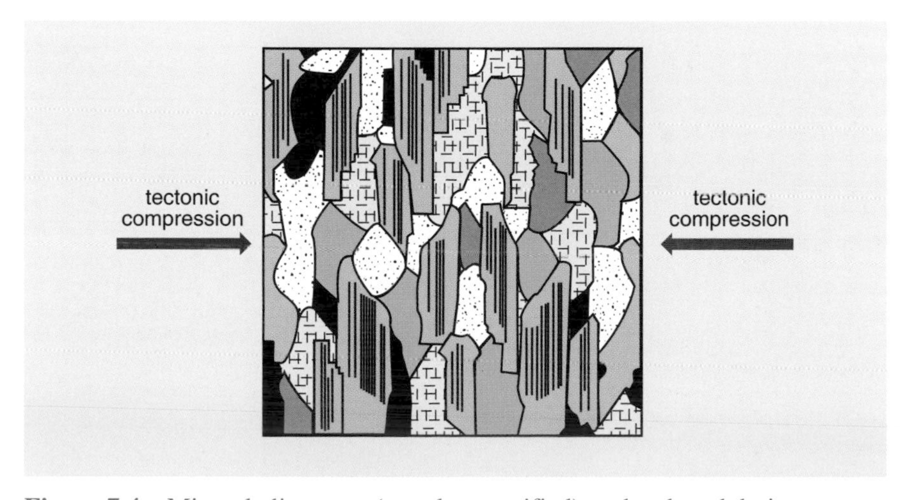

Figure 7.4 Mineral alignment (greatly magnified) as developed during metamorphism at right angles to the direction of tectonic compression.

The schist in the Kit has shiny, but uneven and often crinkly surfaces, made of flaky mica. This unevenness is mostly due to the coarser grain size, and the presence of granular as well as platy crystals. Individual mineral grains are visible, even without a hand lens; there are flakes of dark and pale mica, grains of glassy quartz and pinkish brown garnet.

Gneiss contains even coarser mineral grains, arranged in more or less parallel bands (Figure 7.3b). It contains much less mica because the pale mica, *muscovite*, is not stable at high temperatures. Muscovite breaks down with the loss of water to form alkali feldspar, as follows:

$$\text{muscovite mica(s)} + \text{quartz(s)} \longrightarrow \text{alkali feldspar(s)} + H_2O(l) \quad (7.1)$$

Alkali feldspar is a framework silicate (Section 4, Table 4.2) and has a blocky form, unlike the thin plates of mica it replaces. As a result, gneiss is a more granular rock, and not as easy to split as schist. Instead, it contains rough bands of quartz, feldspar and the dark mica, *biotite* (Figure 7.3b).

- At even higher temperatures, what might happen to a gneiss?

- It might start to melt and form magma.

At very high temperatures (700–1 000 °C) rocks such as gneisses may undergo partial melting to produce magmas and hence igneous rocks. The melting of metamorphic rocks that were formerly igneous or sedimentary rocks closes a major loop of the rock cycle (Figure 7.2).

So, at increasing temperatures of metamorphism, minerals that become unstable break down to form new, more stable minerals. Clay minerals are stable at low temperatures, but are converted to micas at low metamorphic grades, and at high metamorphic grades micas are converted to feldspars. Also, with increasing metamorphic grade, less hydrous minerals replace hydrous ones, so releasing water (as in Equation 7.1). High pressures also affect mineral stability, tending to favour the formation of minerals with dense, compact structures, such as garnet (Activity 4.2).

The progressive change, both in grain size and in the arrangement of mineral grains, in rocks formed from mudstone or shale at increasing grades of metamorphism is summarized in Figure 7.5. The layering that develops due either to the parallel alignment of minerals or to mineral banding is called **foliation**.

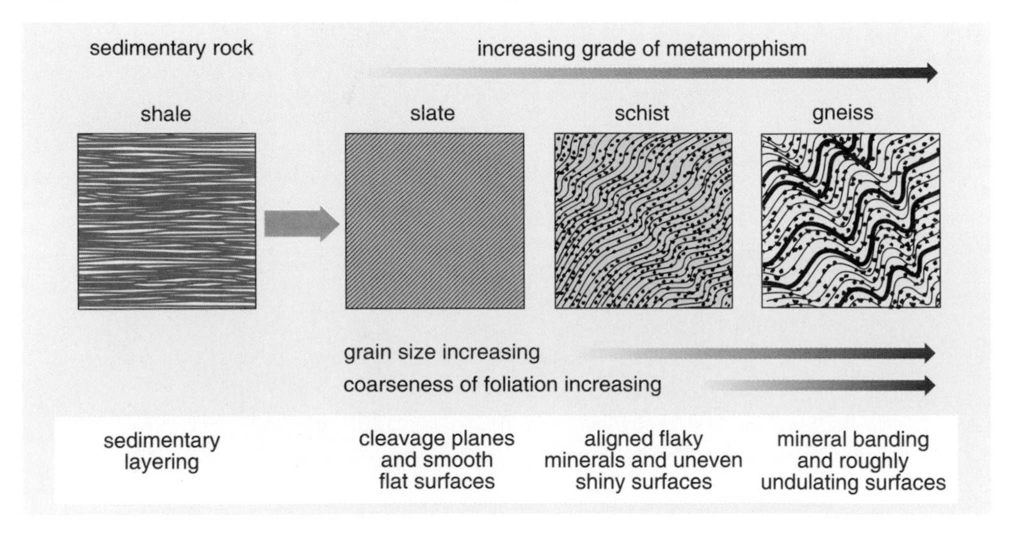

Figure 7.5 Variation in metamorphic rock texture due to increasing grade of metamorphism, as developed from a mudstone or shale.

- How does the foliation change from slate to gneiss?
- The foliation generally gets coarser and more uneven with increasing grain size, and changes from a pervasive alignment of platy minerals (cleavage) in slate, to a rough, often discontinuous, mineral banding in gneiss (Figure 7.3).

The forms of foliation seen in the slate, the schist and the gneiss are typical of regional metamorphism, and are developed through recrystallization of minerals as rocks are moved into different environments of pressure and temperature. These movements occur during plate collision and mountain-building events when tectonic compression causes the alignment of minerals (Figure 7.4). In contrast, contact metamorphic rocks are formed by simple recrystallization without movement or tectonic compression; normally they have no mineral alignment.

Question 7.1 Summarize the main differences between the types of metamorphic rock that can be produced from a mudstone at progressively higher grades of metamorphism. ◀

7.2 Rock deformation

Earth movements, such as those associated with mountain-building, can cause sedimentary rock strata that had once been fairly flat-lying, to be bent, buckled and dislocated to form a variety of contorted shapes (see Figure 7.6). These features are the result of deformation and are common in mountain belts, where they are often associated with metamorphic rocks. They can be developed on all scales, from microscopic, involving mineral banding (Figure 7.6a); to beds in a cliff face (Figure 7.6b); to a grand scale that is best seen in satellite or aerial photos (Figure 7.6c).

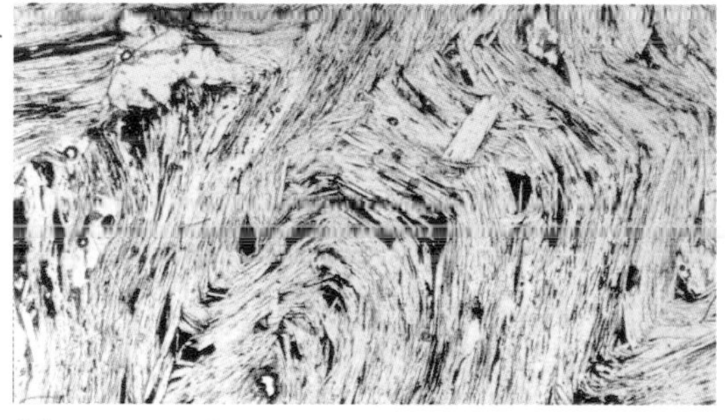

(a)

(b)

(c)

Figure 7.6 Deformation features occur on a variety of scales, including: (a) microscopic folding of mica flakes in a thin slice of rock (2 mm across); (b) a fold exposed in a road cutting (5 m across); and (c) an aerial photo of large-scale folding (20 km across).

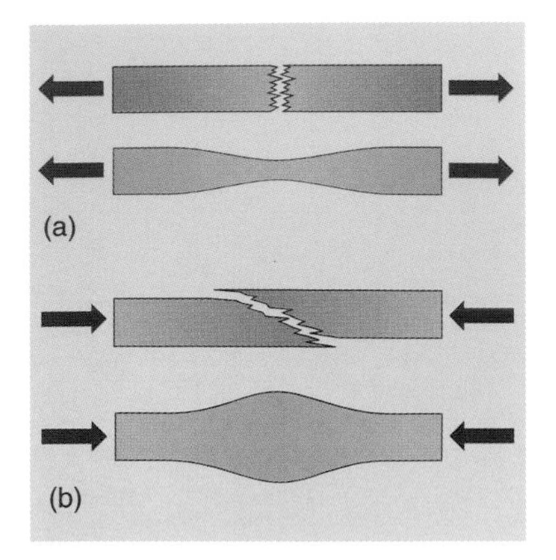

Figure 7.7 Typical effects of (a) tension, and (b) compression, on different types of material. In each part, the upper example shows brittle behaviour and the lower example shows plastic behaviour. The arrows show the direction of forces applied.

What can we learn from deformation features in rocks? Sometimes rocks break apart, sometimes they bend into intricate patterns. Why the difference? Let us consider how deformation occurs in a little more detail. *Deformation* is any process that causes an object (or rock) to change its shape — by breaking, bending, stretching, or squashing — when a force is applied. Forces associated with earth movements can operate in one of two ways. A force directed towards a fixed object produces compression: when operating in the opposite sense it produces tension.

Materials differ in their response to deformation. If you take a thin carrot, grip one end and pull the other, it breaks, but if you try to pull apart a piece of dough, it stretches a long way and gets very thin before breaking. These are different responses to tension; which of them occurs depends on whether the material exhibits plastic behaviour (and stretches like dough) or brittle behaviour (and breaks like the carrot), as shown in Figure 7.7a. What happens under compression? If you compress dough, it bulges or bends (**plastic deformation**), whereas if you compress a carrot with sufficient force it will eventually break (**brittle deformation**), allowing the pieces to move past each other (Figure 7.7b). Compressing material made of layers, like pushing from one edge a pile of cloths or paper in a direction parallel to the layers, produces folded layers.

Rocks also behave in similar ways in response to forces associated with earth movements. But what determines whether they deform in a brittle manner or in a plastic manner? Well, consider a toffee-filled chocolate bar. Try pulling it apart and see if it breaks. If it's warm (on a hot day), it's likely to stretch. If it's very cold (from the freezer), you'll find it more likely to break. So, the extent to which the deformation is plastic or brittle depends not only on the character of the material itself, but on its temperature, as temperature affects its plasticity.

- Given that temperature changes with depth in the Earth, roughly where, in relation to the Earth's surface, would you expect brittle deformation and plastic deformation each to occur?

- Brittle deformation would occur near to the Earth's surface where rocks are cooler; plastic deformation would be more likely to occur at considerable depth, where rocks are hotter.

Figure 7.8 shows the results of deformation experiments on marble subjected to raised temperatures and pressures. Compression causes brittle fracturing under conditions similar to those of the shallow crust, and plastic bulging in the hotter, higher-pressure conditions of the deep crust.

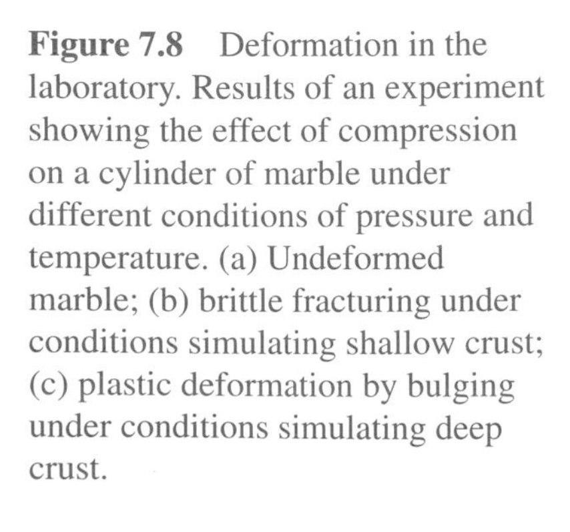

Figure 7.8 Deformation in the laboratory. Results of an experiment showing the effect of compression on a cylinder of marble under different conditions of pressure and temperature. (a) Undeformed marble; (b) brittle fracturing under conditions simulating shallow crust; (c) plastic deformation by bulging under conditions simulating deep crust.

7.2.1 Faulting

Fractures occurring in brittle rocks can be due either to compression or to tension (Figure 7.7). Fractures in rocks are called **faults**: surfaces of dislocation that may have given rise to earthquakes (Block 3, Section 7.2). In rock faces, faults can be recognized where rock layers no longer line up across cracks (Figure 7.9). When we examine a fault, we can sometimes tell whether it formed as a result of compression or tension — try Question 7.2.

Question 7.2 Examine Figures 7.9a and 7.9b and answer the following:

(i) Which of the faults in Figures 7.9a and 7.9b is formed by tension, and which is formed by compression? Remember that compression causes rocks to move closer together: tension causes rocks to move farther apart. Draw arrows parallel to the land surface in Figures 7.9a and 7.9b to show directions of horizontal movement.

(ii) Draw a vertical line downwards from each point A. Imagine these lines represent boreholes. How would the sequences of rocks encountered in each borehole differ?

(iii) The trees shown in Figures 7.9a and 7.9b were the same horizontal distance apart before faulting occurred. How has their separation changed in each case as a result of tension and of compression? ◀

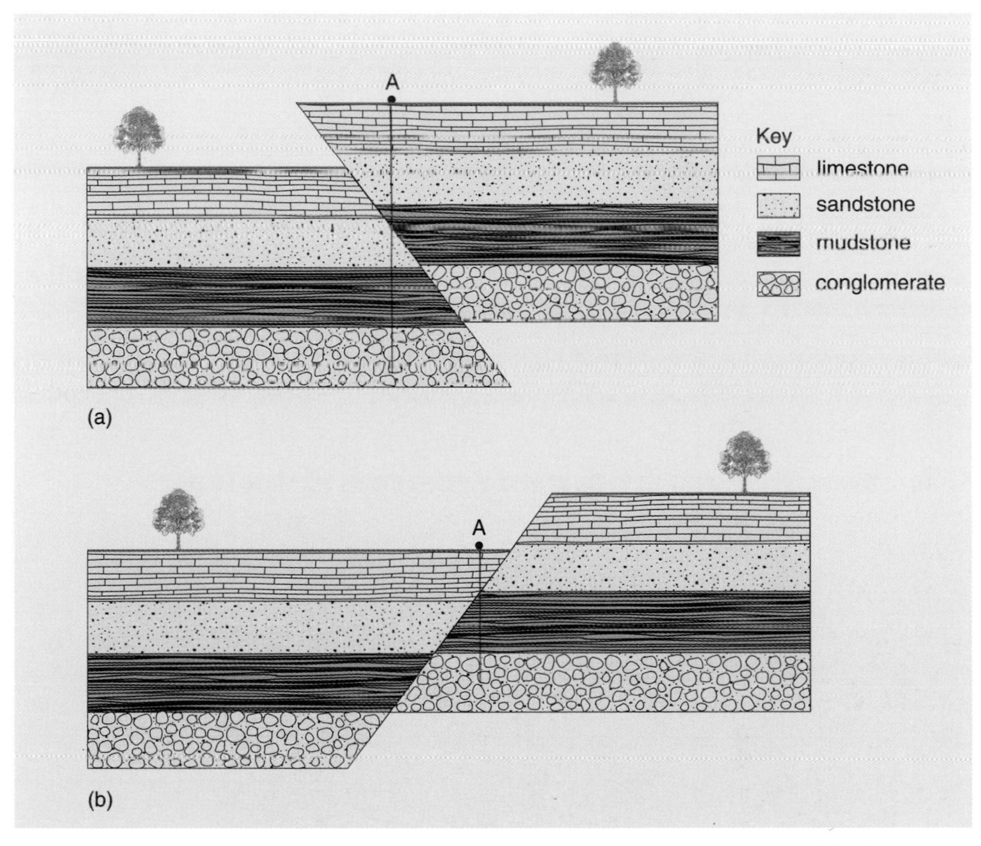

Figure 7.9 (a) and (b) Dislocation of rock strata by faulting. Examples of faults produced in one case by tension and in the other by compression. For use with Question 7.2.

7.2.2 Folding

The plastic behaviour of rocks under compression results in bending or bulging, to give **folds** (Figure 7.10), rather than faults. Folds (and faults) are easy to detect when rocks occur as layers (e.g. in sedimentary strata), but they can occur in any type of rock. There are many different shapes of fold depending on the strength and plasticity of the rocks and on the amount of compression and overall shortening. A small amount of shortening may produce an *open* fold (Figure 7.10a), whereas a large amount of shortening may produce an *overturned* fold in which part of the rock sequence is inverted (Figure 7.10b). When rocks are strong but brittle, as they tend to be at low temperatures, they tend either to fracture or to form simple open folds (Figure 7.6b). When rocks are more plastic, especially at high temperatures, they tend to form tight, intricate fold patterns.

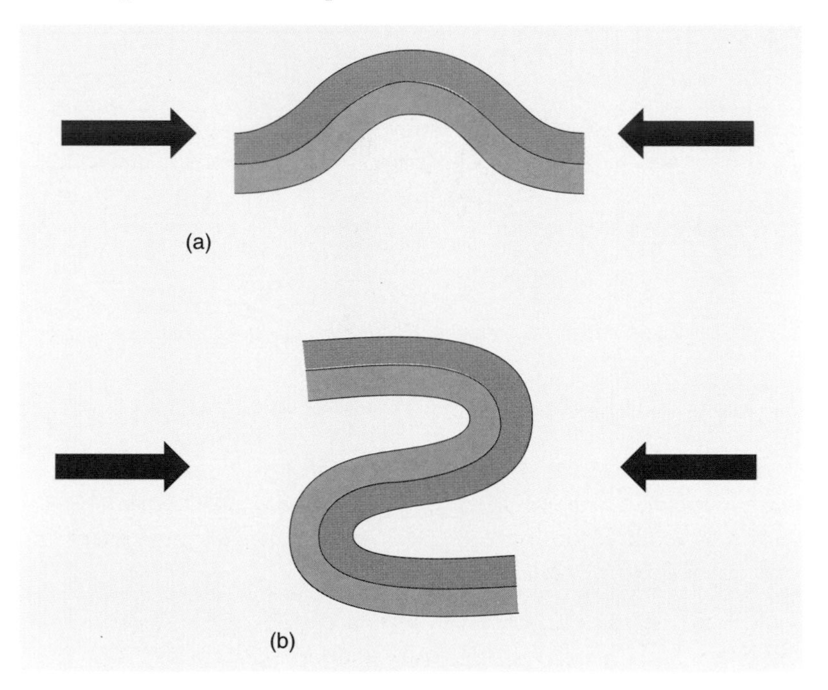

Figure 7.10 Simple folding of rock layers by compressional deformation. (a) An open fold reflects a small amount of shortening. (b) An overturned fold reflects a much larger amount of shortening. Layers such as these are not folded in isolation (as shown): they would be part of a series of layers. The arrows represent compressive pressure, applied over a wide area.

7.3 Mountains and metamorphic belts

Across the world there are linear regions of continental crust where rocks have been strongly deformed. Often, these are also mountain belts, such as the Alps and the Himalayas, and they usually contain belts of metamorphic rocks developed on a regional scale. Hence, both large-scale deformation *and* regional metamorphism are associated with mountain-building. Across these linear zones of deformation, folds and faults in the rocks indicate large-scale compression and, with it, shortening of the crust.

- At what kind of plate boundary might this compression have occurred?

- At a convergent plate boundary, especially where subduction of ocean floor has brought continents into collision (Block 3, Section 14.2).

When collision occurs between continents, mountain belts are formed because continental crust is too buoyant to be subducted. The sediments deposited between converging continents, as well as the continents themselves, are deformed during the collision (Figure 7.11). The compression results in **crustal shortening** and in

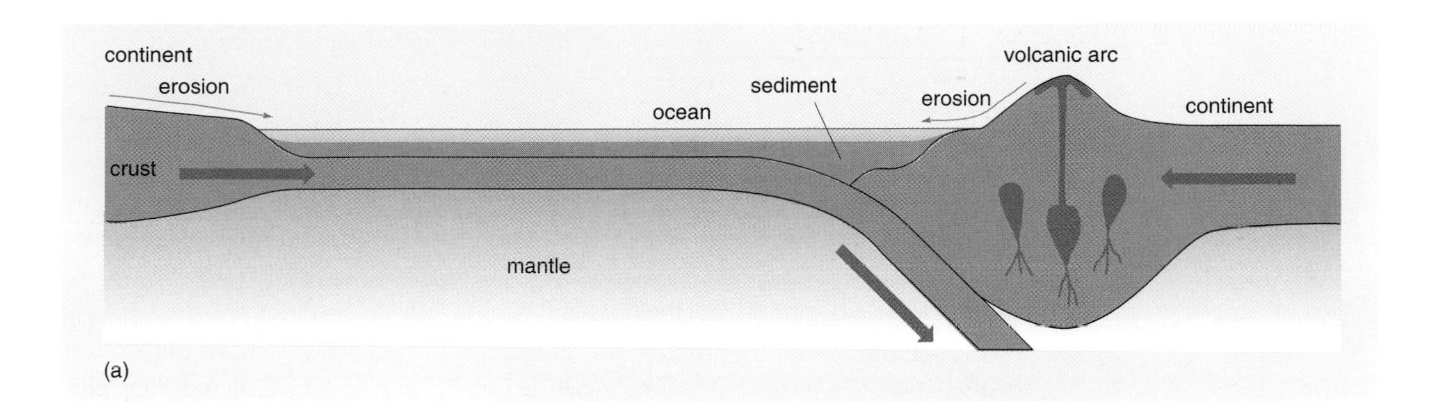

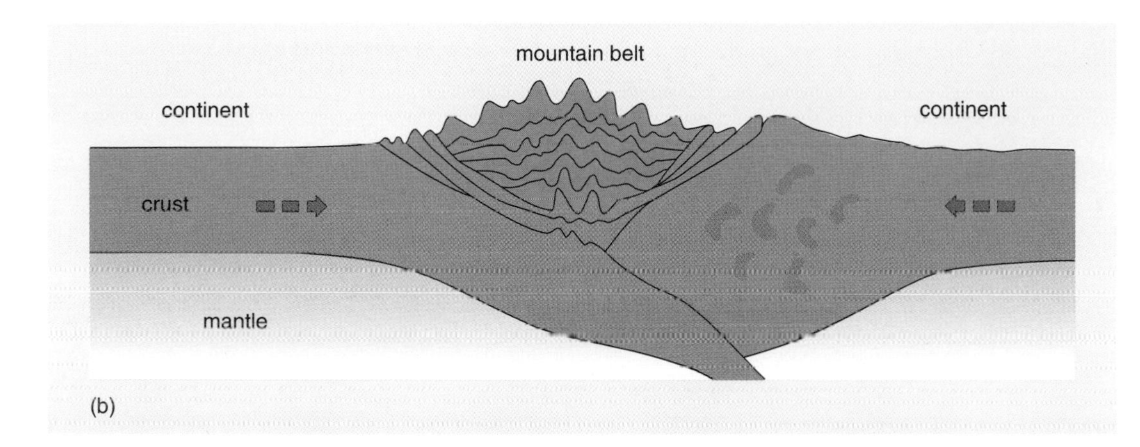

Figure 7.11 Formation of a mountain belt by collision between continents carried on converging lithospheric plates. (a) Converging continents. (b) Deformation and crustal thickening resulting from collision.

thickening of the crust. The crust beneath the Himalayan mountain range, for example, extends down to about 70 km for this reason, compared with a thickness of about 35 km for normal continental crust.

The additional mass of mountains raised up at the surface during the collision (to a height of about 5 km for the Himalayan plateau), and the associated crustal thickening, have caused depression of the mantle beneath the mountains (Figures 7.11b and 7.12a), even though the crust is not as dense as the mantle. Let us consider why this happens and its implications.

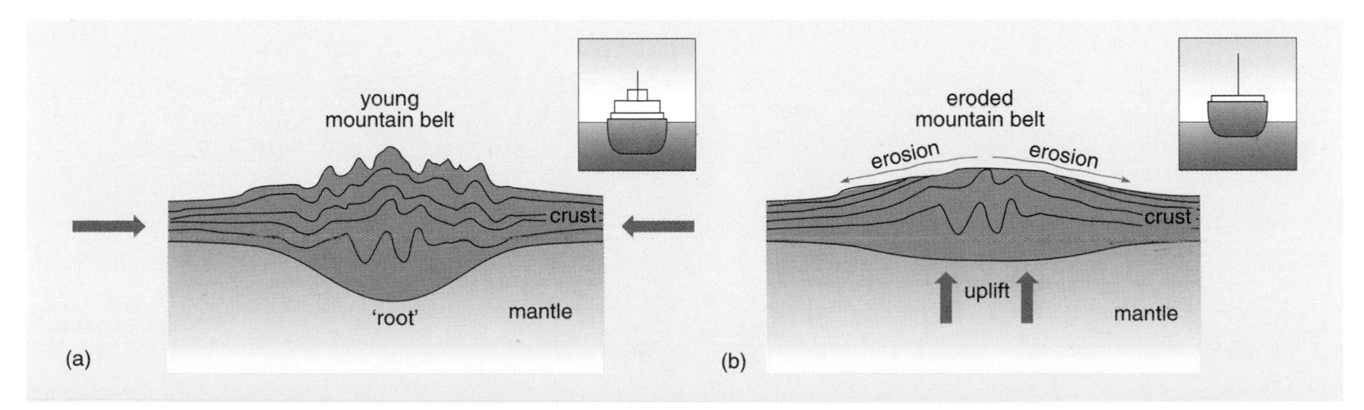

Figure 7.12 The evolution of a mountain belt: (a) compression during mountain-building produces crustal thickening, and (b) subsequent buoyant uplift and erosion of the mountain belt brings metamorphic rocks to the surface. The insets show how the hull of a ship is analogous to the 'roots' of the mountain belt. Note that the ship in (b) has offloaded most of its cargo.

Over geological time-scales, slowly moving solids can behave as liquids do on a short time-scale. The Earth's crust can be likened to a ship floating on a sea of mantle. Building mountains is then rather like adding cargo to the ship (Figure 7.12a); it makes the hull (thickened crust or mountain 'roots') sink deeper in the water (mantle). Just as a ship is buoyed up by the sea, the thickened crust is buoyed up by the mantle: the height of the mountains (the cargo) and the depth to the base of the crust (hull) are in balance. When the mountains are eroded (the cargo is gradually off-loaded), the roots of the mountain belt rise up (the hull, and with it the whole ship, rises) to maintain the balance, as illustrated in Figure 7.12b.

This effect explains how a regional metamorphic belt, seen at the Earth's surface today, can contain rocks that had once been at depths of 30 to 40 km. These rocks were uplifted to the surface *after* the formation of a mountain belt, during which the total thickness of the crust may have reached as much as 70 to 80 km. We know that the Himalayas today are rising by 4–7 mm per year. In a few million years, metamorphic rocks from 10–15 km below the present surface may be revealed. You can see from Figure 7.12 that uplift and erosion would be greater at the central part of a mountain belt, where the crust was at its thickest, than it would be at the edges of the belt.

- How would this variation in uplift be reflected in the grades of metamorphism observed across the belt?

- Rocks of progressively higher grade would be exposed towards the centre of the belt.

Thus low-grade metamorphic rocks, like slates, tend to be found at the edges of metamorphic belts, giving way to schists, and often to high-grade gneisses, in the interior.

Question 7.3 State the two main kinds of evidence that would tell us that rocks seen in field exposures had been affected by earth movements. ◀

Question 7.4 Briefly outline how metamorphic belts form and how their interiors can rise to the surface. ◀

Activity 7.2 Processes of the rock cycle

In this activity you will consolidate your understanding of the processes that produce different kinds of igneous, sedimentary and metamorphic rocks. ◀

The events that produce igneous and sedimentary rocks can be simple and can occur on time-scales of tens of thousands to hundreds of thousands of years, but mountain-building with which metamorphic rocks are associated is complex and takes many millions of years. Piecing together events to discover the geological history of an area affected by mountain-building requires a time framework in which to place evidence from the rocks, whether they are sedimentary, igneous, or metamorphic. Establishing the absolute ages of rocks and their historical framework is the subject of Section 8.

7.4 Summary of Section 7

Metamorphic rocks form below the Earth's surface where minerals respond to the prevailing conditions of temperature and pressure to form new minerals. The change in temperature and pressure with depth, which occurs at different rates in different global settings, gives rise to a wide range of metamorphic conditions and a corresponding range of metamorphic rocks. Both the conditions and the rocks are described in terms of metamorphic grade.

Contact metamorphism occurs locally, adjacent to igneous intrusions, and involves the baking of rocks. Regional metamorphism affects much larger areas and produces foliated rocks containing aligned crystals or bands of minerals formed by recrystallization during tectonic compression. During metamorphism, sandstone transforms to quartzite; limestone to marble; basalt to amphibolite; and shale (or mudstone) to slate, schist and gneiss in order of increasing metamorphic grade. With increasing temperature, hydrous minerals break down and less hydrous minerals become stable. With increasing pressure, denser minerals become stable. Regional metamorphism is associated with the deformation that accompanies mountain-building.

Rocks become deformed as a result of either tension or compression associated with earth movements. Cool rocks near the Earth's surface tend to be brittle and tend to deform by fracturing, or by forming simple folds. Deeper down, where pressures and temperatures are greater, rocks are more plastic in their behaviour and folding is more complex.

Linear mountain belts are the result of tectonic compression and crustal thickening; they form at convergent plate boundaries, especially, when continents collide. Uplift and erosion of thickened crust bring belts of regional metamorphic rocks to the Earth's surface.

8 Geological time

In Sections 2 and 3 we saw how a relative time-scale of geological events and biological evolution can be established by applying some simple principles to the study of sedimentary rocks and fossils. In Sections 4–7 important aspects of minerals and of sedimentary, igneous and metamorphic rocks were described. Together, these different components of the Earth's crust make up the geological record — the detailed history of the outer parts of our planet. Histories, of course, relate to time and the geological record is no exception, but so far we have not explored how the *absolute* ages of rocks, minerals and fossils are determined, as opposed to their *relative* ages. In this section we change the focus of our study from materials to time and look at the *quantification* of the geological time-scale. This aspect of the development of geology as a science has a fascinating history itself, culminating in the use of natural radioactivity for the radiometric dating of rocks and other geological materials.

8.1 Annual events and cycles

Figure 8.1 A section through a timber from the Barley Barn at Temple Cressing, Essex. The tree used to produce this timber has been quite heavily trimmed on three sides. 80 annual growth rings have been counted and used to date the timber to the period AD 1108–1187.

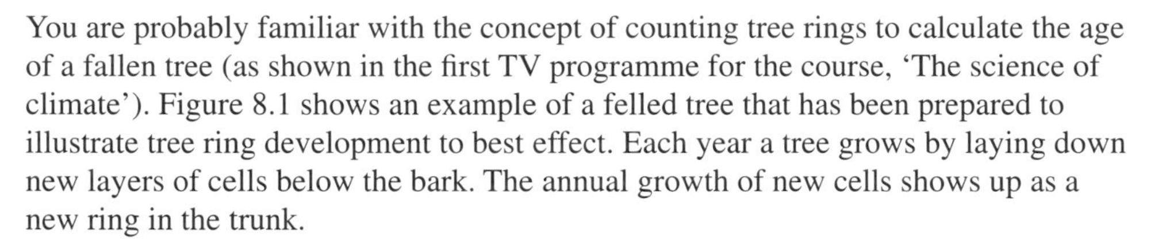

You are probably familiar with the concept of counting tree rings to calculate the age of a fallen tree (as shown in the first TV programme for the course, 'The science of climate'). Figure 8.1 shows an example of a felled tree that has been prepared to illustrate tree ring development to best effect. Each year a tree grows by laying down new layers of cells below the bark. The annual growth of new cells shows up as a new ring in the trunk.

- Are all the tree rings in Figure 8.1 the same width?

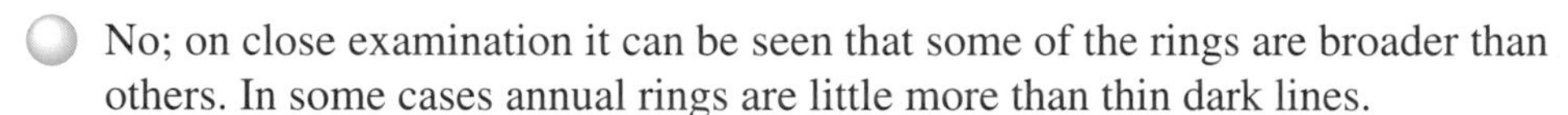

- No; on close examination it can be seen that some of the rings are broader than others. In some cases annual rings are little more than thin dark lines.

- What do you think causes variability in tree-ring width?

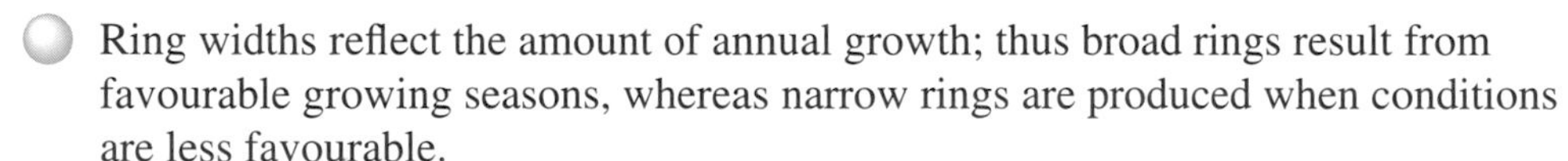

- Ring widths reflect the amount of annual growth; thus broad rings result from favourable growing seasons, whereas narrow rings are produced when conditions are less favourable.

So in addition to acting as a natural clock, a tree is also a recorder of environmental change, although additional evidence is required to interpret fully the meaning of growth ring variations. A narrow growth ring, for example, could mean that the summer was either too hot and dry for much growth, or too cold. More importantly, as all trees respond to annual environmental change in more or less the same way, the pattern of tree rings in different trees from a particular region will be very similar. By comparing ring sequences from different trees that were growing in different but overlapping periods of time, dating by this method — known as dendrochronology — can be extended back thousands of years.

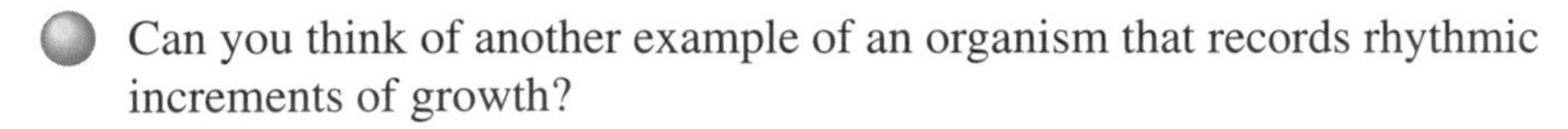

- Can you think of another example of an organism that records rhythmic increments of growth?

- You saw in Sections 2.2 and 3 (Activity 3.1) that the fossil shells of marine organisms may have growth lines, although these do not necessarily record growth at precisely regular intervals such as days, months or years.

In these cases, and that of fossil wood millions of years old, we can sometimes see a detailed record of rhythmic changes or cycles but we have no means of placing those cycles in a historical context — we do not know how many years ago they occurred although we may be able to see for how long the organisms lived. Dendrochronology probes back through past millennia to times before recorded human history, but it cannot take us into the realm of dating solid rocks. We do not have a long enough unbroken tree ring record stretching back through time and, in any case, many rocks predate the advent of the first trees. Thus while tree rings have enormous value in dating recent changes in climate, they are of no use in dating ancient rocks below the surface. Time measured in thousands of years is barely scratching the surface of *geological* time.

But how do we know that geological time is so vast? How do we know, for example, that the age of the Earth is 4 600 Ma and that the dinosaurs became extinct 65 Ma ago? Before showing how such ages can be established, we will delve a little into the historical development of ideas concerning the duration of geological time and explore some of the early attempts to quantify its passage.

8.2 Estimating geological time — reason and religion in the 18th and 19th centuries

The problem of the length of geological time was a particular preoccupation of British science during the 19th century. Notions of its duration were based on observing the rates at which geological processes occur today and comparing them with the record of these processes in rocks. One of the early champions of this cause was Charles Lyell (1797–1875) who, together with James Hutton (1726–1797) 50 or so years earlier, laid the foundations of modern geology. In his *Principles of Geology*, published in the 1830s, Lyell argued from a wealth of observation of geological phenomena that geological processes act very slowly and that geological time must therefore be unimaginably long.

Lyell's and Hutton's arguments form the basis of a fundamental principle of geology: the **principle of uniformitarianism**. This is often summed up in the sound-bite 'the present is the key to the past', which states that the processes that produced rocks in the past are the same as those we can observe today or infer from observation. You will note that we have already applied this principle in our discussion of tree rings and in Section 6 we applied it to sedimentary processes, and to us it seems only common sense. But in the intellectual environment of the 18th and early 19th centuries, dominated by literal interpretations of the Bible, such ideas were, to say the least, controversial.

The alternative to uniformitarianism held that the geological record was one of repeated catastrophes, of which the prime example was Noah's Flood. This was perceived as only the most recent of a series of catastrophic events that had swept the Earth, causing the periodic extinction of life and the episodic construction of rock formations. New species then replaced the old ones, presumably in an act of Divine creation, and populated the newly recreated surface of the Earth. This approach to the geological record, known as **catastrophism,** was more in accord with an Old Testament view of the world and it became the main opponent of uniformitarianism. The debate between their protagonists lasted for many years, but with the publication of Lyell's *Principles* in the 1830s, the basis of modern geology was firmly established.

8.3 Estimating geological time — how old is a volcano?

One of Lyell's many examples in *Principles of Geology* focused on the geology of Etna, an active volcano on the island of Sicily in the Mediterranean, and he outlined a method to estimate its age. He observed from different sections through the main volcanic cone that it is made up of many individual lava flows and layers of ash, exactly similar to those seen to form during eruptions at the present day. This, he deduced, was the way in which the volcano grew to its present dimensions. Therefore, by comparing the total volume of the volcano with the rate at which lava is added, it should be possible to calculate an age. Unfortunately, data on the volumes of individual eruptions were not available to Lyell and he could not follow that calculation through to a solution. But, as we now have access to that information, we can carry out the calculation for ourselves.

During its frequent eruptions, lava flows from Etna present a major geological hazard to the local community, periodically destroying buildings, agricultural land and villages (Figure 8.2). As a result of this risk to life and property, and because of the ease of access to it, Etna has been the subject of longer detailed observation than any other volcano and we can use these accumulated observational data to measure the rate at which the volcano grows.

Figure 8.2 Lava flows in the Valle del Bove below the summit of Etna (June 1994). It was the comparison of new lava flows, such as these, with older flows in the flanks of the Valle that led Lyell to his conclusions regarding the growth of Etna.

One way of illustrating how Etna grows is to plot a graph of eruption volume against the date of the eruption. This is shown in Figure 8.3. The volume of each eruption is simply determined by multiplying the area of a lava flow, calculated from detailed mapping, by its average thickness. Clearly, these volume estimates are subject to uncertainties because of difficulties in measuring flow thickness, but a reasonable estimate can be deduced by taking many different measurements of the thickness over the whole area of each flow.

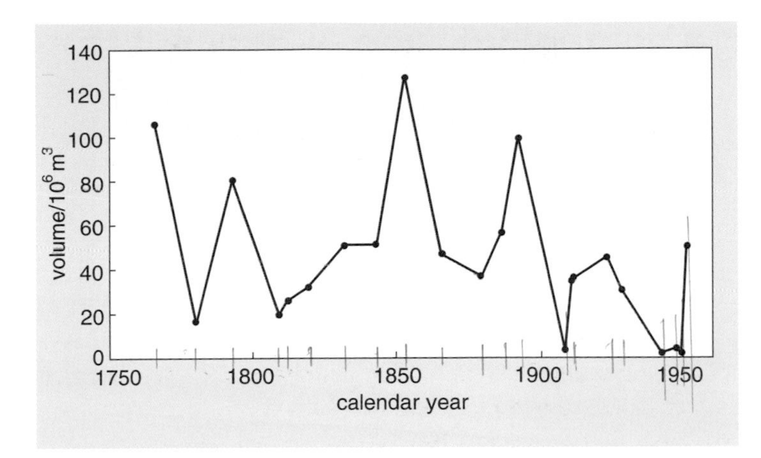

Figure 8.3 The volume of eruptions at Etna, 1766 –1951.

- Do the eruptions appear to be regular in size and frequency? Is there a long period of inactivity before every large eruption?

- No. There seems to be no regularity, no pattern to the length of time between each eruption, and no evidence that a large delay is followed by a large flow. Eruptions appear to be random in both size and frequency.

It is quite clear that different eruptions produced different volumes of lava and that we would get very different estimates of the rate of growth from individual flow volumes. Therefore, to calculate a rate of growth we need to take an average over a long period of time.

Activity 8.1 Calculating an average growth rate for Etna

In this activity you will use data on the volumes of Etna's recorded lava flows to plot a cumulative volume graph from which you can determine the average growth rate of the volcano. ◀

- Now that we know the average growth rate, what extra information do we need to calculate an age for the volcano?

- We need to know the total volume of lava in the mountain. An estimate of the age of Etna can then be derived by dividing its volume by the rate of growth.

The shape of Etna is well known because it has been mapped in some detail. It has a roughly circular base, with a summit at 3 000 m above sea-level. A recent determination of Etna's volume, using modern topographic surveying techniques and seismic profiles to define the detailed shape of the surface on which it is built, gives a volume of close to 350 km^3.

Question 8.1 Using the volume of 350 km^3 and the growth rate calculated in Activity 8.1, calculate the age of Etna. (*Hint:* Make sure that you use consistent units.) ◀

On a human scale the calculated age of Etna is a very long period of time, equivalent to about a thousand average human lifetimes, or three thousand generations. All of written human history represents less than one-tenth of this period. However, Etna is a relatively young geological feature, and is built on a foundation of sedimentary rocks.

- What does this tell us about the age of these sedimentary rocks?

- They must be older than Etna.

The youngest of these sedimentary rocks contain fossils of marine animals that are very similar to, and in some cases indistinguishable from, animals living in the present-day Mediterranean.

- What does this observation tell us about the rate of evolution of these marine animals, as far as their preservable features are concerned?

- It has been very slow or zero over the time taken for Etna to form.

The inescapable conclusion is that even the time required to construct Etna must be insignificant in relation to the time required for the development of the geological sequences in which fossils are preserved. This was one of the major philosophical breakthroughs that Lyell made in his analysis of the geology of Etna, and it contributed to his conclusion that geological time must be measured in terms of many millions of years.

Before we leave Etna, look at the cumulative graph in Figure 8.4. This includes more recent data on volumes of Etna lava flows covering the time period from 1951 to 1985. There is quite clearly a marked change in the eruption rate in 1951.

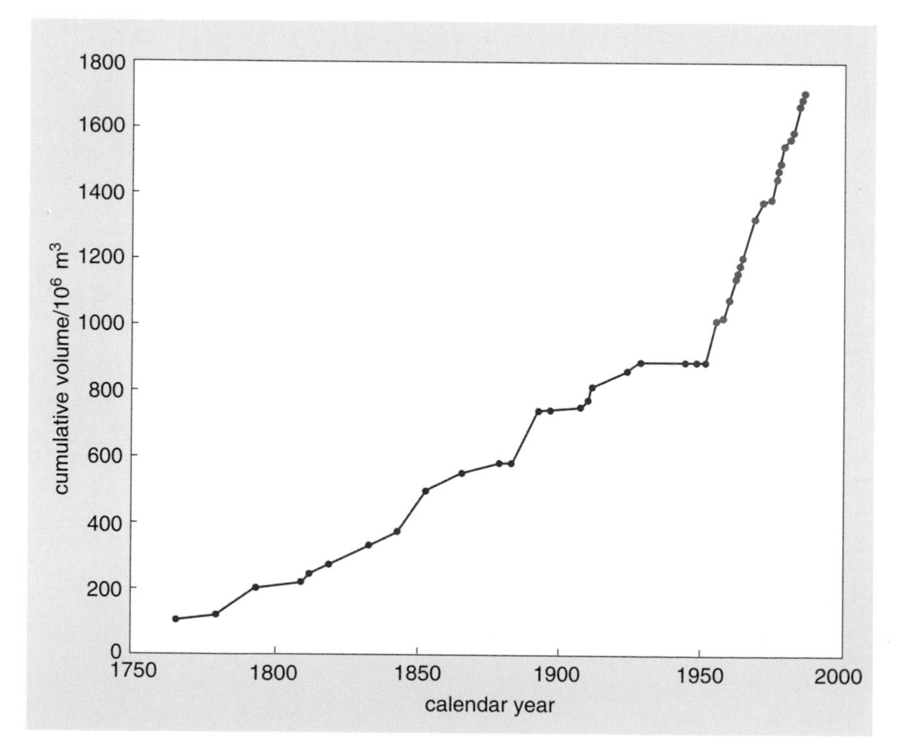

Figure 8.4 The cumulative volume of lava flows from Etna, 1766–1985. Note the marked change in the general slope of the line in 1951.

- Did the eruption rate increase or decrease in 1951?

- The graph steepens, so the eruption rate increased.

In fact, the eruption rate increased four-fold from about $0.005\,km^3\,y^{-1}$ to about $0.02\,km^3\,y^{-1}$.

- Is the change in eruption rate a violation of the principle of uniformitarianism?

- No, it is not. Although the rate of growth between 1951 and 1985 was greater than that in the period since 1766, the mechanism of eruption remained the same.

The term 'uniformitarianism' is often misinterpreted to mean a uniformity in the *rate* of geological processes and a denial of the occurrence of rapid, catastrophic events. In fact what Lyell meant when he coined the term was a 'uniformity of natural law', i.e. that all geological events and processes can be understood within the bounds of known physical laws.

- How would the estimate of the age of Etna change if we based it on the measured eruption rate since 1951?

- The volume of Etna remains the same, so the increase in the eruption rate would decrease the age we calculate.

If we based our estimate of the age of Etna on the eruption rate between 1951 and 1985, it becomes:

$$\frac{350\,\text{km}^3}{0.02\,\text{km}^3\,\text{y}^{-1}} = 17\,500\,\text{y}$$

or 20 000 y to one significant figure, which is only a quarter of our original estimate.

This example of Etna illustrates that although we can gain *some* quantitative insight into the duration of geological time, and the time-scale of evolution, through the observation of geological processes, such methods cannot form the basis of a reliable method of determining the absolute ages of rocks. The rates of geological processes are simply too variable on long time-scales. To determine the absolute age of a rock we need to utilize a natural process that occurs inside rocks at a constant rate and which is independent of external influences.

8.4 Estimating geological time — geology and physics in the late 19th century

Having settled one argument concerning the great duration of geological time in the early 19th century, the new science of geology had to do battle with the scientific establishment in the late 19th century. As we have seen, Lyell argued from observations of the very slow rates of geological processes, and by applying the principle of uniformitarianism, that the Earth must be many millions of years old. In fact, his general opinion was that the age of the Earth was indeterminate and that geological time had no bounds. Others, however, thought otherwise; towards the end of the 19th century attempts were made to calculate the age of the Earth.

John Joly, for example, made a quantitative estimate of the age of the Earth in 1898, by calculating the time required for the oceans to attain their present concentration of sodium — an idea initially proposed in 1715 by Sir Edmund Halley. Sodium is readily removed from the rocks of the continents by chemical weathering (Section 6.2.1), and is washed by rivers down to the oceans where it gradually accumulates — hence the contribution of sodium to the saltiness of the sea. From the volume of the oceans and the concentration of sodium in river water, Joly deduced that the oceans must be 80–90 Ma old. Other estimates of the age of the Earth were also made at around this time and most pointed, albeit rather imprecisely, to ages of 100–1 000 Ma.

A counter-argument to these large and variable age estimates was proposed at the end of the 19th century by a leading physicist, William Thompson (later, Lord Kelvin, after whom the SI unit of temperature was named). He recognized that the Earth is losing heat from its interior. As you go down a mine the rocks get hotter — in the deepest gold mines in South Africa, for example, rock temperatures of 100 °C are not uncommon (see Box 7.1). Therefore, Kelvin argued, the Earth must be cooling from a hotter state which he assumed was initially molten. He also assumed that there was no additional source of energy within the Earth and that the Earth was cooling by conduction of heat from its centre to the surface. The time taken for the Earth to cool to its present, rather solid, condition could then be calculated from the present temperature gradient within the Earth, as measured in mines.

Kelvin's results demonstrated that the Earth could only be at most 20–40 Ma old. Herein lay the source of the controversy: a scientific estimate of the age of the Earth based on fundamental physical principles — and a few well-reasoned assumptions — pitted against an array of qualitative and semi-quantitative estimates based on geological observation. And all of the geological estimates were substantially greater than the 20–40 Ma which the physical arguments demanded.

Early in the 20th century, shortly after Lord Kelvin's death, severe doubts were raised about his conclusion when it was recognized that at least one of his assumptions was incorrect — there *is* a long-lived internal source of energy within the Earth: natural radioactivity.

All radioactive decay processes liberate energy (Block 7, Section 5) and the low-level but ubiquitous occurrence of radioactive isotopes in rocks provides a long-lived source of energy within the Earth. Although radioactivity was discovered in 1896, a decade before Kelvin's death, it was only with the later recognition that natural rocks contain small but measurable amounts of radioactive isotopes that the possible implications for the thermal history of the Earth were realized (see Box 8.1, *The real reason why Kelvin got the age of the Earth wrong*).

Box 8.1 The real reason why Kelvin got the age of the Earth wrong

A popular version of the development of geochronology, and one loaded with false irony, is that Kelvin arrived at his erroneously low estimate of the age of the Earth because he ignored heat production by radioactive decay. When radioactivity was discovered and estimates of radiogenic heat production within the Earth were added into Kelvin's calculations, they increased the calculated age of the Earth, bringing it more in line with geological estimates. This is because the Earth would need more time to get rid of the excess radiogenic heat in order to cool to its present state. However, we now know that early assumptions about the distribution and concentrations of potassium, uranium and thorium, the most important radioactive elements in the Earth, were inaccurate and too high. When modern estimates are used, the effect on the age of the Earth calculated by taking into account the contribution of radiogenic heat is much less significant.

The real reason for Kelvin's low estimate of the age of the Earth was that his other major assumption, that the Earth cools by conduction alone, was also wrong. We now know from plate tectonics that the Earth's mantle moves and this movement is driven by thermal *convection* — hot material rises and cold material sinks. This process 'evens out' the temperature within the deeper Earth but maintains a higher temperature gradient near the surface than is generated by purely conductive cooling. In other words, the Earth cools by conduction near the surface but by mainly convection in the deeper layers. By using the surface gradient in a model which assumed that conduction is the only way of transporting heat throughout the whole Earth, Kelvin arrived at his erroneously short age; and he would have done so even if he had included the correct estimates of radiogenic heat production. The failure to account for radioactivity was cited at the time as the main reason why he was wrong but it was not until the advent of plate tectonics, in the latter half of the 20th century, that the real reason for the discrepancy between Kelvin and the geologists was finally resolved.

8.5 Measuring geological time — radiometric dating

Radiometric dating exploits naturally occurring radioactive isotopes to determine the ages of geological and archaeological materials.

Activity 8.2 Revision: radioactivity

This activity will help you revise important aspects of radioactivity that have been covered earlier in the course in Block 7 and at the residential school. You should satisfy yourself that you fully understand the answers to the questions in this activity before continuing with this section. ◀

Radioactive isotopes each decay with a half-life that is constant for that isotope (Block 7, Activity 5.1). The half-lives of all commonly occurring radioactive isotopes are known from laboratory measurements of pure samples; Figure 8.5 illustrates various decay schemes commonly used in radiometric dating, together with their half-lives. The constancy of each half-life is the critical factor that allows us to use radioactivity as a natural clock. But to determine the ages of rocks and minerals we have to learn how to 'tell the time' using that clock.

One of the better known radiometric techniques used in dating is the $^{14}_{6}C$ (carbon-14) method. It is based on the β^--decay of $^{14}_{6}C$ to $^{14}_{7}N$ and is frequently used to date organic remains and archaeological, or even historical, artefacts — for example the Turin Shroud. The technique assumes that the ratio of $^{14}_{6}C$ to the other isotopes of carbon, $^{12}_{6}C$ and $^{13}_{6}C$, in a sample of living material was the same thousands of years ago as that measured in living things today. This is because the ratio of $^{14}_{6}C$ to the other carbon isotopes in the CO_2 of the atmosphere is assumed to have remained constant (new $^{14}_{6}C$ being produced at a constant rate in the atmosphere by cosmic ray bombardment). However, when organisms die, the proportion of $^{14}_{6}C$ starts to fall, as no more $^{14}_{6}C$ is being absorbed by the living tissue. By measuring the amount of $^{14}_{6}C$ in the sample now, its age can be calculated from a knowledge of the half-life of $^{14}_{6}C$, 5 700 years.

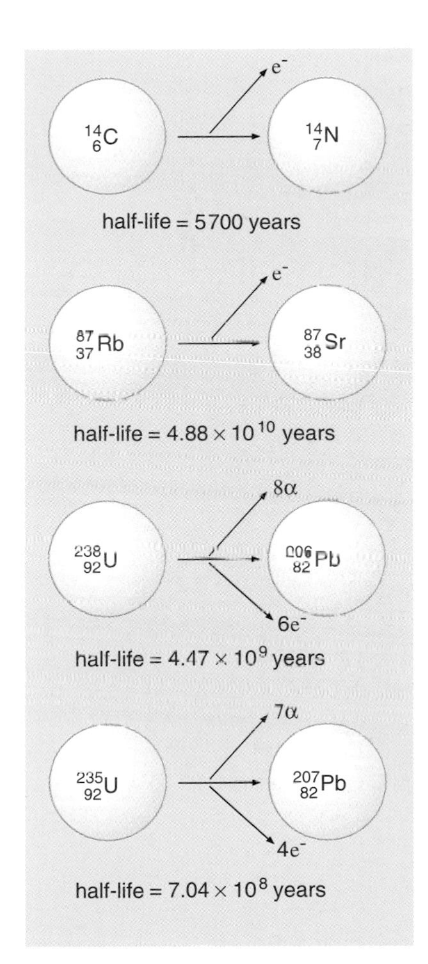

Figure 8.5 Some radioactive decay schemes commonly used in radiometric dating. The decay of $^{235}_{92}U$ to $^{207}_{82}Pb$, and of $^{238}_{92}U$ to $^{206}_{82}Pb$, occurs via a number of intermediate, short-lived radioactive isotopes, and the numbers of alpha-particles (α) and electrons (e^-) emitted in each chain are indicated.

● Why is the $^{14}_{6}C$ method inappropriate for dating most geological specimens?

○ Most geological specimens are many hundreds or thousands of times older than the half-life of $^{14}_{6}C$, so virtually all of the $^{14}_{6}C$ they may once have contained will have decayed away. Also, many geological specimens do not contain organic carbon.

$^{14}_{6}C$ is extremely useful for dating organic remains less than 60 000 years old, i.e. those that are within the realm of archaeology and history. To date geological samples we need to make use of radioactive isotopes with much longer half-lives. But before we can use these decay schemes, we have to solve another problem.

In the $^{14}_{6}C$ method, we can calculate the original amount of $^{14}_{6}C$ present in a given mass of organic material from knowledge of the proportions of carbon isotopes present in living organisms. However, when dealing with other radioactive decay schemes we do not know the amount of the parent isotope present when a rock or mineral was formed. What we see is a snapshot of a radioactive system at the present day. In this snapshot there are both parent and daughter isotopes, the amounts of which can be measured. The parent isotope atoms have been decaying and the daughters growing in number since, for example, a mineral crystallized as magma cooled to form a solid rock. How can we use this information to date the time that the rock or mineral formed?

To do this we need to explore a little of the mathematics of radioactive decay. We know from Activity 8.2 that the general equation for radioactivity can be expressed as:

$$P = P_0\left(\frac{1}{2}\right)^n = \frac{P_0}{2^n} \quad (8.1)$$

where P_0 is the number of parent atoms present when the rock or mineral crystallized and P is the number of parent isotope atoms left after n half-lives.

As the number of parent atoms declines, so the number of daughter atoms increases, but the total number of atomic nuclei remains the same. For example, in the β^--decay of $^{87}_{37}Rb$ (rubidium) to its daughter isotope $^{87}_{38}Sr$ (strontium) (Figure 8.5), each time a $^{87}_{37}Rb$ atomic nucleus decays, a new $^{87}_{38}Sr$ nucleus is formed, so the total number of atomic nuclei in the system is constant. In the general case we are considering here, this can be stated as:

$$D + P = P_0$$

where D is the number of daughter isotope atoms present. This can be re-arranged to calculate D:

$$D = P_0 - P \quad (8.2)$$

What we measure in a rock or mineral sample is the relative number of daughter and parent isotope atoms, which, in our terminology is D/P. From Equations 8.1 and 8.2 we can find an expression for the value of D/P in the following way.

Rearranging Equation 8.1 to make P_0 the subject we get:

$$P_0 = 2^nP$$

Substituting this expression for P_0 into Equation 8.2 leads to:

$$D = 2^nP - P = P\,(2^n - 1)$$

and so:

$$D/P = 2^n - 1 \quad (8.3)$$

In other words, for every value of n, the number of half-lives elapsed since the rock or mineral crystallized, there is a unique value of D/P. The important observation from this exercise is that:

> the value of D/P (known as the **daughter to parent (D/P) ratio**) depends on the number of half-lives that have elapsed since a rock or mineral was formed, and this value can be used to calculate the age of a rock or mineral without knowing the amount of parent isotope originally present.

Activity 8.3 Calculating the value of D/P for a simple radioactive decay scheme

In this activity you will use the simple equations derived above to calculate values of D/P for different numbers of half-lives. This produces the graph that is used in subsequent exercises. ◀

We have now shown in two ways, the first mathematical, and the second graphical, that we can relate the values of *D/P* in a rock or mineral to its age. However, certain conditions must be met for our simple version of a radioactive clock to work. First, the sample must act as a closed system — atoms of parent and daughter isotopes must neither enter nor leave the sample after its formation. Second, there must be no daughter isotope atoms present in the sample at the time of its formation. For many radioactive systems this is not the case and corrections for the initial concentrations of isotopes have to be applied. Such procedures are beyond the scope of this course and the following examples of radiometric dating are restricted to the use of decay schemes and systems in which such corrections are not necessary.

8.5.1 Examples of radiometric dating

One of the most precise dating techniques uses a mineral called zircon that contains high concentrations of uranium. Uranium has two isotopes, ${}^{235}_{92}\text{U}$ and ${}^{238}_{92}\text{U}$, both of which decay through a series of intermediate isotopes of other elements to stable isotopes of lead: ${}^{235}_{92}\text{U}$ decays to ${}^{207}_{82}\text{Pb}$, and ${}^{238}_{92}\text{U}$ to ${}^{206}_{82}\text{Pb}$ (Figure 8.5). Thus, from a knowledge of the *D/P* values of ${}^{207}_{82}\text{Pb}/{}^{235}_{92}\text{U}$ and ${}^{206}_{82}\text{Pb}/{}^{238}_{92}\text{U}$ in a zircon sample, its age can be calculated. This is a particularly powerful technique because zircon is a mineral that occurs in many igneous rocks, albeit in very tiny amounts, typically much less than 1% of the rock. Moreover, it can survive the chemical effects of weathering and other processes that may modify a rock after formation. In this sense it is as close as we get to a geological closed system. It also contains practically no lead when it is newly crystallized. All we have to do to determine the age of a zircon crystal is to determine the value of *D/P* for one or both decay schemes and compare the result with our graph (Figure 8.6) to find the number of half-lives that have elapsed. Knowing the number of half-lives and the value of the half-life, it is then easy to find the age of the crystal. Here are two worked examples that demonstrate how age information can be derived from zircons.

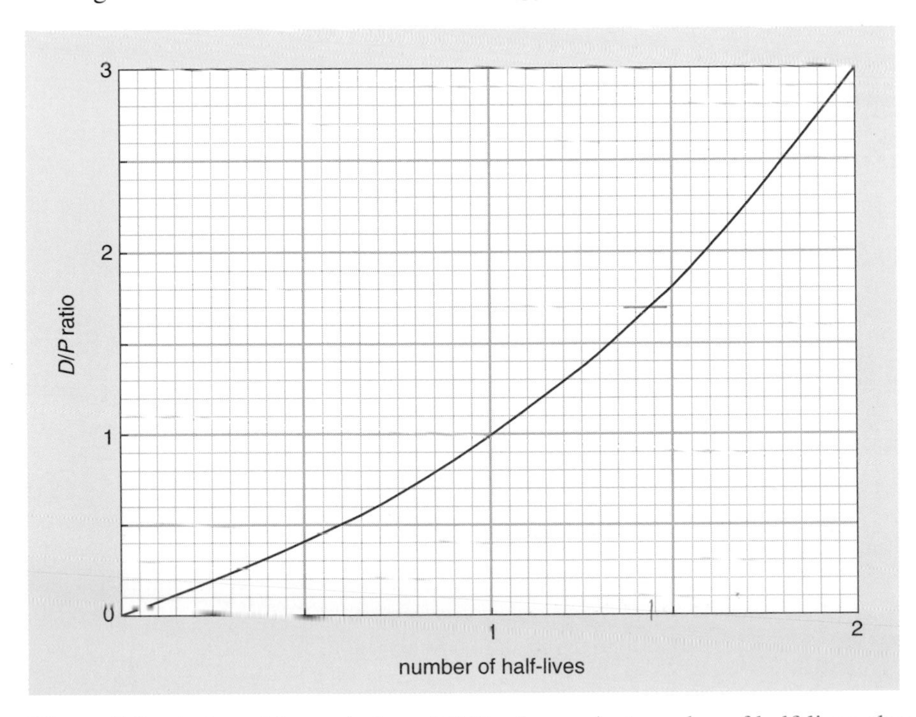

Figure 8.6 A plot of the variation of *D/P* value against number of half-lives elapsed.

Example 1

The value of ${}^{207}_{82}\text{Pb}/{}^{235}_{92}\text{U}$ in a zircon sample from a granite intrusion is 3.0. What is the age of the zircon and hence the granite?

${}^{235}_{92}\text{U}$ is the parent to ${}^{207}_{82}\text{Pb}$ and it has a half-life of 704 Ma. The *D*/*P* value is 3.0 and from Figure 8.6 we can see that this *D*/*P* value corresponds to 2.0 half-lives. As the half-life of ${}^{235}_{92}\text{U}$ is 704 Ma, two half-lives is equivalent to an age of 2.0×704 Ma = 1 408 Ma old. Thus the zircon, and hence the granite, are 1 400 Ma old, to two significant figures.

Example 2

The ${}^{206}_{82}\text{Pb}/{}^{238}_{92}\text{U}$ value of another zircon sample from a different granite is 0.50. What is the age of this granite?

From Figure 8.6 we can read off that a *D*/*P* value of 0.50 corresponds to 0.58 half-lives. As the half-life of ${}^{238}_{92}\text{U}$ is 4 470 Ma, this is equivalent to an age of $0.58 \times 4\,470$ Ma = 2 593 Ma. Thus the granite is 2 600 Ma old, to two significant figures.

These ages are subject to uncertainties, one of which is associated with reading the number of half-lives elapsed from Figure 8.6, although this source of uncertainty can be removed by using Equation 8.3. A much more important source of uncertainty concerns the accuracy with which the long half-lives of naturally occurring radioactive isotopes can be determined. Yet more uncertainties are associated with the measurement of the relative amounts of the lead and uranium isotopes in a sample. A full treatment of the uncertainties associated with radiometric dating is well beyond the scope of this course, but it is important to appreciate that even with all of the technologically advanced instruments available to modern geochronology, absolute ages always have uncertainties associated with them. The zircon technique is in fact the most precise method currently available, and ages are frequently determined to a relative precision of between ±0.1% and ±1%, but even at ±0.1% those uncertainties represent ±2 Ma on an age of 2 000 Ma. This would be expressed as 2 000 Ma ± 2 Ma. Notwithstanding these uncertainties, radiometric dating has revolutionized our knowledge of the Earth's history, having given us the absolute ages of igneous and metamorphic rocks, in which correlation using fossils is not possible.

To consolidate your understanding of radiometric dating you should now attempt the following two questions.

Question 8.2 (a) A zircon in a granite has a ${}^{207}_{82}\text{Pb}/{}^{235}_{92}\text{U}$ value of 1.7. What is the age of the granite? ◀

(b) A zircon in a second granite has a ${}^{238}_{92}\text{U}/{}^{206}_{82}\text{Pb}$ value of 2.5. What is the age of this granite? ◀

Question 8.3 In practice, ages are calculated using a variant of Equation 8.3 and the uncertainty of the calculated age is dependent on the uncertainty with which *D*/*P* has been measured. Express the unrounded ages calculated in Question 8.2 in the form *a* Ma ± *b* Ma, assuming the uncertainty in the final calculated age is ±1%. ◀

8.6 Calibrating the stratigraphic column

So far in this block you have learnt how sedimentary rocks can be dated relatively using fossils and the principle of superposition (Section 3.4), and how igneous rocks are dated absolutely using radiometric methods. We shall now combine these two approaches to demonstrate how sedimentary rocks are dated *absolutely* to reveal the true time-scale of biological evolution.

Igneous rocks crystallize at high temperatures and their constituent minerals become closed to external influences before they cool to surface conditions. The same cannot be said for sedimentary rocks. Sediments form at low temperatures on the Earth's surface by a combination of physical and chemical processes (Section 6). After deposition, they are subjected to further processes, such as compaction and cementation, heating and interactions with fluids, that turn sediments into sedimentary rocks. All of these processes have an effect on the ability of a sedimentary rock to retain the parent and daughter isotopes of the radioactive decay schemes. Hence the closed system condition is rarely met in sedimentary rocks, and this prevents the successful application of radiometric dating in all but a few specific cases. How then do we date sedimentary rocks absolutely? To do this we need to turn to some other geological principles that allow us to determine the relative ages of rocks in slightly more complex situations than those explored earlier.

Although igneous rocks are uncommon in association with sedimentary sequences, when they are found in place they provide critical markers that can be dated absolutely using radiometric methods. The best examples are lavas because these are younger than the rocks below them and older than those above them, i.e. they fit into the sequence according to the principle of superposition (Section 3.4). However, we saw in Section 5.1.1 that not all magma reaches the surface; sometimes it is trapped in fissures, to form dykes and sills, or it forms larger bodies (plutons). In these cases we cannot resort to the principle of superposition to deduce relative ages, but it is obvious that the surrounding rocks must have existed for the magma to intrude into them! The surrounding rocks must be older than the intrusion, whatever its size.

The relationships seen in the field between igneous and sedimentary rocks are therefore very important if the igneous rocks are to be used for dating purposes.

- What happens to sedimentary rocks when they are intruded by hot magma?

- The heat of the magma bakes the sedimentary rocks, causing physical changes (e.g. recrystallization) and may induce the growth of new minerals — this is contact metamorphism (Section 7.1).

Figure 8.7 (*overleaf*) shows two examples of granite intrusions surrounded by sedimentary rocks. In Figure 8.7a, the intrusion, labelled B, cuts across the bedding of the adjacent strata (A) and is surrounded by a zone of contact metamorphic rocks (C), so the granite intrusion must be younger than the surrounding strata. In Figure 8.7b, the relationship between strata A and the granite intrusion B is similar. Strata D, however, cut across both the older strata (A) and the granite intrusion (B), and are not metamorphosed where they are in contact with the granite. In this case the granite intrusion must have been exposed at the surface and have undergone a period of erosion before the later sediments were deposited over it. The sedimentary rocks above the granite intrusion are unmetamorphosed, so we can deduce that they are younger than the granite.

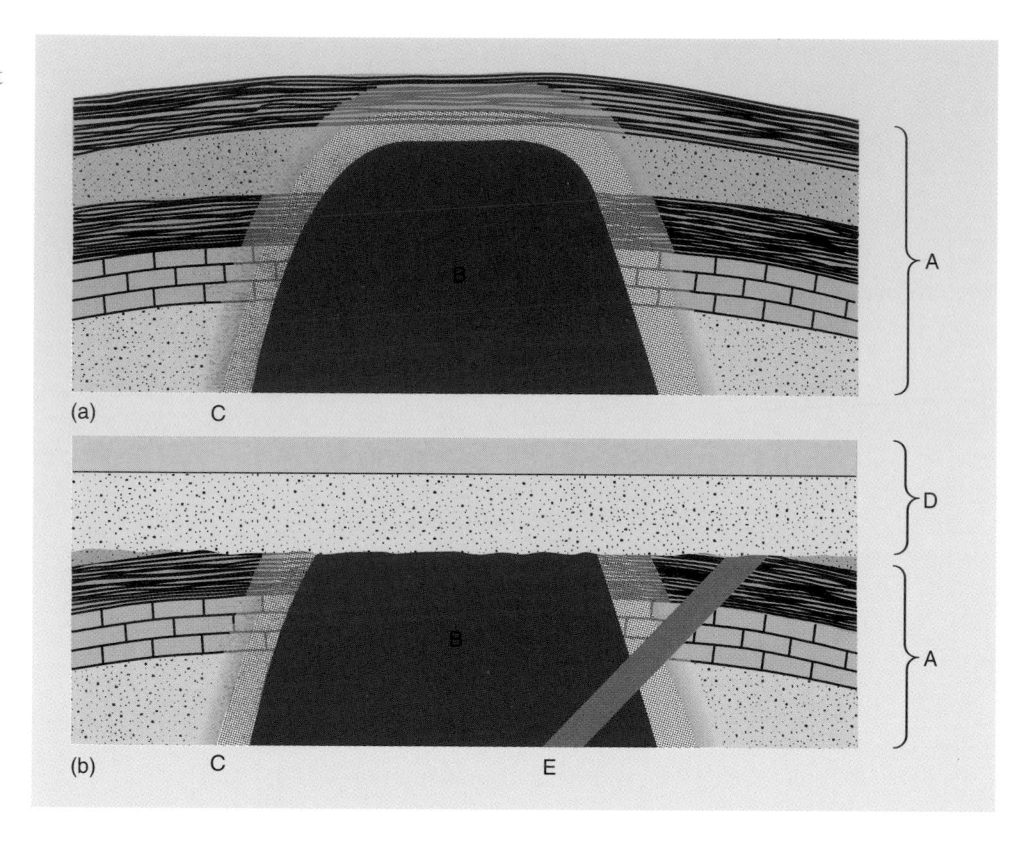

Figure 8.7 Sections through two granite intrusions showing different relationships with the surrounding sedimentary rocks. See text for discussion.

- What is the boundary in Figure 8.7b between strata D and the older strata A and the granite intrusion called?

- An unconformity (Section 3.4).

Unconformities indicate periods of erosion and often represent long intervals of geological time for which there are no sediments preserved in that particular area.

- What is the relative age of the dyke (E) in Figure 8.7b? Explain your answer.

- The dyke cuts across the older strata (A), the granite (B) and the zone of contact metamorphism (C), but is truncated by the unconformity between A and D. It is therefore younger than the granite but older than the younger group of strata (D).

Activity 8.4 From relative to absolute: ages of rocks

In this activity you will use the principles outlined in this section and earlier in the block to deduce relative and absolute ages for igneous and sedimentary rocks. ◀

The technique you have used in Activity 8.4 is commonly used to establish absolute ages of sedimentary rocks and is known as **bracketing**. Each time a particular radiometric date is used to calibrate some part of the stratigraphic column, a similar age can be applied to rocks elsewhere that are known to be of the same age because they contain similar fossils. Thus, by combining the relative ages derived from fossil evidence and the principle of superposition with absolute dates from occasional igneous intrusions or lava flows, we can calibrate the whole stratigraphic column, world-wide.

- How far back in time can we routinely use fossils in the correlation of sedimentary rocks?

- Only as far back as the beginning of the Cambrian, 545 Ma ago.

As we discovered in Sections 2 and 3, rocks older than the Cambrian Period rarely contain fossils. It is therefore not surprising that the development of radiometric dating revolutionized our perspective of the Precambrian, which we now know represents about 88% of Earth history.

This completes our introduction to the concept of geological time — or 'deep time', as it is sometimes described. Geological processes and evolution involve time on a grand scale. Indeed, the combination of the spatial scale of the Universe, which can be deduced from modern astronomical observation, as you will see in Block 11, and the time-scale of the geological record emphasize the limits of individual human experience. However, on a more practical level, our present knowledge of the way the Earth works owes much to the recent quantification of geological time through radiometric dating.

8.7 Summary of Section 8

Many living things record cyclical changes in their environment each year, or over some other period, and these cycles can sometimes be seen in the fossil record. However, it is usually difficult to place these changes in an absolute time frame, and techniques such as dendrochronology are useful only as far back as 5 000–10 000 years.

The principle of uniformitarianism states that the processes that produced the Earth's rocks in the past are the same as those we can observe acting on the Earth today, or infer from observation. Uniformitarianism developed as the successful alternative to catastrophism in the early 19th century.

The geological time-scale cannot be quantified accurately by extrapolating from observed rates of active geological processes because these rates are too variable over long periods of time.

The only way in which geological time can be measured absolutely is through the use of naturally occurring radioactive isotopes with very long half-lives. Examples of radioactive decay schemes used in radiometric dating are the decay of uranium to lead; rubidium to strontium; and potassium to argon. We can use the ratios of daughter to parent isotope atoms in rocks and minerals to calculate their ages, but care must be taken to ensure that the sample has remained a closed system since the rock or mineral formed. Ages determined by this method are always subject to experimental uncertainty. Although the uncertainty can be as low as ±0.1%, even this small value translates to an absolute uncertainty of ±2 Ma for a determined age of 2 000 Ma, and the uncertainties associated with radiometric ages are often greater than this.

Sediments can only rarely be dated using radiometric techniques. The stratigraphic column is calibrated by bracketing sedimentary formations with intrusive or extrusive igneous rocks that can be dated radiometrically.

9 Scenes from Britain's geological past

Having established some of the basic ideas of geology, and briefly explored the depth of geological time, we are in a good position to bring these ideas together to investigate the geological history of a particular part of the Earth's surface. And where better to focus on than the British Isles? This small area contains sedimentary, igneous and metamorphic rocks ranging in age from the mid-Precambrian (about 3 000 Ma ago) to much more recent deposits, such as those left by retreating glaciers about 10 000 years ago. Few areas of the Earth's surface of comparable size have such a rich geological heritage, and this was one of the reasons why so much of the development of the science of geology in the 18th and 19th centuries took place in Britain.

Figure 9.1 is a simplified geological map of Britain and Ireland. The different colours show where rocks of particular ages (or origin in the case of igneous rocks) occur either at the surface or below the soil. This map contains essential information for guiding us through the geological evolution of Britain. Activity 9.1 includes another map showing the location of many places mentioned in this section.

Activity 9.1 The geological map of the British Isles

This activity will help you to become familiar with the geological map in Figure 9.1 and will develop your map interpretation skills. ◀

Clearly, the British Isles have had a long and complex geological history. Here we will focus on a few episodes that emphasize some of the variety of rock types that occur in Britain and the story that they tell. However, as well as a journey through geological *time*, this section is also a journey through *space* as we study the plate-tectonic movements of what we now call the British Isles across the surface of the Earth.

As you may have noticed in Activity 9.1, Precambrian rocks outcrop mainly in northern Scotland, the western isles, and north-west Ireland, with scattered, smaller outcrops in Wales, the Welsh borders and elsewhere.

Question 9.1 Think about the likely nature and distribution of Precambrian rocks, and suggest three reasons why unravelling the Precambrian history of Britain is likely to be especially difficult compared with the study of much more recent times. ◀

Not surprisingly, during the immensely long Precambrian history of the British Isles there were many episodes of sedimentation, igneous activity and regional metamorphism, as plate-tectonic forces moved the rocks of the crust over the globe and around the rock cycle. Many Precambrian rocks have not only undergone high-grade regional metamorphism on more than one occasion, but they have also been affected by numerous faults and folds, so piecing together the detailed sequence of events is very challenging. We will therefore confine our discussion to some important events affecting Britain in the Phanerozoic Eon.

Figure 9.1 (*opposite*) A simplified geological map of the British Isles. Sedimentary and metamorphic rocks are colour-coded according to age. Igneous rocks are colour-coded according to whether they are intrusive or volcanic.

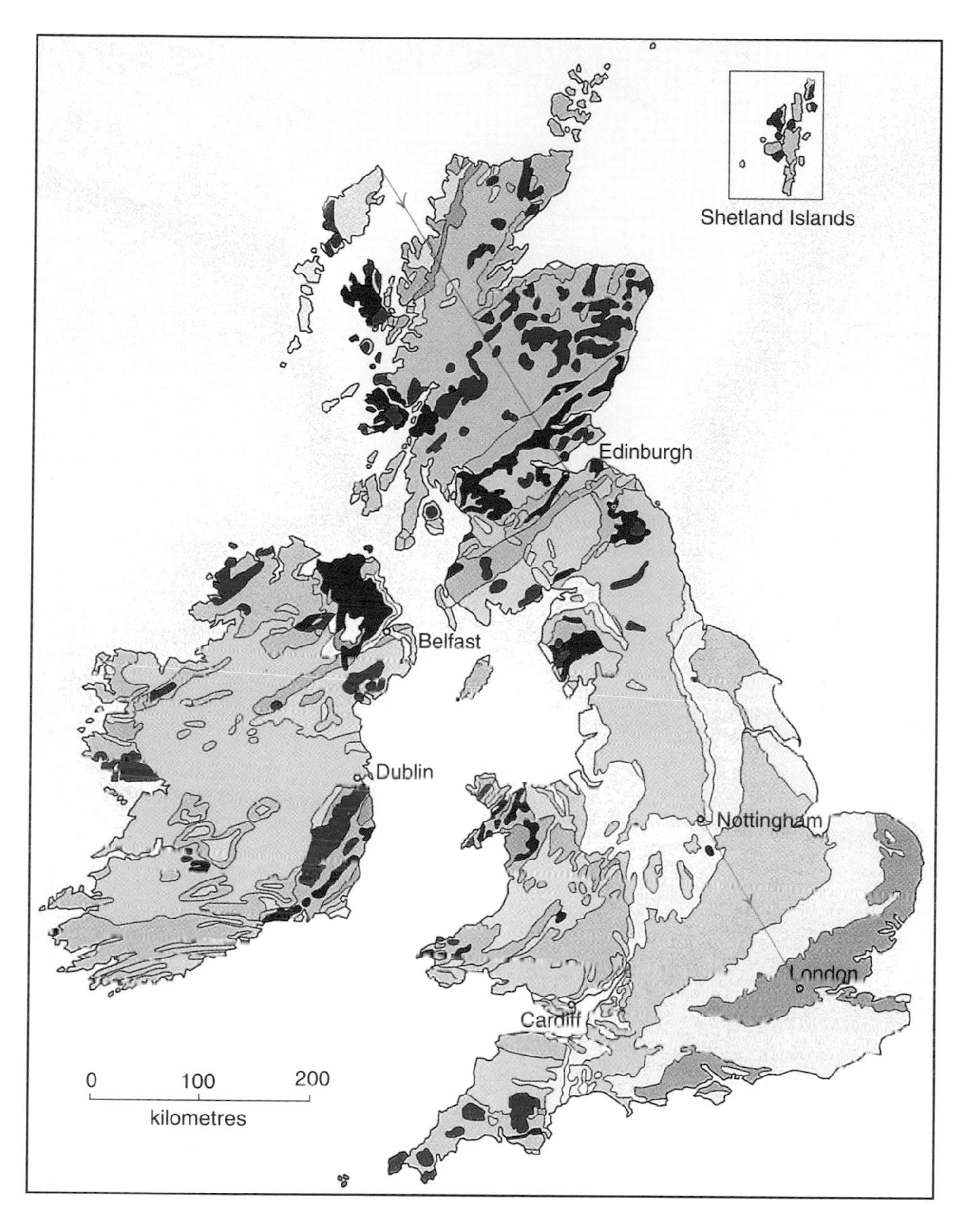

SEDIMENTARY ROCKS

CENOZOIC

Period	Description	Age
Tertiary and marine early Quaternary	mainly clays and sands; Quaternary glacial deposits not shown	up to 65

MESOZOIC

Period	Description	Age
Cretaceous	mainly chalk, clays and sands	65–142
Jurassic	mainly limestones and clays	142–206
Triassic	mudstones, sandstones and conglomerates	206–248

PALAEOZOIC

Period	Description	Age
Permian	mainly limestones, mudstones and sandstones	248–290
Carboniferous	limestones, sandstones, shales and coal seams	290–354
Devonian	sandstones, shales, conglomerates; slates and limestones	354–417

PALAEOZOIC continued

Period	Description	Age
Silurian	mainly shales, mudstones, some limestones	417–443
Ordovician	mainly shales and limestones; limestone in Scotland	443–495
Cambrian	mainly shales and sandstones; limestone in Scotland	495–545
Late Precambrian	mainly sandstones, conglomerates and siltstones	545–1000

HIGHLY METAMORPHOSED ROCKS

Period	Description	Age
Late Precambrian, Cambrian and Ordovician	mainly schists and gneisses	443–1000
Mid Precambrian	mainly gneisses	1500–3000

IGNEOUS ROCKS

Type	Description
Intrusive	mainly granite, gabbro and dolerite
Volcanic	mainly basalt, rhyolite, andesite and volcanic ashes

Numbers indicate age in millions of years

9.1 The Caledonides and the building of Britain (545–400 Ma ago)

The Caledonides are an ancient mountain range that gradually came into existence over a period of at least 100 Ma, ending about 400 Ma ago in the Devonian Period. Although the Caledonides have since been deeply eroded, parts are still exposed, forming much of the high ground in Scotland, the Lake District, north and mid-Wales, parts of Ireland and, further afield, in the Appalachians (eastern USA) and in Scandinavia. To understand how these ancient mountains arose, and how the various bits of what was to become Britain were assembled, we need to reconstruct the arrangement of oceans and continents at the time.

During the early Palaeozoic Era, unlike today, the continents were mainly located in the Southern Hemisphere (Figure 9.2). Palaeomagnetic evidence (Block 3, Section 11) reveals that at the start of the Ordovician Period, southern Britain was part of a small continent situated about 60 degrees south of the Equator. Meanwhile, northern Britain was part of a larger continent at a latitude of about 15° S, with the Baltic area (including Scandinavia) forming yet another continent (Figure 9.2a).

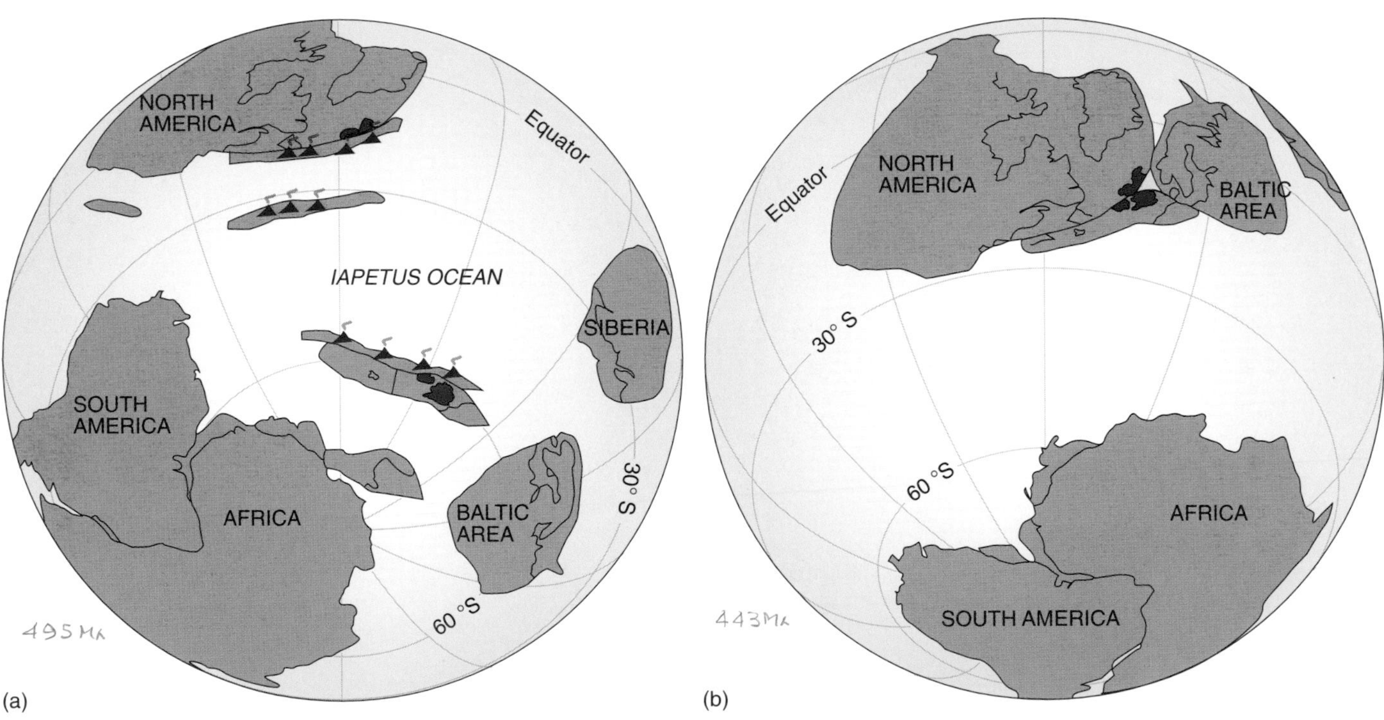

Figure 9.2 A reconstruction (one of several that have been proposed) showing the distribution of continental areas and oceans at two stages in the early Palaeozoic. (a) In the early Ordovician, 'Britain' (shown in red) was in two main pieces on either side of the Iapetus Ocean; together with some slivers of volcanic island arcs, these pieces were later to combine to form Britain. The purple triangles indicate volcanoes. (b) By the early Silurian, the Iapetus Ocean had closed, and the continuing collision of continental areas until the mid-Devonian formed the Caledonides. The thin slivers of island arcs incorporated into Britain are not discernible in (b).

The ocean that formed an original 'north-south divide' between the northern and southern parts of the British Isles is called the *Iapetus Ocean* (after Iapetus, who in Greek mythology was the father of Atlas, after whom the Atlantic Ocean is named). The Iapetus Ocean was at its widest — perhaps about 4 000 km across — during the early Ordovician (Figure 9.2a). Its subsequent narrowing, or closure, as the rate of subduction overtook sea-floor spreading, eventually led to continental collision. As we've seen before, when two or more plates collide, mountain belts are produced. Such a mountain-building event, with the associated metamorphism and tectonic deformation described in Section 7.3, is called an **orogeny** (from the Greek for mountain, *oros*, and genesis). The closure of the Iapetus Ocean and associated collisions led to the Caledonian Orogeny — one of the most important events in the geological history of the British Isles. We shall now investigate it further in Question 9.2.

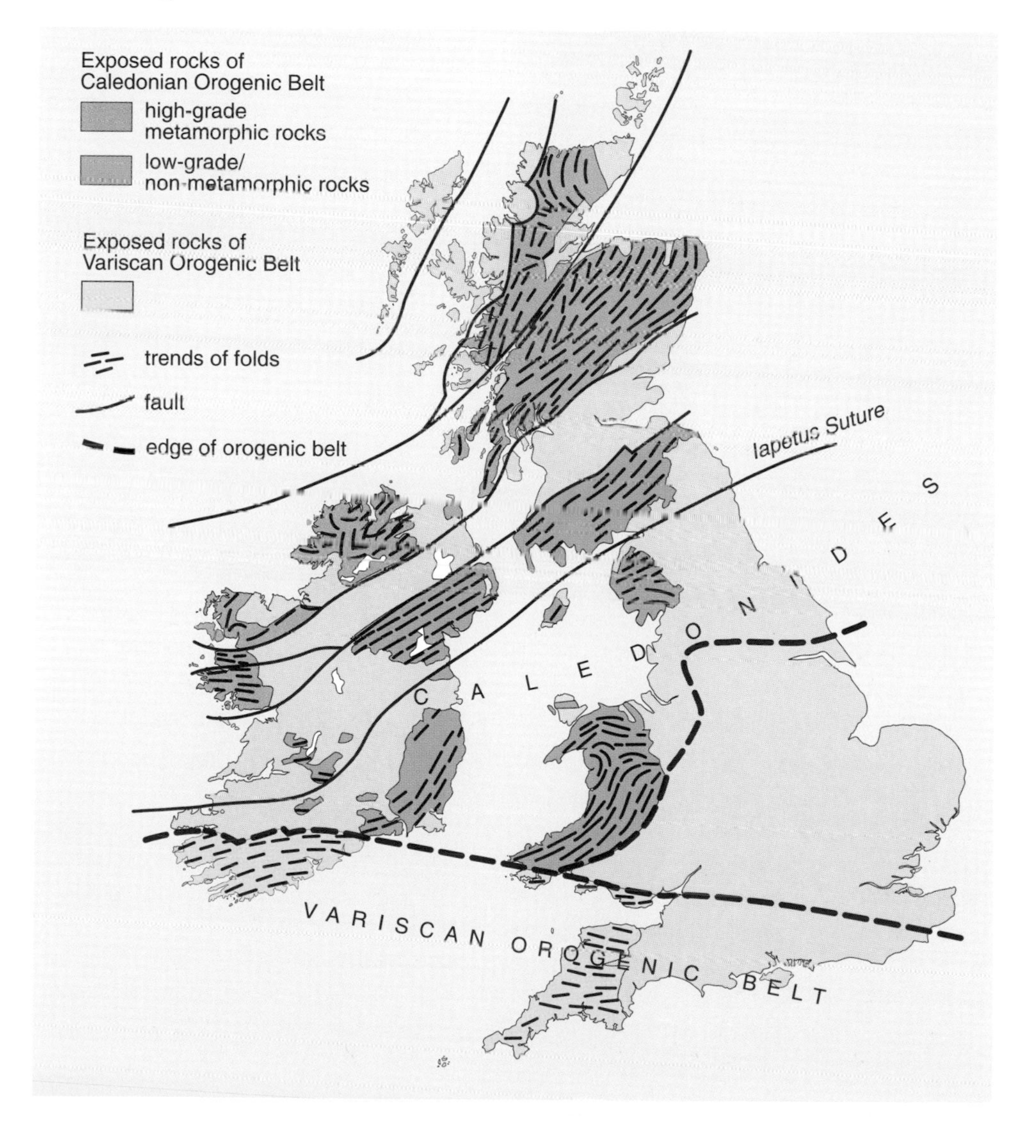

Figure 9.3 The main elements of the British Caledonides, showing areas where rocks of the Caledonian Orogenic Belt are exposed, major faults, the trends of folds, and location of the Iapetus Suture. Also shown are areas where rocks affected by the later Variscan Orogeny are exposed.

Question 9.2 All but *one* of the following paragraphs correctly summarize various aspects of the history of the Iapetus Ocean and the Caledonian Orogeny as it affected the British Isles. The story is based on the interpretation of a huge number of field observations of rocks, fossils and geological structures, relative and absolute dates, and so on. Most of the details, although new to you, should make geological sense and ring true on the basis of what you have already learnt in this block and in Block 3, and from studying Figures 9.1–9.3; some references are given to related information in earlier sections. You should simply read the paragraphs, taking in this important story, and find the *one* paragraph that clearly contains major errors, and correct those errors within it.

1 The Cambrian, Ordovician and Silurian sedimentary rocks of Britain are typically mudstones, shales, siltstones, and sandstones, with some limestones (Figure 9.1). They often contain fossil groups such as trilobites, brachiopods, cephalopods and, in the case of the limestones, also corals and crinoids, indicating that much of Britain then lay under the sea (Activities 2.1, 3.1). Most of these deposits accumulated in shallow seas on continental shelves, rather than on the deep ocean floor.

2 When the Iapetus Ocean was at its widest during the early Ordovician (Figure 9.2a), the ocean itself was a physical barrier that maintained separate, independently-evolving groups of marine species on each side. It was finding a marked difference between fossil faunas in Ordovician rocks of similar ages and environments as close together as southern Scotland and the Lake District that first led geologists to suggest the existence of a lost ocean.

3 As the Iapetus Ocean closed, and as both sides became more similar in latitude, the faunas on both edges of the ocean became increasingly alike, as species were able to migrate across progressively smaller distances into increasingly similar environments. By early Devonian times, the *freshwater* environments on the newly-merged continental edges were inhabited by the same species of fish and arthropods.

4 The oceanic crust itself was eventually all subducted, apart from some small slivers of ophiolite (Section 5.4) and some ocean floor sediments that were scraped up onto the continental edges. This subduction led to much igneous activity, especially along the southern margin of the Iapetus Ocean. For example, as is typical of subduction under continental crust (Section 5.4), andesitic lavas and ashes were erupted, often into shallow seas, in areas such as the Lake District and Wales.

5 As continental collision proceeded, many of the sedimentary rocks deposited during the Cambrian, Ordovician and Silurian were subjected to regional metamorphism (Section 7.1), and to extensive folding and faulting (Section 7.2; Figure 9.3). Those rocks that escaped subduction were uplifted at various times during the protracted history of the Caledonian Orogeny to form part of the Caledonian mountain chain. In the later stages of collision, granites were intruded into the crust of northern England and Scotland (Figure 9.1). Although some of these granites are exposed today, others remain hidden several kilometres below the current erosion surface.

6 The areas of the British Isles subject to the most intense Caledonian metamorphism were in Wales, the Lake District, and east and south-east Ireland (Figure 9.3). In these areas schists and gneisses are common at the surface today (Figure 9.1); many such rocks were originally derived from limestones, and underwent high-grade metamorphism at a depth of about 3 km (Section 7.1). The prevailing directional trend both of the major faults and of the folds in the British Caledonides is NW–SE (Figure 9.3).

7 The join between the main northern and southern continents — the *Iapetus Suture* — runs roughly through the England/Scotland border, from near Alnwick on the east coast, westwards to the Solway Firth and across into Ireland (Figure 9.3). Today, this fundamental boundary is inconspicuous at the land surface, but a major junction deep within the crust can be detected by geophysical surveys. ◀

So, numerous lines of evidence support the existence of an ancient ocean, at its widest in the early Ordovician, that eventually closed by subduction at its edges, giving rise to igneous activity and, on continental collision, a mountain belt composed of metamorphosed and deformed rocks. The closure of this Iapetus Ocean brought together the main pieces of continental crust that still make up the British Isles today. Most of the major faults crossing northern Britain shown in Figure 9.3, and some others not shown, form the boundaries of long, narrow, slices of crust that, late in the Caledonian Orogeny, slid *sideways* into place along these faults, like boats docking alongside a quay. Parts of the volcanic island arcs seen in Figure 9.2a were finally incorporated into Britain in this way. Some such slivers were originally hundreds of kilometres apart, and were eventually brought adjacent to each other by lateral movement somewhat like that along the San Andreas Fault today (Block 3, Section 7). Sorting out the details of what was a continually changing jigsaw puzzle when we don't have all the pieces today, nor the complete picture to look at, is not easy.

9.2 Britain in the Devonian and Carboniferous Periods (417–290 Ma ago)

By the end of the Caledonian Orogeny, the crust of Britain had mostly been assembled into its modern configuration, and was part of a stable continental landmass about 20° south of the Equator (see Figure 9.4). Erosion of the Caledonian mountains progressed throughout the Devonian Period (417–354 Ma ago), producing large volumes of sediment that were laid down to give thick deposits of red sandstone. Eventually the land surface was eroded to such an extent that the sea began to reinvade the land. Such an advance of the sea marked the beginning of the Carboniferous Period (354–290 Ma ago). Look at the geological map (Figure 9.1) to see the areas where Carboniferous rocks are exposed today.

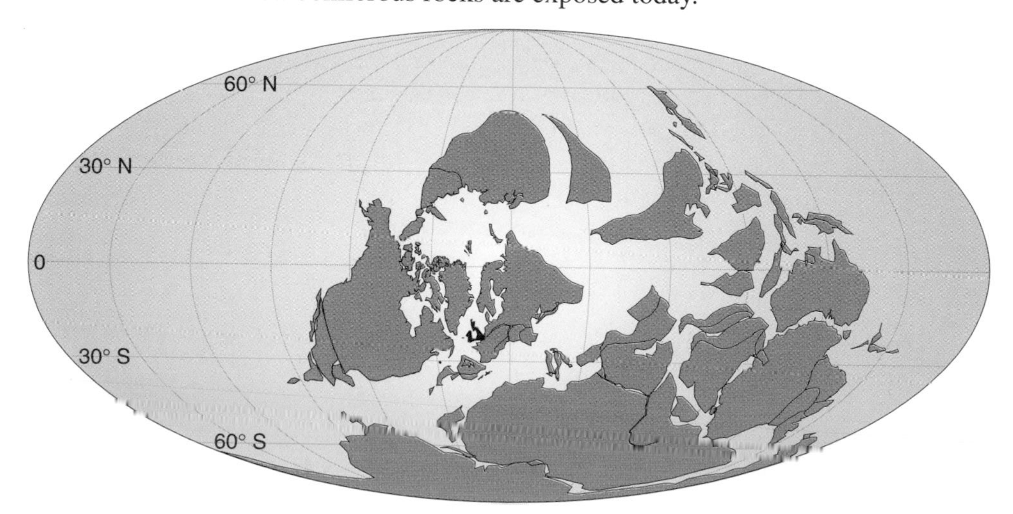

Figure 9.4 Plate reconstruction highlighting the global position of the British Isles (in red) in the Devonian Period 400 Ma ago, at the end of the Caledonian Orogeny. They have been drawn with their current outline for ease of recognition.

The early Carboniferous was characterized by thick coral-rich sediments that were deposited over the newly submerged areas. The resulting limestones are well exposed today, for example, in the Peak District and the northern Pennines. With time, these areas filled up with sands, silts and muds from sediment-laden rivers; deltas started to grow, and the seas became shallower, allowing extensive swamps to develop.

- What general conditions were required, first, for the deposition of coral-rich limestones and, later, for the development of extensive, low-lying swamps?

- Warm, clear shallow seas for the limestones (Section 2, Activity 2.1, and Section 6.3.3), and then warm, wet conditions over large areas near sea-level for the swamps.

Palaeomagnetic evidence shows that Britain moved northwards across the Equator during the Carboniferous Period, consistent with independent sedimentary evidence of a warm and wet tropical climate. The compacted remains of the dense swamp and forest vegetation (Figure 3.4) were destined to become the coal of the British coalfields.

Towards the end of the Carboniferous Period, about 300 Ma ago, there was another mountain-building period — the Variscan Orogeny, which this time mostly affected southwest Britain. Much of what is now Devon and Cornwall was not land until this time. Instead, this area was part of an ocean that lay to the south of Britain. The closing of this intervening ocean pushed the crust northwards to form a mountain belt. The remains of this mountain belt stretch from southern Ireland through south Wales and southwest England, and across to Kent. The folds (such as those shown in Figure 9.5) which formed the belt are orientated nearly east–west (Figure 9.3), and these Variscan structures still shape the modern landscape. For instance, the long fjord-like inlets on the southwest coast of Ireland are eroded-out folds of soft Carboniferous rocks, with intervening headlands of older, harder Devonian rocks (Figure 9.1). The granite plutons of SW England (Figure 5.4) are of Variscan age, as is the Whin Sill (a basaltic intrusion) in northern England (Figure 5.5c).

(a)

(b)

Figure 9.5 Some spectacular folds in Carboniferous rocks produced during the Variscan Orogeny, now exposed on the north Cornwall coast at (a) Millook Haven and (b) Bude.

9.3 Britain in the Permian and Triassic Periods (290–206 Ma ago)

The closing of the southern ocean in the Variscan Orogeny marked the formation of the supercontinent Pangaea. (You might like to revisit Activity 16.1 in Block 3 to replay the continental drift sequence on the CD-ROM and remind yourself how Pangaea developed.) By Permian times (290–248 Ma ago), Britain had become locked within Pangaea, and was at a latitude of about 10°–20° N, fairly similar to that of the Sahara Desert today. Britain was entering a period of tectonic stability, as Pangaea was a long-lived landmass.

- Look back at Figure 9.1 and identify the areas where sedimentary rocks of Permian and Triassic age occur near the surface.

- They occur mainly on either side of the Pennines, stretching down into Devon, and up into southern Scotland. They also occur in the north of Ireland.

The Permian and Triassic Periods left behind a varied sedimentary record in Britain, part of which you will examine in Activity 9.2.

Activity 9.2 A geological field trip

This CD-ROM activity involves three 'field visits' to the Permian and Triassic rocks of southwest England, and introduces some basic geological field techniques. ◀

Southwest Britain in the Permian and Triassic

What was going on in southwest Britain during these periods? To help us summarize events, we need to piece together the palaeogeography of the region, i.e. the physical geography of the time. The sediments deposited are crucial to establishing such a palaeogeography, since they reveal the type of environments that prevailed in different areas (Block 3, Section 11.3).

- In Activity 9.2 you saw some Permian deposits at Dawlish in Devon. What did their features imply about the prevailing climate? (You may need to refer back to your 'field' notes in the Study File.)

- The large-scale cross-bedding like that of modern sand dunes, and the red colour of the sandstone, suggested that the sediments were laid down by winds in a hot desert environment (Section 6.3.1).

In addition, the quartz grains are well-rounded and well-sorted, consistent with this interpretation (Section 6.3.1). The extent of the early Permian sand dune area around Dawlish is shown in Figure 9.6.

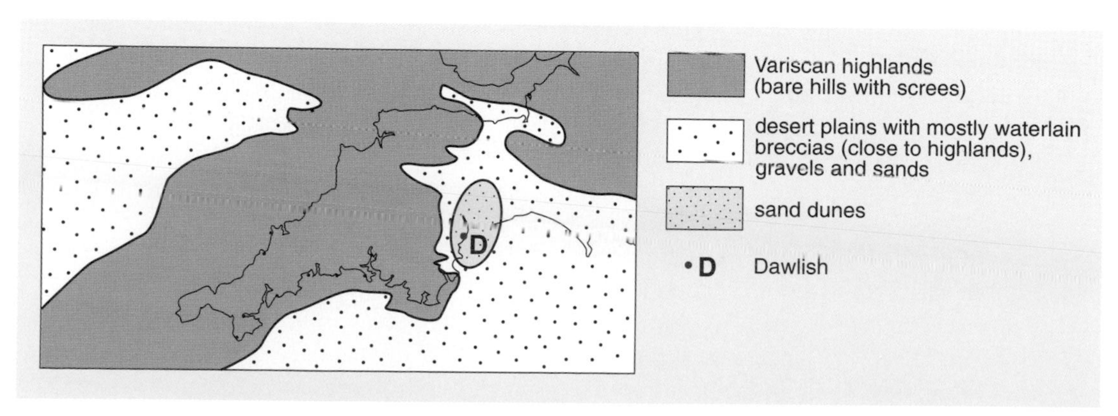

Figure 9.6 Palaeogeography of southwest Britain during the early Permian.

- What other types of environment are shown in Figure 9.6?
- Bare hills with screes; desert plains with mostly waterlain breccias (close to the highlands), gravels and sands.

The breccias, gravels and sands, mostly laid down in river beds, were derived from erosion of the highland areas (part of the Variscan mountains). The dune sands were probably also derived from these eroding highlands, but being readily carried by the wind (Activity 6.2 and Section 6.3.1), the sand grains were transported some distance from the eroding mountains before being deposited in the lowland area which formed a sedimentary basin (Section 6.2.3).

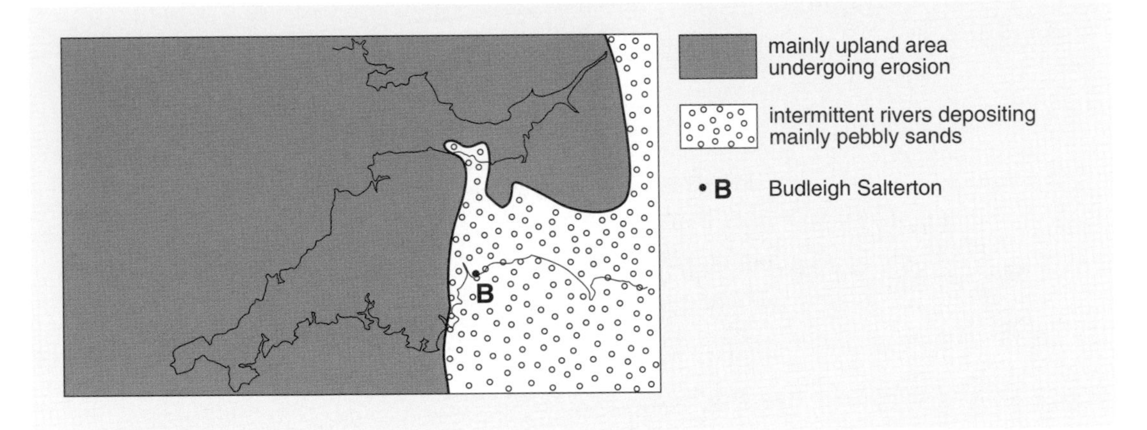

Figure 9.7 Palaeogeography of southwest Britain during the early Triassic.

At Budleigh Salterton you saw some red, pebbly sediments that are thought to be of Triassic age, i.e. younger than the Dawlish sands. Figure 9.7 shows the lateral extent of these deposits: it is clear that, in Triassic times, river-transported sediments derived from the highlands covered the entire basin, and that the Dawlish sand dunes were buried beneath them. These pebble beds, or conglomerates, were deposited by a complex system of intermittently flowing rivers that covered the basin (Figure 9.7). In the early Triassic, an overall desert environment still held sway over southwest Britain. However, the observations at Aust Cliff suggested that the environment changed later on in the Triassic Period.

- Can you remember what those observations were? (Check your 'field' notes again if you're not sure.)
- The upper strata at Aust Cliff are marine mudstones and limestones, which contain teeth and scales of marine fish, as well as bits of reptile bones.

The rocks at the top of the locality at Aust Cliff mark a major change in the palaeogeography of the region. As you can see from Figure 9.8a, the lowland areas had been inundated by the sea, as was implied by the teeth and scales of marine fish in the sediments. Erosion had finally worn away much of the Variscan highlands, so the sea was able to encroach into channels and inlets between the remaining areas of higher ground.

Britain in Permian and Triassic times: an overview

In early Permian times the desert conditions seen in southwest England prevailed over much of Britain. Hot, dry dune-fields covered some of the plains, and erosion cut down into the new Variscan mountains and the remnants of the Caledonian highlands. Then, in the later Permian, some low-lying areas were invaded by ocean

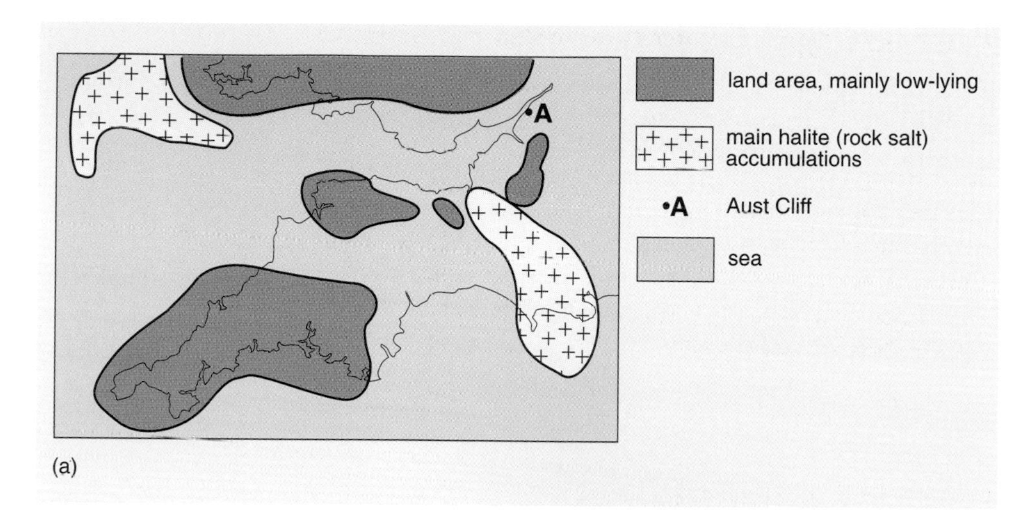

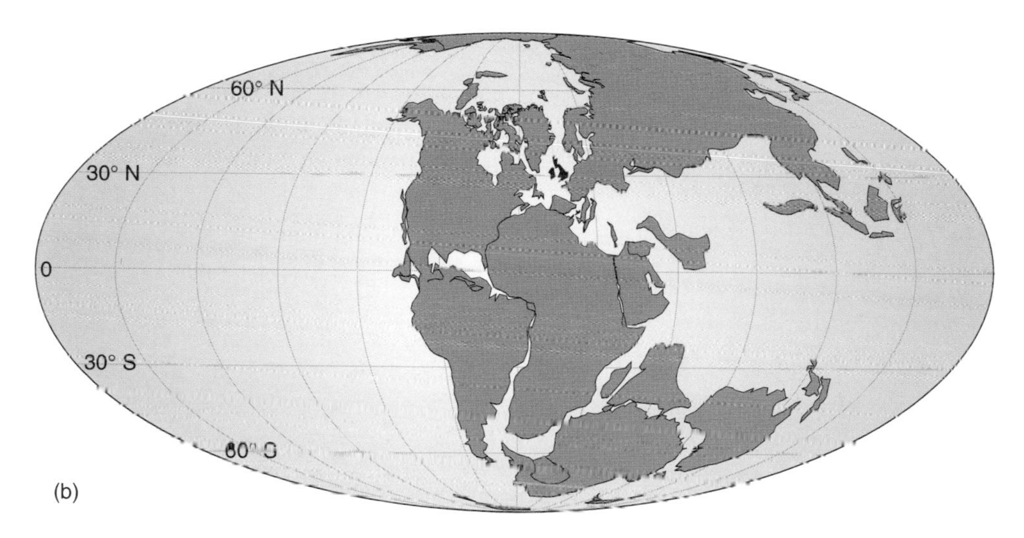

Figure 9.8 (a) Palaeogeography of southwest Britain during the late Triassic. (b) Plate reconstruction highlighting the global position of the British Isles (shown in red) in the late Triassic, drawn with their current outline for ease of recognition.

water to form warm, inland seas (on continental crust), including one that stretched from northern England to Poland (Figure 9.9, *overleaf*). For about 20 Ma, this extensive shallow sea went through cycles of flooding, evaporation, and desiccation (drying up). Each part of the cycle left a distinctive sedimentary rock behind — limestone, mudstone, and evaporites, respectively. The cyclic sequences finally gave way again to desert sediments.

At the start of the Triassic, large rivers carried sand and gravel great distances, as you saw at Budleigh Salterton. Sands and gravels were deposited in an area stretching from Devon to the English Midlands, and also east of the Pennines. The sediments deposited in the English Midlands are believed to have originated in northern France: there was then no intervening sea (Figure 9.9). As time passed, the highland areas eventually wore down, resulting in a flat, featureless landscape. A hot desert climate still prevailed and a lot of fine red dust accumulated in temporary lakes in lowland areas. Due to occasional rainstorms on higher ground, repeated cycles of flooding followed by evaporation deposited red muds and gypsum, such as observed at Aust Cliff. Then, towards the end of the Triassic Period, when Britain was at about 30° N (Figure 9.8b), shallow seas once again flooded over the land. In these waters lived sharks and other fishes whose teeth can be found in the muddy limestones deposited at this time. In some areas of Britain the shallow seas dried up, depositing further evaporites.

Figure 9.9 Artist's impression of a view of Britain from a satellite during the late Permian.

9.4 Britain in the Jurassic and Cretaceous Periods (206–65 Ma ago)

As Britain continued to move northwards as part of Pangaea during the Jurassic Period (206–142 Ma ago), shallow branches of the ocean spread northeast to inundate most of southern Britain. Much of Scotland and Ireland formed low-lying areas of land that were sources for sediments deposited in marine basins to the south and east.

- Where do Jurassic sedimentary rocks mainly outcrop in Britain? (Look back at Figure 9.1.)

- Jurassic rocks are chiefly found in England, where a wide band crosses the country from Yorkshire to Dorset. Small patches of Jurassic rocks also occur elsewhere, such as west of Cardiff.

The Jurassic rocks are mainly composed of limestones and shales, with some sandstones.

- Many of the limestones contain fossils of the three types that you studied as replicas in Activity 3.1. What are these types?

- Ammonites, brachiopods and echinoids.

The marine shales, such as the deposit called the Oxford Clay (used for brickmaking), also contain a wealth of fossils — especially ammonites, oysters and other bivalves, and occasional marine reptiles such as ichthyosaurs and plesiosaurs.

In some places, such as in the North Sea area, dense 'blooms' of algae and other plankton grew seasonally, and then sank to the stagnant muds below, enriching them in organic material. Subsequent burial by younger sediments compressed these muds into shales, and this burial, together with a rise in temperature, generated oil and gas. These fossil fuels (Block 2, Section 8) were eventually trapped in overlying sandstones, and today the energy from Jurassic sunlight stored in them is being used to fuel our energy-hungry society.

The depth of individual sedimentary basins was controlled by localized subsidence and uplift of parts of the crust. This was a symptom of the tectonic instability in northern Europe as the central Atlantic Ocean opened to the south: Pangaea was breaking up. Periodically, the basins filled up with muds and sands, eventually becoming deltas and sometimes emerging as land, before yet again subsiding, and being flooded by the sea once more.

Look back at Figure 9.1, and study the outcrop pattern of Cretaceous rocks (142–65 Ma old). Where does the pattern differ markedly from that of the Jurassic rocks?

In southeast England, where there is a broad band of Cretaceous rocks running roughly E–W to the south of London.

The early Cretaceous deposits in southeast England show cycles of deepening and shallowing similar to those in the Jurassic, although, rather than being marine, the Cretaceous deposits were formed when a large lake repeatedly filled up with sediment and then became inundated again.

Later on in the Cretaceous — around 100 Ma ago — a rise in sea-level flooded much of Britain, and sea-level remained high for over 25 Ma (Figure 9.10). The lack of land areas meant that little erosion could take place, so the only sediments available for deposition in the seas were those that the oceans themselves could supply, mainly the microscopic remains of planktonic plants and animals. Coccolithophores (Block 2, Figure 8.5a) were the minute phytoplankton whose calcite plates accumulated in countless numbers on the late Cretaceous sea-bed to form the Chalk deposits. The Chalk is a widespread deposit found in England, northern Ireland, northern France and elsewhere in Europe. However, increasing tectonic movements due partly to the opening of the North Atlantic eventually ended this quiet depositional situation. The sea-bed was uplifted in many areas, and much of the fairly recently deposited Chalk was removed by erosion. As we saw in Section 3.2, the mass extinction at the end of the Cretaceous Period wiped out many species, including many of those whose remains had been accumulating to form the Chalk.

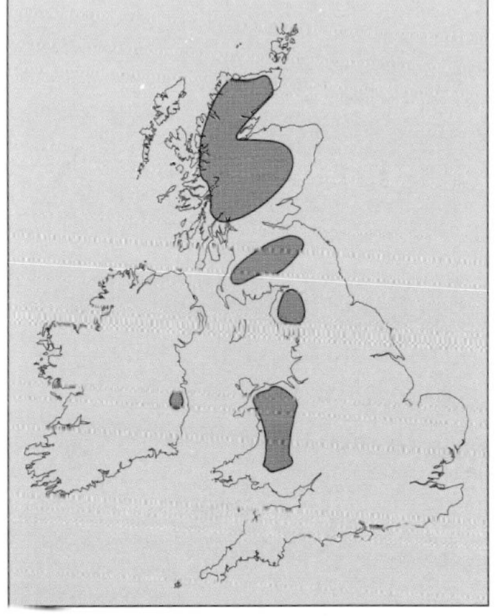

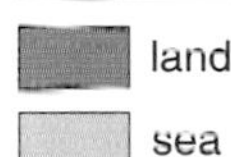

Figure 9.10 Map showing the extent of sea across Britain in the late Cretaceous Period, about 75 Ma ago, when Chalk deposits were forming. Note that the land areas chiefly consist of eroded remnants of the Caledonides.

9.5 Volcanic Britain in the early Cenozoic Era (65–53 Ma ago)

At various times in the past, Britain has been the location of volcanic activity. The geological map in Figure 9.11 (*overleaf*) shows the age distribution of Britain's igneous rocks, some of which were formed during the Caledonian and Variscan orogenies (Section 9.1).

Where are Tertiary (early Cenozoic) igneous rocks mainly located in Britain?

The Tertiary igneous rocks are concentrated in northwest Scotland and Northern Ireland.

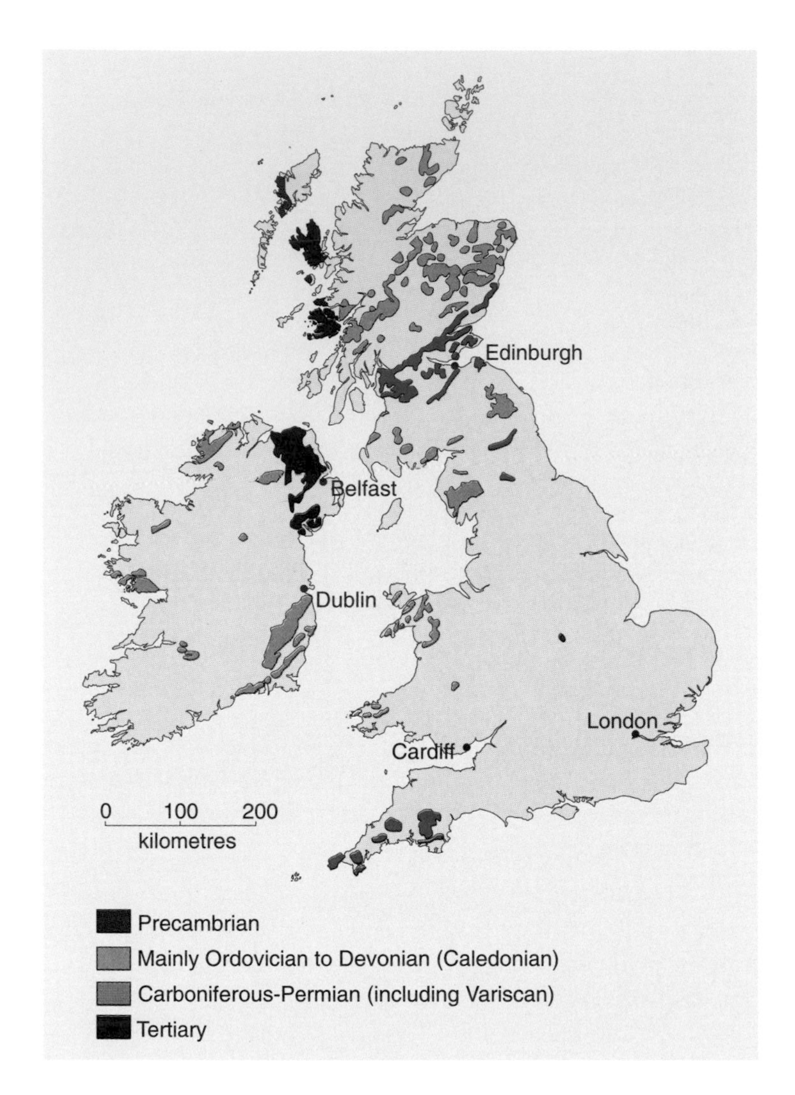

Figure 9.11 Igneous rocks of the British Isles, colour-coded according to age.

Apart from northwest Scotland and Northern Ireland, there are smaller outcrops of Tertiary igneous rocks (not in Figure 9.11) as far south as Lundy (in the Bristol Channel) and as far east as the Yorkshire coast. All these outcrops are collectively known as the Tertiary igneous province. Some of these locations represent the eroded remnants of long-dead volcanoes, each of which has its own characteristics. One of the best developed and most studied of these extinct Tertiary volcanoes is on the Isle of Skye in the Inner Hebrides, and we shall now look at this area a little more closely.

9.5.1 Rock types, environments and volumes: evidence from Skye

- Look at Figure 9.12, which is a simplified geological map of Skye showing its igneous rocks. What is the most abundant volcanic rock type on Skye?

- Basalt, which covers much of the north of the island.

The basalts in the northern part of Skye are formed of accumulations of numerous individual lava flows which in places have a total thickness of about 1 km. Similar sequences of lava flows occur on Mull and in Northern Ireland (such as the famous Giant's Causeway in Antrim, shown in Figure 5.3). However, these are just the remnants of more extensive lava flows that have been much reduced by erosion.

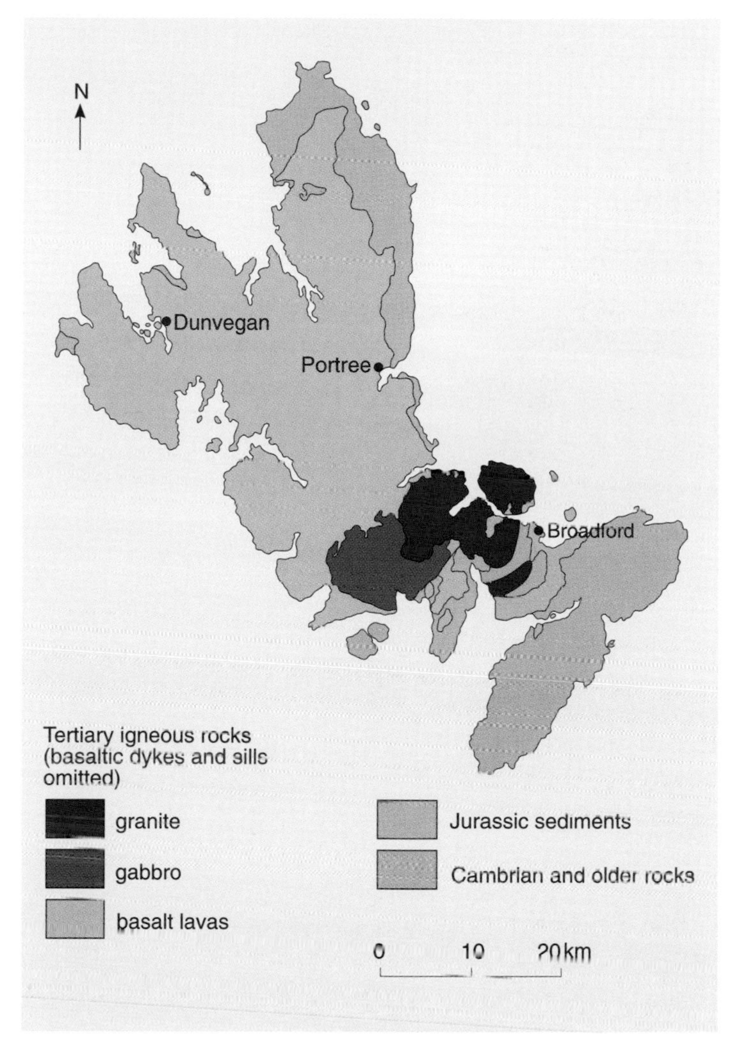

Figure 9.12 A simplified geological map of the Isle of Skye, showing the distribution of igneous rocks.

Interbedded between different lava flows are remains of ancient soils, produced by weathering and erosion of the basaltic flows.

- What does the presence of these soils tell us about the frequency of eruptions?
- Soils such as these take a long time — hundreds or even thousands of years — to develop. Therefore eruptions must have been rather infrequent on a human time-scale.

Within the soils are the fossilized remains of plants, including whole tree trunks in some localities. However, the most useful fossils are microscopic pollen grains. These record evidence of a mixed flora of deciduous trees, resembling modern-day walnut and hickory, along the banks of freshwater streams, with coniferous forests dominated by trees similar to giant redwoods at higher altitudes. Despite being at a similar latitude to its present position (56° N), the environment of northwest Scotland was different from that of today — warmer, although it was also wet! From this geological evidence we can build up a picture of a lush mixed forest surrounding scattered active volcanoes that periodically erupted large volumes of basaltic lava, cutting a broad dark swathe through the green vegetation.

Basalt is not the only rock type shown on the map — others shown are granite and gabbro.

- What is the difference between basalt and gabbro?
- Grain size. Gabbro is coarser-grained than basalt but has the same composition and mineralogy (Section 5.1.2).

- What is the significance of differences in grain size in igneous rocks?
- Grain size in igneous rocks reflects the rate of cooling from a liquid state — intrusive rocks like granite and gabbro are coarse-grained because they have cooled more slowly than volcanic rocks (Section 5.1.1).

- What is the difference between granite and gabbro?
- They contain different minerals and have distinct chemical compositions (Section 5.1.2). Granites are more felsic than gabbros and basalts, having a mineralogy dominated by feldspars and quartz, whereas gabbros are mafic, containing abundant pyroxene, plagioclase feldspar and sometimes olivine.

The map of Skye shows that basalts and gabbros cover a much greater area than granites. Granites are restricted to a small area in the central part of the island adjacent to the gabbros. In fact, the granites are sills (flat-lying sheets), about 1 km thick, roughly the same thickness as the basalt lava pile. They therefore occupy a much smaller volume than the basalts.

The gabbros cover an area of Skye similar to that of the granites. However, unlike the granites, they extend to very great depths, possibly to the base of the crust, some 30 km below the surface. Given that gabbros and basalts have similar compositions, it becomes clear that basaltic rocks overall occupy a much greater volume of the crust beneath Skye than do granitic rocks. The greater volume of basaltic rocks compared with granites in Skye is typical of most of the Tertiary volcanoes and the difference is more extreme than the map suggests at first glance. This conclusion emphasizes the three-dimensional nature of geology — one must always consider what's going on underground as well as what can be seen on the surface.

9.5.2 Relative and absolute timing of events

While rock types and their volumes are important, we now need to unravel the sequence in which the rocks were formed in order to understand the development of this volcanic activity. Which came first, the basalts or the granites? In Section 8.6 you saw that the relative ages of igneous rocks can be determined from their relationship to each other and to the surrounding sedimentary rocks, whilst absolute ages can be derived from radiometric dating. By examining the cross-cutting relations of different igneous bodies on Skye, it has been deduced that the first igneous activity was the eruption of the basaltic lavas. Gabbros were intruded next because they cut across the lava flows.

- How would you expect the cooled basalt lavas to respond to the intrusion of hot gabbro?
- They would undergo contact metamorphism.

The gabbros were in turn followed by the granites, and finally there were more basalts in the form of dykes, which cross-cut the lavas, gabbros and granites. This sequence of events appears to be typical of most Tertiary volcanic centres, but how do we know that these igneous rocks were all emplaced at about the same time? Here we have to resort to radiometric dating and fossil evidence.

Radiometric methods offer us a chance to put a more precise date on volcanic activity, but ages from these Tertiary igneous rocks have been notoriously difficult to obtain. The ages with the least uncertainty have been derived from granites, and two granites from Skye have been dated at 53.4 Ma ± 0.8 Ma and 59.3 Ma ± 1.4 Ma, whereas granites from other parts of the province generally lie within the range 55–60 Ma.

- What does this tell us about the age of *basaltic* volcanism on Skye?

- It must be older than about 60 Ma because the granites are younger than the basalts and gabbros.

Unfortunately, there are no radiometric dates for the lavas themselves, but feldspar crystals from a volcanic ash at the base of the Tertiary lavas on the island of Muck (fifty kilometres south of Skye) have yielded ages of 62.8 Ma ± 0.6 Ma and 62.4 Ma ± 0.6 Ma.

- What does this tell us about the age of volcanism on Muck?

- It has a maximum age of about 63 Ma.

The total duration of both intrusive and volcanic activity in the Skye area was therefore from about 63 Ma ago — the age of the oldest volcanic rock on Muck — to about 53 Ma ago, the age of the youngest granite on Skye. The timing of igneous activity, however, varies in different parts of the province. For example, biostratigraphic evidence from pollen grains in soils between basaltic lavas reveals that in other centres, such as Mull and Antrim in Northern Ireland, the activity occurred between 58 and 55 Ma ago. The total duration of Tertiary igneous activity in Scotland and Ireland therefore appears to be about 10 Ma, although the details are still being investigated.

9.5.3 What caused Tertiary volcanism?

Basalts are generated by partial melting in the upper mantle (Section 5.2) but as Scotland is volcanically *inactive* today, something must have changed since 60 Ma ago. The best way to see what has happened is to look at a reconstruction of the North Atlantic region at about that time (Figure 9.13). This is done by 'removing' oceanic crust generated in the last 60 Ma, and putting the plates back to their positions 60 Ma ago (you met this type of reconstruction in Block 3, Activity 16.1).

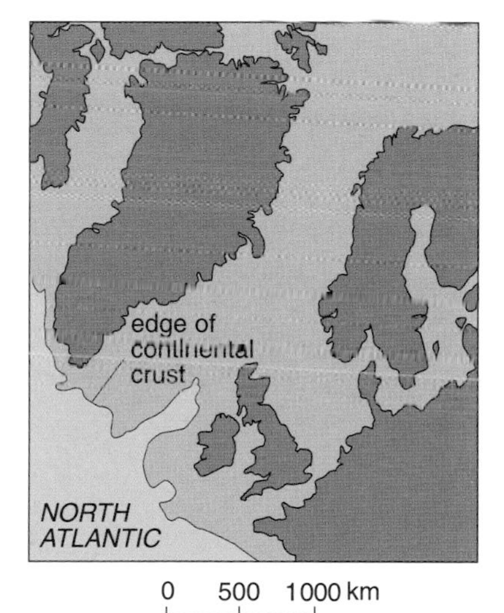

Figure 9.13 Reconstruction of part of the North Atlantic area 60 Ma ago, showing the approximate edge of the continental crust and the relative position of the large areas that form land today. (The edges of the land and sea at that time are not shown accurately.) By 60 Ma, volcanic activity had been occurring for several million years in parts of Scotland and Greenland, and a new divergent plate boundary had just started to form.

- Which large island in the North Atlantic today, between the UK and Greenland, is missing from the 60 Ma map?

- Iceland.

As you saw from some Icelandic eruptions in the 'Volcanoes' video (Block 3, Activity 8.1), Iceland is currently one of the most volcanically active areas on Earth. It sits astride an unusually active section of the Mid Atlantic Ridge. In fact, so much basaltic magma is produced that extremely thick oceanic crust is generated — so thick that it rises above sea-level, giving the landmass we see today. This excessive volcanic activity is produced by a mantle hot spot beneath Iceland, similar to the one beneath Hawaii described in Block 3, Section 15.1.

Northwest Britain was much closer to this region of hot mantle in the early Tertiary than it is today, and it is generally considered that the Iceland mantle hot spot was the cause of magmatism in northwest Britain during the early Tertiary. The break-up of the large American–Eurasian continental landmass close to or over the Iceland hot spot caused melting in the hotter parts of the mantle. The cracking of the lithosphere as the two plates separated allowed basaltic magma to rise into the crust and produce volcanic activity at the surface. As more Atlantic Ocean began to form at the newly-created divergent plate boundary, the continents on either side of this boundary moved away from the hot spot and so basaltic volcanic activity on the margins of the continents ceased. This model therefore not only explains the location of magmatism but also why it only lasted for a limited period — plate motions simply moved Britain away from the hot mantle now beneath Iceland.

Having explained the origin of the basaltic rocks, we have now to explain the presence of the granites.

- What are the two most common ways of producing granitic rocks?
- By melting the crust and by fractional crystallization of more mafic magmas (Section 5).

The present consensus is that the granites are mainly the products of local crustal melting, but that fractional crystallization may also play a small role. Regardless of which process is dominant, the granites can be considered as a secondary feature caused by the heat brought into the crust by the large volume of basaltic magma rising from the mantle.

This brings us to the end of the Tertiary volcanic episode, the most recent to have affected the British Isles. The eastward movement of the Eurasian Plate that ended this volcanic activity continues to the present day as the Atlantic continues to widen.

9.6 Post-volcanic Britain and into the future

The Tertiary geological record for the rest of Britain is mainly restricted to sedimentary deposits in the south. The retreat of the seas that covered much of Britain during the Cretaceous (Section 9.4) continued, and the emerging land surface and shallowing marine environment produced sequences of Tertiary clays and sands that are today exposed in various areas of southeast and southern England (see Figure 9.1).

It was certainly warmer in Britain in the early Tertiary than it is now. We know this from the fossil plants in soils within the lava piles on Skye and Mull, and from a variety of fossil flora, such as palms, found in Tertiary rocks in the south of Britain, such as the London clay. However, as time progressed, the climate in Britain — and more globally — slowly began to cool.

Beginning about 30 Ma ago, the distant collision of Africa with Europe produced the Alps, and the effect of this on Britain is seen in the large-scale folds of the North and South Downs of southern England (Figure 9.14). More dramatic effects are seen locally, as in the vertically tilted Jurassic and Cretaceous sediments along the Dorset coast and on the Isle of Wight, but elsewhere in Britain this was a relatively uneventful period.

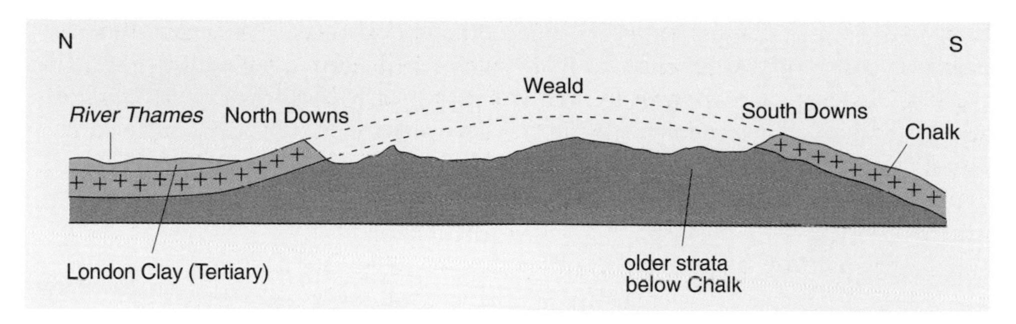

Figure 9.14 A simplified cross-section of the North and South Downs of southern England. The large-scale folding of strata resulted mainly from the distant plate movements that threw up the Alps. Note that the fold has been deeply eroded since it was formed, so that the Chalk and some beds below it are now completely missing in the Weald area.

Throughout the later Tertiary the global climate continued to cool, culminating in the glaciations of the Quaternary (late Cenozoic) Ice Age, discussed in Block 2, Section 3. In Britain, ice-sheets and glaciers reached almost as far south as the Thames, and much of Britain's scenery to the north owes its character to this most recent of major geological events. Glaciers carved out deep, U-shaped valleys in the hard, high rocks of the north and west, and transported eroded material to the lowlands of the south and east. When the glaciers retreated, this material was left behind as till with erratic boulders, and gravel, silt and clay were deposited on the bedrock from rivers and lakes flushed with meltwaters.

As the glaciers finally retreated and melted, and global sea-level rose, Britain became separated from mainland Europe, and about 6 000 years ago it took on the outline of its islands that we see today. This brings us to the end of our journey through space and time, but it's certainly not the end of the story. What we see today is only the latest scene in the ongoing evolution of the British Isles.

Activity 9.3 Predicting the future for Britain

In this activity you will speculate on what the future may hold for Britain on a geological time scale, thousands and millions of years ahead. ◀

The speculations that you made in Activity 9.3, and those in the comments on this activity, cannot possibly be confirmed, and many millions of years in the future Britain's situation may be very different from them. But whatever the future holds, one thing is certain: the rocks and scenery of Britain are not static; change on a geological time-scale is inevitable.

9.7 Summary of Section 9

The rocks of the British Isles are exceptionally diverse, reflecting an immensely long and complex history spanning at least 3 000 Ma. The palaeogeography of Precambrian times is often difficult to interpret, especially as many of the Precambrian rocks are highly metamorphosed.

By about 500 Ma ago, southern Britain was part of a small continent situated about 60° S of the Equator, whilst northern Britain was part of a larger continent about 15° S, between which lay the Iapetus Ocean. The closure of this ocean (at its widest in the early Ordovician), by subduction at its edges, consumed the oceanic crust and caused much igneous activity, especially andestic volcanism. When the continents collided, a mountain belt — the Caledonides — was thrown up, and granites intruded its deformed crust. By the Devonian (400 Ma ago), the Caledonian Orogeny had brought together the main pieces of continental crust that make up the British Isles today.

Erosion of the Caledonides in the Devonian gave thick deposits of red sandstone. Britain, moving northwards, crossed the Equator during the Carboniferous, experiencing tropical environments represented at first by coral-rich limestones, and later by coal-bearing shales and sandstones (deposited in swamps and deltas). At the end of the Carboniferous, the closing of another ocean in the south caused the Variscan Orogeny, which deformed the rocks of southwest Britain, south Wales and southern Ireland.

In the Permian and Triassic, wind-blown deposits of dune sands reveal that much of Britain experienced desert conditions. Away from the eroding Variscan highlands, low-lying areas were occasionally inundated by seas that dried up, depositing evaporites. In the Jurassic, cycles of deepening and shallowing caused a variety of limestones, shales and sandstones to be deposited in the seas that covered much of eastern and southern Britain. By the late Cretaceous, after a large rise in sea-level, there were few areas of land undergoing erosion, and much of Britain became blanketed by the Chalk, a deposit mainly composed of the tiny calcite plates of phytoplankton.

The most recent of many volcanic episodes to have affected Britain is represented by the Tertiary igneous province in western Scotland and Northern Ireland. Between 63 and 53 Ma ago, the British Isles were much closer to the mantle plume presently located beneath Iceland. Melting within the hot mantle of the plume generated large volumes of basaltic magma that were subsequently emplaced within and on the continental crust. Today, this magma is preserved (in places such as Skye) as large gabbro intrusions and areas of basalt lava flows. The heat transported into the crust by the basaltic magma induced crustal melting and the intrusion of small granite plutons. As the Atlantic continued to open and develop into the ocean we see today, the British Isles drifted further away from the mantle plume, and volcanism ceased.

Elsewhere, Cenozoic rocks can be found in southeast and southern England, where mainly clays and sands were deposited. During the later part of the Cenozoic, global climate cooled, and Britain was eventually plunged into the Quaternary Ice Age, which began about 2 Ma ago. Much of Britain's scenery owes its character to the effects of the ice-sheets and glaciers that scraped away bedrock and draped it with till, while rivers and lakes flush with melted ice deposited thick sands, silts and muds. The last glaciers retreated from Britain about 10 000 years ago, and, as global sea-level rose, the British Isles gained more-or-less their current outline about 6 000 years ago.

Connections

10

In the previous section we looked mainly at the way in which the solid structure of the British Isles has developed through time. In this final section we'll take a highly selective look at some of the connections between the four *Earth systems* (i.e. the solid Earth, the hydrosphere, the atmosphere, and the biosphere), using the solid Earth as a thread to link the different topics together. You'll encounter some concepts and processes that were discussed in earlier blocks and also touch on a few areas that are the subjects of active research.

We begin by considering the energy sources for the four Earth systems before looking at examples of processes in the hydrosphere, atmosphere, and biosphere that are influenced by the solid Earth. The section concludes with two examples of how the solid Earth influences climate.

10.1 Energy sources

It is mainly energy from the Sun that drives cycles in the atmosphere, hydrosphere, and biosphere (Blocks 2 and 3). But the solid Earth is different. The interior of the Earth is hot (Section 8.4) and the energy released inside the Earth drives plate movements. The Earth's internal energy escapes to the surface (the process called heat loss), and volcanism is a particularly noticeable manifestation of this heat loss. But the rate of heat loss has not been constant throughout geological time. Studies of very old rocks — combined with mathematical modelling of how the early Earth gained and lost its internal energy — suggest that heat loss was about *five times* greater some 4 000 Ma ago.

The solid Earth is highly dynamic (Block 3), and events such as volcanic eruptions, earthquakes, and landslides occur on time-scales between seconds and days. Because of their rapid release of energy (and the distress caused to human society), we regard these events as catastrophic, and yet in energy terms they are greatly overshadowed by far slower events such as continental drift and the formation of mountain belts — which take place over millions of years. Such large-scale processes are driven by a combination of convection currents within the asthenosphere (the deformable part of the Earth beneath the more rigid lithosphere described in Block 3, Section 13.1), and plate-driving forces such as the slab-pull force (Block 3, Box 15.1). The source of energy that drives these processes is the internal energy of the Earth, and much of this derives from the energy released in radioactive decay.

- If the Sun stopped shining, what would happen to the rate of sea-floor spreading at mid-ocean ridges, subduction at island arcs, and collisions between continents?

- Virtually nothing. As the Earth's internal energy is the driving force for these processes, their rates would not be significantly affected.

10.2 The hydrosphere

The term 'hydrosphere' was introduced in Block 3, Section 6, and you'll recall that this includes *all* of the Earth's water. Of the estimated 1.46×10^9 km^3 of water at or near the Earth's surface (Block 2, Section 7), there are about 1.4×10^9 km^3 of water in the oceans (about 96%), and a mere 1.5×10^4 km^3 (about 0.001%) in the atmosphere. The remainder (about 4%) is on the continents — in glaciers, lakes, rivers, living plants, underground, and so on. As they contain the vast bulk of the Earth's water, there is a natural bias towards talking about the oceans when discussing the hydrosphere.

10.2.1 Where did all the water come from?

There is no *precise* answer to this question — but there is a simple answer! Scientists believe that the Earth's water has come from two sources: from volcanoes, and from the melting of icy bodies such as comets (discussed in Block 3, Section 3.1) that impacted on the Earth's surface early in its formation. There is considerable debate about the respective contributions from each source, although most scientists currently agree that the contribution from volcanoes has been dominant. Block 12 covers this topic in more detail. Look at Table 10.1, which gives the composition of gases expelled by a currently active volcano.

Table 10.1 The composition of volcanic gases emitted by a typical modern-day Hawaiian volcano, and the average abundances of the various gases in today's atmosphere at sea-level.

Constituent	Gases from an active Hawaiian volcano/% by number of molecules	Abundance in atmosphere/% by number of molecules
water, H_2O	80.4	0.5
sulfur dioxide, SO_2	13.6	—
carbon dioxide, CO_2	3.7	0.04
hydrogen sulfide, H_2S	1.0	—
hydrogen, H_2	0.9	—
hydrogen chloride, HCl	0.2	—
hydrogen fluoride, HF	0.2	—
carbon monoxide, CO	0.1	—
nitrogen, N_2	0.04	77.6
argon, Ar	trace	0.93
oxygen, O_2	—	20.9

- What is the dominant gas emitted by a typical Hawaiian volcano?

- The dominant gas is water (H_2O).

A large amount of the water vapour emitted by volcanoes (Figure 10.1) is simply rainwater trapped in near-surface rocks that is boiled off, but there is always some *completely new* water vapour emitted (which was dissolved in the magma), and this means that, every time there is a volcanic eruption, new water is added to the atmosphere and/or hydrosphere from the solid Earth — where it has been since the planet formed. As the Earth's early heat loss was about five times higher than it is now (Section 10.1), this almost certainly stimulated greater amounts of volcanic activity, and expelled correspondingly larger amounts of volcanic gases into the early atmosphere. It is believed that the large amounts of water released during this activity (de-gassing) might have led to the existence of early 'oceans' on the young Earth. Supporting evidence for this is found in the most ancient sedimentary rocks (Section 2.3), suggesting that oceans have been around for about the last 3 850 Ma.

Figure 10.1 An active volcanic area in Iceland, with large amounts of water vapour (and other volcanic gases) released into the atmosphere after a recent eruption.

10.2.2 Salt in seawater

From Section 6.3.2 you may recall that seawater consists of approximately 96.5% water, and 3.5% dissolved substances that collectively we call 'salt' (Block 1, Section 6.1.2, and Table 10.2 of this block). The elements sodium and chlorine together constitute about 90% of these dissolved substances, so where have the sodium and the chlorine come from?

Table 10.2 (a) Percentages by mass of the nine most abundant elements dissolved in seawater. (b) Percentages by mass of the nine most abundant elements in the Earth's continental crust.

(a) Element	% by mass in seawater	(b) Element	% by mass in continental crust
chlorine, Cl	1.950	oxygen, O	46.6
sodium, Na	1.077	silicon, Si	27.7
magnesium, Mg	0.129	aluminium, Al	8.3
sulfur, S	0.091	iron, Fe	5.0
calcium, Ca	0.041	calcium, Ca	3.6
potassium, K	0.038	sodium, Na	2.8
bromine, Br	0.007	potassium, K	2.6
carbon, C	0.003	magnesium, Mg	2.1
strontium, Sr	0.001	titanium, Ti	0.4

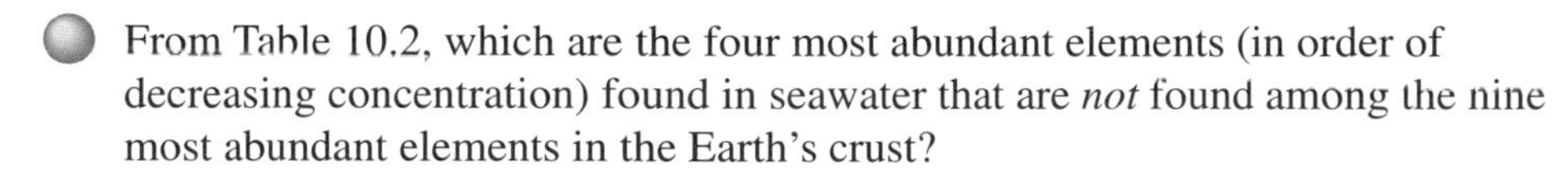

From Table 10.2, which are the four most abundant elements (in order of decreasing concentration) found in seawater that are *not* found among the nine most abundant elements in the Earth's crust?

In order of decreasing concentration, these are chlorine, sulfur, bromine, and carbon.

The sodium, magnesium, calcium, potassium, and strontium found in solution in seawater largely have a continental origin: they are mostly the soluble products of chemical weathering of continental rocks (Section 6.2.1). So we've found part of our answer — that the sodium in seawater has a mainly continental origin. But is this true for chlorine as well?

- Table 10.1 shows that chlorine (in the form of HCl) and sulfur (in the form of SO_2 and H_2S) are important constituents of volcanic gases. Why are they largely absent from the lower atmosphere?
- Because they soon get washed out of the atmosphere by rain (Block 2, Section 9.2.2) — and so end up in the hydrosphere. The chlorine in seawater therefore has its origins in volcanic activity.

So to a fascinating conclusion: the two elements that unite to give us common salt — sodium and chlorine — have two quite *different* sources — sodium from the chemical weathering of continental rocks, and chlorine from volcanic gases.

One might imagine that the overall salinity of seawater would steadily increase with time, but in fact it seems to have remained remarkably similar for much of the Earth's history. Salinity is maintained in an approximately steady state by a variety of processes. One of these is the interaction between the hydrosphere and the solid Earth in the vicinity of mid-ocean ridges. For example, in the case of sodium, the alteration of the oceanic crust by circulating hot water causes much sodium (originally derived mainly from continental weathering) to be absorbed by basalt in exchange for calcium ions that are released into seawater. The deposition of carbonate-rich sediments (mostly formed from the shells of organisms, Section 6.3.3) removes calcium (derived from both oceanic and continental crust) from the oceans, causing the calcium to be 'locked up' — buried in limestone strata — often for hundreds of millions of years.

- Which group of sedimentary rocks is more or less entirely composed of elements such as sodium and chlorine that are present in large quantities in seawater?
- Evaporites (Section 6.3.2), which form when seawater evaporates.

Evaporites, along with limestones and altered oceanic crust, thus form a major underground store for those elements whose concentrations in seawater would otherwise tend to increase mainly as a result of chemical weathering of the continental crust.

10.2.3 The restless oceans

Think of the oceans and it's natural to think of how restless they are. Waves and tides are familiar phenomena, but beyond the coastal waters there are large and powerful currents that greatly influence our weather and climate. These currents were mentioned briefly in Block 3 (Section 6.1.2).

- Can you recall, from Block 3, the two different types of ocean current systems?
- Surface currents, and deep-ocean currents.

Although these have distinctly different circulation systems, which are driven by different processes, they both involve the large-scale transport of energy around the surface of the planet.

Mariners know only too well about the surface circulation driven by the prevailing winds, but the less well-known (and very important) deep-ocean circulation system is driven by density differences.

- What happens when seawater starts to freeze?

- The ice that forms contains no salt (i.e. it is non-saline), and so the remaining unfrozen seawater becomes richer in salt (i.e. it becomes more saline). The higher the concentration of salt, the denser the seawater. The more saline seawater has to sink as it is more dense than the underlying water.

The deep-ocean circulation system has its origins at high latitudes, where temperatures at the sea surface are low enough to freeze seawater. Cold, saline and relatively dense water that sinks at high latitudes gradually makes its way towards the Equator and beyond (Block 3, Figure 6.2b). As it circulates within the ocean, this water remains recognizable by its 'fingerprint' of low temperature and high salinity for many hundreds of years.

Interactions between the world-wide network of water currents — both surface and deep — are exceedingly complex. These have been summarized in the term 'oceanic conveyor belt' (Figure 10.2). As shown in the diagram, surface waters bring warm water from the Pacific and Indian Oceans to the North Atlantic, with the net result that the North Atlantic is warmed and the North Pacific is cooled. The driving force behind this oceanic conveyor belt is the sinking of cold and relatively saline water at high latitudes (mentioned above). At the present time, the conveyor belt benefits the North Atlantic, but it's been speculated that it could reverse and benefit the North Pacific instead — which would cool the North Atlantic and surrounding land by approximately 6 °C. There are indications in the climatic record that such changes may have happened in the past — but oceanographers do not yet know what could trigger these changes.

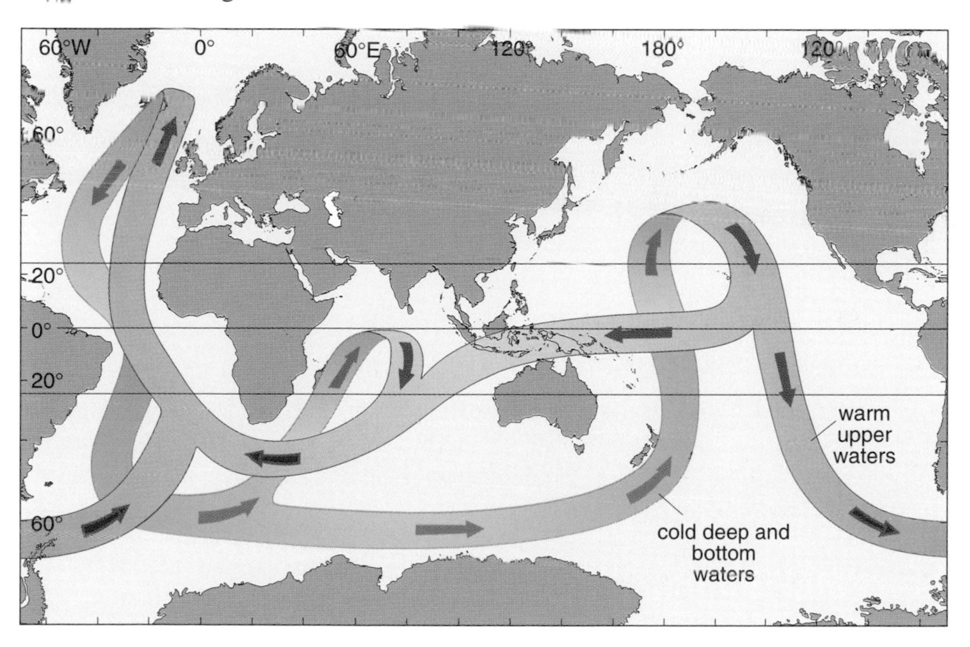

Figure 10.2 The 'oceanic conveyor belt', a highly schematic representation of how warm water in the upper 1 000 m or so of the ocean generally flows towards the northern North Atlantic, where water that has been sufficiently cooled sinks, and then generally makes its way towards the northern Pacific and northern Indian Oceans. Do not worry that there is not much similarity between this diagram and Block 3, Figure 6.2a. The picture is intended to show the *overall effect* of surface and deep currents (Block 3, Figures 6.2a and 6.2b) on the transport of heat around the oceans.

10.3 The atmosphere

Although the atmosphere is a fairly insubstantial 'skin' surrounding the Earth's surface (Block 2, Section 6), without it there would, for example, be no wind-driven surface ocean currents (Section 10.2.3 of this block), no wind-driven transport of sand grains across beaches and deserts (Section 6.3.1), and no oxygen for organisms to use in aerobic respiration (Block 9, Section 4). The atmosphere also plays an important role in regulating the global mean surface temperature (GMST), as we saw in Block 2.

In Block 2 we also saw that the large-scale circulation of the atmosphere is driven by the difference in solar heating between equatorial regions (where more solar radiation is absorbed) and high latitudes (which receive much less solar radiation), with a net transfer of warm air towards high latitudes. This seemingly simple Equator-to-pole circulation is made more complex by the presence of continental landmasses (especially mountain belts), which deflect the paths of wind systems, induce cooling of air that is forced to rise, and have a major effect on the pattern of precipitation (Block 3, Section 6.2.1).

10.3.1 Where did all the oxygen come from?

Having read the discussion of the combined volcanic and extraterrestrial origins of the Earth's water in Section 10.2.1, you might suspect similar origins for the gases in the atmosphere. But — and it's a big BUT — there's a problem with oxygen, as its presence in the atmosphere cannot be accounted for either by volcanic processes (see Table 10.1), or by known extraterrestrial processes. So how did we get an atmosphere with nearly 21% oxygen — a highly reactive gas (Block 3, Section 18.2) found nowhere else in the Solar System in comparable amounts?

Although oxygen is produced chemically in the upper atmosphere when ultraviolet radiation breaks apart water vapour, this produces only minute amounts of oxygen. Furthermore, Section 18.2 of Block 3 shows that oxygen molecules readily combine with other elements — especially on the surface of the Earth — and that this oxygen stays combined! So there needs to be an efficient process somewhere on our planet that generates lots of 'surplus' oxygen.

- Think back to Section 2. What type of organism was mainly responsible for producing atmospheric oxygen prior to 2 000 Ma ago?

- Cyanobacteria were believed to be responsible for producing enough atmospheric oxygen so that by 2 000 Ma ago a stable aerobic environment had been established (Section 2.3). These organisms were photosynthesizers, and released oxygen as a by-product of photosynthesis.

Early, primitive cyanobacteria lived under water, where they were protected from DNA-damaging ultraviolet (UV) radiation, because water absorbs UV radiation (Block 3, Section 18.2). Oxygen levels gradually increased until there was sufficient oxygen in the upper atmosphere to form ozone. This is produced when molecular oxygen (O_2) dissociates at high levels in the atmosphere (about 30 km) into single atoms of oxygen (O), which then combine with oxygen molecules (O_2) to form ozone (O_3). Ozone is extremely important to life as it strongly absorbs UV radiation; the establishment of an 'ozone layer' in the atmosphere helped to protect the organisms that started to colonize shallow waters (Section 2.3) and, later, the land.

By about 2 000 Ma ago atmospheric oxygen had formed a permanent accumulation (about 1% of the gases in the atmosphere), and it became possible for organisms to respire aerobically — a highly significant step as aerobic respiration is a much more efficient process and one that allowed the development of more complex organisms (Section 2.3). About 430 Ma ago, plant and animal life emerged onto land, and this evolutionary step had the effect of greatly increasing atmospheric oxygen levels.

Terrestrial habitats offered a multitude of 'new' environments for evolving organisms to colonize. The huge increase in land plants, which greatly increased the amount of photosynthesis, led directly to a major increase in the amount of atmospheric oxygen and a decrease in the amount of atmospheric CO_2. By about 380 Ma ago, the atmospheric oxygen level was similar to that of the present day (21%, Table 10.1). Towards the end of the Carboniferous Period (354–290 Ma ago), the formation of the great tropical forests led to a surge in the production of atmospheric oxygen, and some scientists believe that the oxygen level in the late Carboniferous atmosphere may have been as high as 35%.

In summary, the evolution of the Earth's atmosphere has essentially been one of balancing its carbon dioxide and oxygen concentrations. Table 10.1 shows that CO_2 typically constitutes about 4% of volcanic gases, and yet it constitutes only 0.04% of the atmosphere. Where has it all gone? As we saw in the carbon cycle in Block 2, Section 8, photosynthesizing plants play an important role by reducing the amount of carbon dioxide in the atmosphere. The locking up of carbon from atmospheric CO_2 in limestones (mainly calcium carbonate), and in hydrocarbons (including oil and natural gas) contained in other sediments, has also been important in reducing CO_2 concentrations in the atmosphere. A crucial point is that the oxygen-rich atmosphere of the Earth owes its origin *exclusively* to the presence of life on this planet. If scientists discovered an oxygen-rich atmosphere on a planet in another solar system this would be a cause for considerable excitement, as it would hint at the presence of organisms with a metabolism similar to those that live on the Earth. This idea was suggested in Block 3, Section 18.2 and is discussed further in Block 12.

10.4 The biosphere

We've seen that life is remarkably durable — it has, for example, survived several mass extinctions (Section 3). Some scientists hold the view that once life has started on a planet, it is extremely difficult to eradicate. So what are the limits to life in our biosphere?

In the past few decades much research has focused on *extremophilic* organisms. These are specialized micro-organisms that normally thrive under extreme conditions (i.e. conditions that seem extreme and inhospitable to us), such as exceptionally: high temperature; low temperature; high salinity; high alkalinity; high acidity; high pressure.

For example, extremophiles have been collected from muds in the deepest part of the Mariana Trench some 11 km beneath the sea surface, from boiling water springs in volcanic regions (Figure 10.3, *overleaf*), from cracks in permanently frozen Antarctic rocks, and from oil reservoirs thousands of metres beneath the surface. The thermophilic (heat-loving) bacteria have been the subject of special attention as it is thought that the sulfur-dependent varieties which thrive in present-day hot springs between 85 and 100 °C may be similar to micro-organisms that were present in the Precambrian. There's speculation that some of these may be 'living fossils', and ongoing research will help us to understand the evolution of these unusual organisms.

Figure 10.3 The water from these two hot springs in Iceland is at boiling point, and yet adjacent to the outflows are colonies of thermophilic bacteria which thrive on the mineral-rich hot water. The bacteria and the precipitation of minerals give rise to the bright colours surrounding the springs.

As we saw in Section 3.3, some species benefit from the disruptive events of mass extinctions as they are able to adapt to the habitats vacated by those species that become extinct. In Block 4 (Sections 4 and 5 and Activity 7.1 on the oak tree ecosystem) we discussed species diversity, habitat, and adaptation, and here we'll focus on just a few facets of the biosphere that are strongly influenced by the solid Earth.

Species are able to live and breed only in favourable habitats where they have sufficient food, where there is the correct range of physical and chemical conditions, and where they can sufficiently avoid their predators. The topography of the solid Earth exerts a strong influence on the abundance and distribution of suitable habitats. If you look again at the hypsometric plot (Figure 6.8 in Block 3), you'll see that only about 30% of the Earth's surface lies between 1 km above and 1 km below sea-level, yet within this limited vertical range are the habitats that support the vast majority of terrestrial and marine species. There is also a polar dimension to this restriction of habitats. For instance, we can contrast the twenty or so species of indigenous mammals in the Arctic with the several thousands of species of indigenous mammals that flourish in tropical ecosystems — and similar patterns of diversification towards the tropics are found for birds, fish, insects, and many other groups. Arctic species have evolved metabolic processes and patterns of growth that can cope with extreme seasonal variations, prolonged cold, and rapidly changing weather conditions.

So, although the biosphere is influenced by the solid Earth, it is also affected by climatic conditions (involving the hydrosphere and the atmosphere), all of which exert strong controls over the creation and distribution of habitats suitable for promoting species diversity and abundance. However, the interactions between the different Earth systems and how they influence the biosphere are very complex, and much work needs to be done before we fully understand the relative importance of the different links and connections.

Activity 10.1 A sunless world?

This activity asks you to speculate about what you think might happen to the four Earth systems if the Sun stopped shining tomorrow. ◀

10.5 Climate and the solid Earth

Climate can be regarded as a synthesis of the day-to-day weather experienced by a particular region (Block 2, Section 1), usually averaged over at least a 30-year period. Climate is determined by latitude, altitude, and by a region's proximity to continental margins — and by how it is affected by major atmospheric and oceanic circulation systems (Block 3, Section 6.1.2).

10.5.1 What controls climate?

Climate varies across the globe largely as a result of variations in the way that energy (heat) is transferred from the tropics to the temperate and polar regions via atmospheric and oceanic circulation systems (Block 3, Section 6.1).

- Why is there more heat energy at the tropics, compared with polar regions?

- A higher intensity of solar radiation is received at the Equator than at the poles.

Two complicating factors that affect these circulation systems are, first, the rotation of the Earth (which exerts a 'sideways' force on water and air masses in motion), and second, the tilt of the Earth's axis of rotation (currently 23.5°). The surface ocean currents are driven by the prevailing winds in the atmosphere. But the presence of landmasses (plus the rotation of the Earth) causes these surface ocean currents to move in roughly circular paths, and on the western sides of oceans they tend to become 'squeezed' against the margins of landmasses (Figure 10.4). One consequence of this that affects climate in northwestern Europe is the rapidly-moving stream of warm water called the Gulf Stream, which essentially transports heat to this region and gives it a warmer climate than expected for its latitude. The tilt of the Earth's axis produces seasonal variations, which are more extreme at the poles and less extreme at the Equator (Block 2, Section 9.2.2).

Figure 10.4 The wind-driven surface circulation of the oceans (long-term average pattern). Note the compression of the flow paths on the eastern coast of North America and the northeasterly flow of warm water from the Gulf Stream towards NW Europe. Cold currents flowing from higher latitudes are dashed. This figure is a more detailed version of the map of surface currents shown in Block 3, Figure 6.2a.

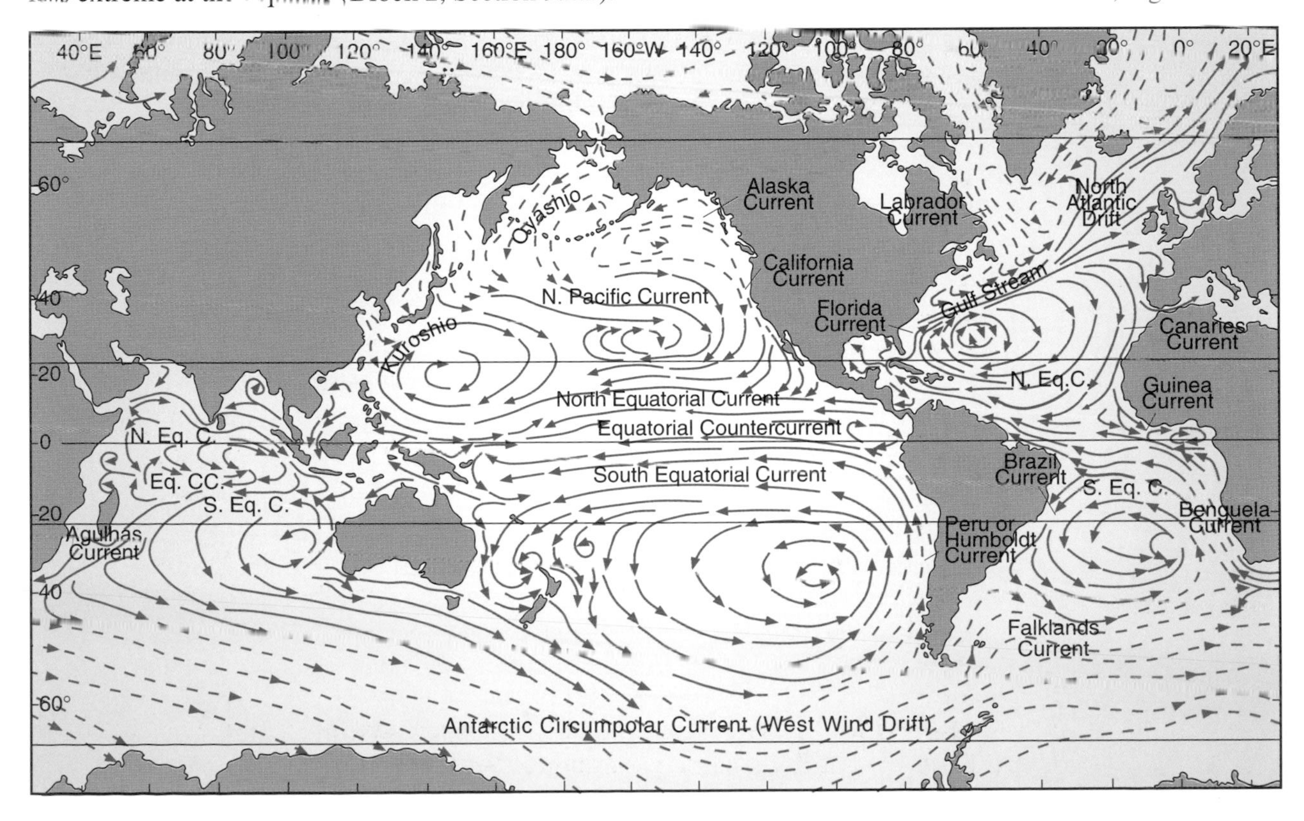

The global climate represents the balance achieved between the influence of many factors — with interactions between the atmosphere and the hydrosphere being especially important. But does this mean that the solid Earth plays only a passive role in influencing climate?

- Consider what might happen if the solid Earth did not have any topography. If we smoothed out all the ups and downs of the solid Earth, we would have a rocky surface that lay at a uniform depth beneath the surface of the oceans. What effect might this lack of topography have on atmospheric and oceanic circulation?

- There would be no mountain belts or other land protruding above the sea surface to deflect winds (and the moisture within them). Likewise, there would be no landmasses to deflect ocean currents (and any nutrients within them) either horizontally or vertically. Transport of energy (heat) from the tropics polewards would be more rapid and efficient without these barriers.

Climate change is triggered by events such as variations in solar radiation, movements of continents affecting major ocean and atmospheric currents, mountain-building, the carbon dioxide content of the atmosphere, impact events (such as that described in Section 3.2.1), and major volcanic eruptions. Activity in the solid Earth can stimulate climate change — either rapidly or over longer time-scales. We shall now look briefly at how volcanic eruptions and mountain-building can affect climate.

10.5.2 Volcanic eruptions and climate change

There is good evidence that volcanic eruptions can give rise to rapid and short-term effects on global climate, and the effects on GMST were modelled in the 'Global warming and cooling' CD-ROM activity in Block 2. Direct evidence comes from studies of a few historical eruptions, which are relatively modest in size compared to some of the enormous eruptions that we know about from the geological record. Some of these historical eruptions have caused the mean temperature in the Northern Hemisphere to drop by up to 1 or 2 °C for a year or two. This is not a trivial temperature drop, as it could have a swift and detrimental effect on parts of the biosphere (e.g. agriculture; Block 2, Section 10).

So how do volcanic eruptions actually affect climate? The answer lies in the products of volcanism. From Block 3, Section 8.1, you'll be aware that explosive eruptions generate fragmented magma (pyroclasts), and you'll recall from Table 10.1 that carbon dioxide is one of the gases expelled during volcanic eruptions. But another gas is expelled in substantial quantities — sulfur dioxide, which has a rapid but short-lived effect on climate. Table 10.1 shows that SO_2 forms 13.6% of gases expelled by a typical volcano.

The sulfur dioxide gas reacts with water vapour to form tiny airborne droplets (of sulfuric acid) called aerosols (Block 2, Section 5.1.1). In addition to the sulfuric acid aerosols there will be tiny, *solid* (pyroclastic) aerosols from the eruption. If these two types of aerosol reach the stratosphere (the part of the atmosphere above the troposphere), they can remain there for months or years. These aerosols interact with incoming solar radiation and with radiation emanating from the Earth's surface, such that there is a net *cooling* of the Earth's atmosphere in the region occupied by the aerosols (Block 2, Sections 9 and 10).

From Table 10.1, you'll see that there's no sulfur dioxide normally present in the lower atmosphere (troposphere). Why is this?

Sulfuric acid aerosols eventually get washed out of the lower atmosphere.

Generally speaking, the larger the eruption, the greater the amount of aerosols released into the atmosphere — and the greater the potential amount of cooling. But there are complications:

- Eruptions taking place near the Equator are more likely to produce global cooling effects. Global wind patterns prevent aerosols from high-latitude eruptions being as widely distributed as aerosols from low-latitude eruptions, which can more easily spread into both hemispheres.
- Highly explosive eruptions are much more effective at injecting sulfur dioxide and tiny pyroclasts into the stratosphere, and hence these types of eruptions are more likely to lead to global effects.

In the geological record there are numerous examples of eruptions much larger than the modest historical eruptions that we know have influenced climate. Among the largest of these are the massive outpourings of basalt known as *flood basalts* (so called because they flooded the landscape). Figure 10.5 shows the locations of large basaltic igneous provinces, including flood basalts erupted on continents. These major effusive eruptions would have expelled large amounts of sulfur dioxide, carbon dioxide, and water vapour into the atmosphere (Table 10.1) — and a substantial proportion of these would have reached the stratosphere. (Note, however, that *effusive* eruptions inject only minor amounts of pyroclasts into the stratosphere — *explosive* eruptions are much more effective at doing this.) At the moment we have no clear idea of what effects these massive effusive eruptions have had upon global climate in the past, as there is too much uncertainty in trying to scale up the known effects of small eruptions to the possible effects of these much larger eruptions.

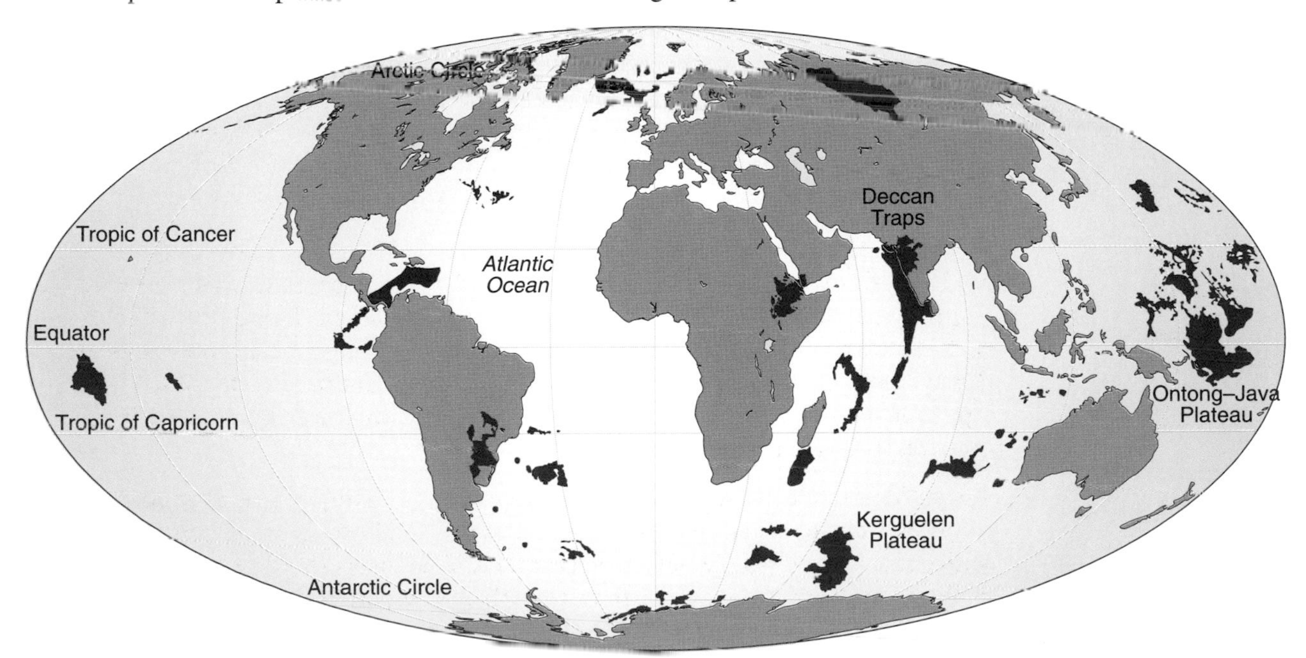

Figure 10.5 The locations of large basaltic igneous provinces (shown in purple). Those erupted on continents are flood basalts. The oldest (in Siberia) are of Permian age. The huge Ontong-Java and Kerguelan oceanic plateaux were probably erupted above sea level in mid-Cretaceous times.

Finally, there is an intriguing and vigorous debate about the apparent coincidence of flood basalt eruptions and mass extinctions — and (in some cases) possible links with impact events (such as the one at the K–T boundary discussed in Section 3). Could impacts have triggered these massive outpourings of basalt? The timing of eight extinction events correlates fairly well with eight major episodes of flood basalt volcanism. Notwithstanding the massive volumes of sulfur dioxide expelled during these eruptions (which would have had a cooling effect), there is a question mark over the possible global effects caused by the massive amounts of carbon dioxide that would also have been expelled (with a warming effect). Was the *net* result a change in the GMST? Did these eruptions trigger mass extinctions? These important questions are the subject of ongoing research.

10.5.3 Shifting lands and climate change

We've seen from studies of recent volcanic eruptions that the solid Earth can exert rapid but short-lived effects on climate. But can the solid Earth induce more substantial and longer-lived effects on the GMST? Let's look briefly at the solid Earth's influence on ocean currents and then consider a more spectacular example — the sudden rise of the Himalayas.

Ocean currents transport heat from the Equator to higher latitudes, but it is not a straightforward journey: there are topographic features such as mid-ocean ridges and island arcs blocking the free passage of water. Figure 10.6a shows the probable pattern of ocean circulation about 175 Ma ago, when the present-day continents were joined into a supercontinent, and the circulation pattern was fairly simple. Contrast this with the more complex circulation pattern of roughly 30 Ma ago shown in Figure 10.6c.

- What main difference is there in the currents in the Antarctic region 30 Ma ago compared with 175 and 100 Ma ago?

- Currents could flow unimpeded around the Antarctic continent 30 Ma ago.

It is thought that this would have resulted in colder water being transported more easily towards the Equator (and beyond). Given the large amounts of heat energy transported by such currents, any substantial change to the circulation patterns of major currents will probably have a knock-on effect on global climate. Again, we lack sufficient knowledge and understanding in this area — but ongoing research may help to clarify this important issue.

Turning now to larger-scale and more persistent changes to the GMST caused by processes in the solid Earth, let us consider the Himalayas and the Tibetan plateau (created due to the collision between the Indian and Eurasian Plates). Any mountain range encourages precipitation of moisture-laden winds on the windward side — with correspondingly dry conditions on the leeward side (the 'rainshadow' effect) — and the Himalayas are no exception (Figure 10.7, *p. 142*). But is this the only influence that mountain belts can have on climate?

As we saw in Section 3.3 of Block 2, the geological record shows that the Earth's surface has cooled markedly during the past 50 Ma — during the same period that the Himalayas were being formed — and one hypothesis argues that these events are linked. But how could the creation of a mountain belt and high plateau lead to global cooling? Think back to the discussion of the carbon cycle in Block 2, Section 8.

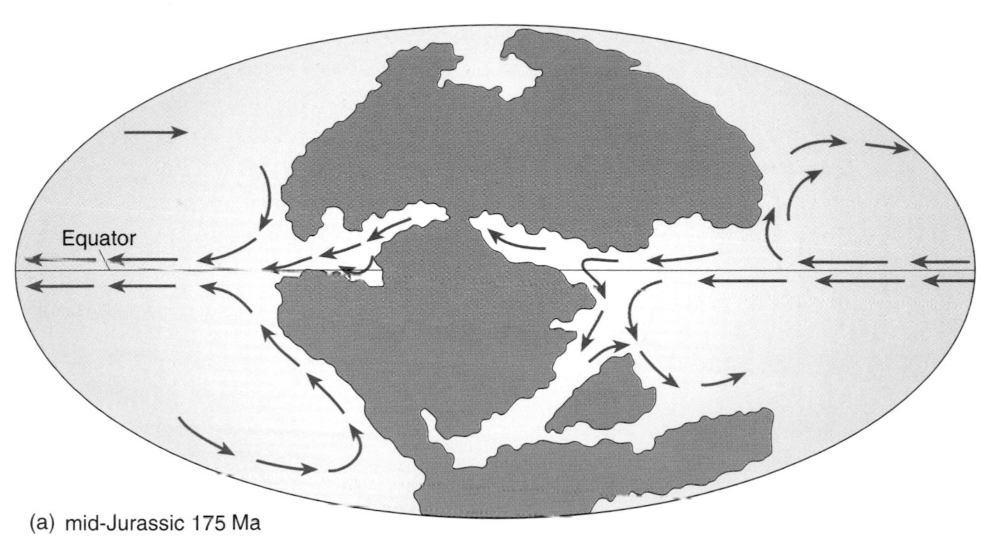

(a) mid-Jurassic 175 Ma

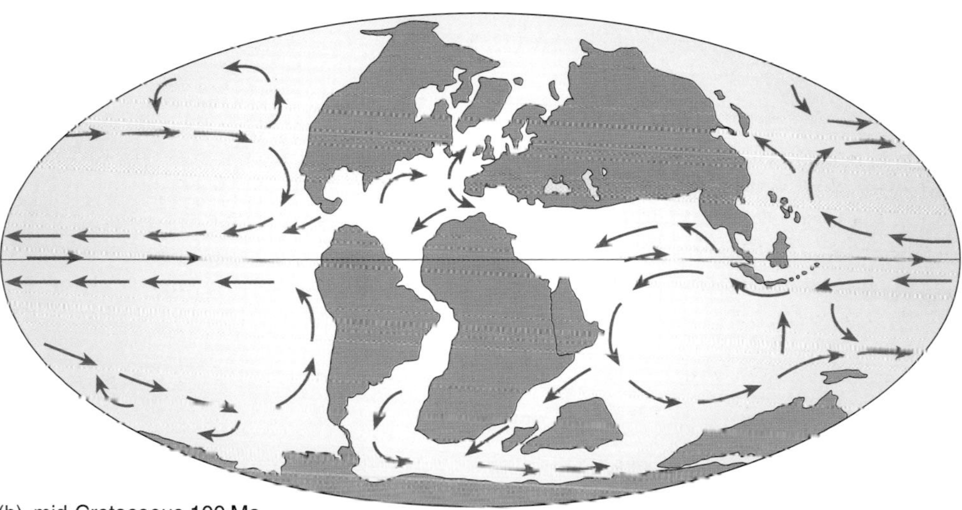

(b) mid-Cretaceous 100 Ma

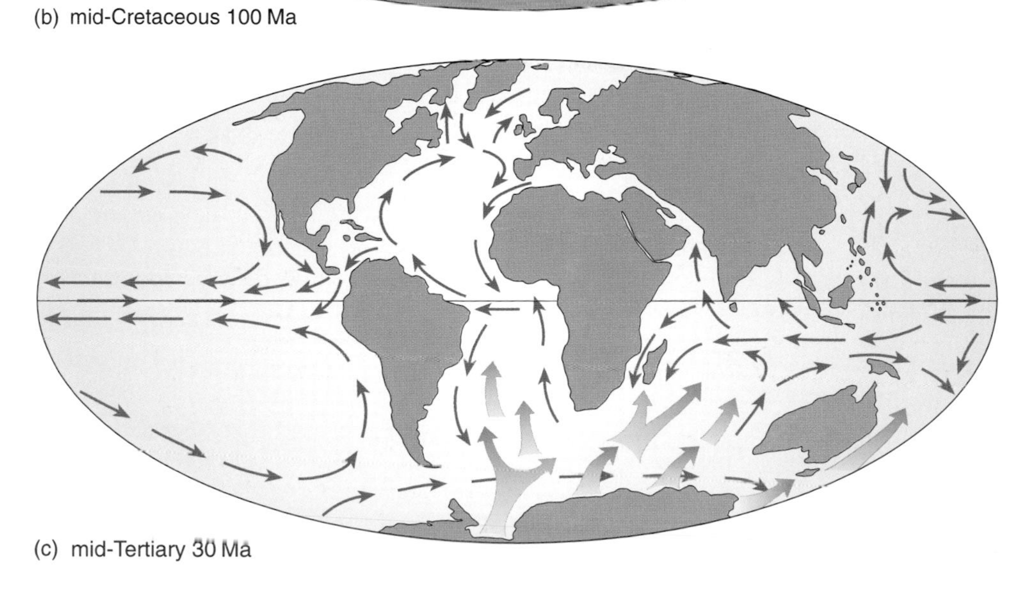

(c) mid-Tertiary 30 Ma

Figure 10.6 The changing distribution of the continents and surface-water current patterns, shown at (a) 175 Ma; (b) 100 Ma; and (c) 30 Ma ago. Note the free flow of water in equatorial regions 100 Ma ago; this very warm water could spread to higher latitudes, making the globe, on average, warmer than it would otherwise have been. Actual coastlines are not shown.

(a)

(b)

Figure 10.7 Himalayan mountains with (a) forested slopes on the windward side, and (b) arid desert conditions in the rainshadow.

There's no direct link, but there is a subtle (yet powerful) indirect link. The uplift of the mountain range and plateau increases precipitation on the windward side, and this in turn leads to increased rates of chemical and physical weathering. (Indeed, the rivers flowing from this elevated region carry huge loads of sediment and dissolved material within them due to this high rate of weathering.)

Now comes the subtle part. The dissolving of silicate minerals in river water requires the involvement of atmospheric CO_2, and so any process that increases the large-scale weathering of silicate minerals leads to an *extra* extraction of atmospheric CO_2 — and therefore to a consequent reduction in the amount of atmospheric CO_2. Once the water reaches the sea, much of the dissolved carbon precipitates (mainly via the bodies of organisms) as carbonate which then becomes buried in ocean sediments, and so the carbon becomes removed from the terrestrial and marine parts of the carbon cycle (Block 2, Section 8 and Section 10.3.1 above). At the same time, organic carbon is removed from the mountainsides by physical weathering, and is transported to the oceans (by rivers), where it too is buried in ocean sediments. In both cases the carbon is then locked up for millions of years as part of the long-term geological carbon cycle. As we've seen, this *increased* deposition of carbon-bearing sediment and dissolved material has the net effect of reducing the concentration of global atmospheric CO_2, and this in turn leads to global cooling.

We can summarize this quite simply by saying that as weathering of the continents removes CO_2 from the atmosphere, any process that *increases* continental weathering should lead to *global cooling*. This provides a plausible explanation for the marked cooling of the Earth's surface during the past 50 Ma.

So, we have seen how processes within the solid Earth can influence global climate. Modest but short-lived eruptions trigger rapid and short-term changes to global climate (which may be quite localized), whereas larger-scale but slower processes such as the growth of a mountain belt can trigger longer-term global climate changes.

10.6 Summary of Section 10

There are many complex interactions between the four Earth systems — the solid Earth, the hydrosphere, the atmosphere and the biosphere. The solid Earth plays an important (but variable) role in these interactions. Its topography influences the availability of habitats for organisms within the biosphere, and also affects the large-scale circulation patterns in the oceans and the atmosphere.

Climate is sensitive to changes within each of the Earth systems. Processes in the solid Earth — such as volcanic eruptions and the construction of mountain belts — exert short-term and/or long-term effects on either the climate of a particular region or on the GMST. Among the many and complex controls limiting the carbon dioxide concentration in the atmosphere is the deposition, mainly via the bodies of organisms, of sediments rich in carbonate and organic carbon; this effectively removes carbon from parts of the carbon cycle for millions of years.

The oxygen-rich atmosphere of our planet is unique within the Solar System. The only feasible process we are aware of that can give rise to an atmosphere such as ours containing 21% oxygen is photosynthesis — and this indicates the presence of carbon-based organisms. Some of the more evolved carbon-based organisms are searching for their origins — all the way back to the formation of the Universe — and this search is the subject of Blocks 11 and 12.

Activity 10.2 Revision at the end of the course

In this final activity, you will begin to plan your revision programme for the period leading up to the course examination. ◀

Questions: answers and comments

Question 2.1 (i) The garden slug is extremely unlikely to find its way into the fossil record because it has only soft parts, and these will be eaten or rapidly decay after death. In any case, living on land, it is in an environment with little chance of long-term burial by sediment. (ii) The garden snail at least has a shell, but this too is readily destroyed, and overall the snail also has a low preservation potential because it lives on land. (iii) The whale has huge bones, and being marine should stand a fair chance of fossilization. (iv) The jellyfish, although living in the sea, has no hard parts, and, not surprisingly, fossil jellyfish are very rare.

Question 2.2 (i) As we saw in Question 2.1, any *individual* whale has, on average, a high preservation potential, but there are very few blue whales so the species is likely to be very rare in the fossil record. (ii) The garden earthworm occurs in huge numbers, and is widespread, but, because it is soft-bodied and lives on land, both its body and its burrows are unlikely candidates for inclusion in the fossil record. (iii) Despite having hard bones and teeth, the low numbers of individuals, the non-marine setting, and the fact that organic material on land in the tropics tends to rot away very quickly, largely explain why early human fossils are so rare. (iv) The oyster species is abundant, thick-shelled and marine, all of which give it by far the best preservation potential of these four species.

Question 2.3 (ii), (iii) and (v). (ii) The trace fossils record its activities; (iii) the other groups could provide independent evidence of the environment; (v) the more complex the hard parts, the more clues to go on. Conversely, having few living relatives (i) tends to make fossils difficult to reconstruct as living organisms, and, (iv), the more separated the hard parts, the more difficult to see where they fitted together, or whether they came from the same individual.

Question 2.4

$$\frac{4\,600\,\text{Ma} - 545\,\text{Ma}}{4\,600\,\text{Ma}} \times 100\% \approx 88\%$$

The Precambrian therefore represents about 88% of geological time. Another way of expressing this is about seven-eighths of geological time ($7/8 \times 100\% = 87.5\%$.)

Question 2.5 The events in order, starting with the oldest, are as follows:

- origin of the Earth: 4 600 Ma
- first evidence of life (chemical fossils) in oldest sedimentary rocks: 3 850 Ma
- first fossil structures (including stromatolites): 3 500 Ma
- first eukaryotic cells in the fossil record: 2 100 Ma
- permanent accumulation of free atmospheric oxygen: 2 000 Ma
- rapid diversification of eukaryotes: 1 200 Ma
- first multicellular organisms (algae): 1 000 Ma
- first animals (Ediacaran fauna): 610 Ma
- Cambrian explosion: 545 Ma
- Burgess Shale fossils: 520 Ma
- Wenlock Limestone fossils in the Kit: 425 Ma

Question 3.1 Fossils are absent from virtually all igneous rocks (formed from molten magma) and metamorphic rocks (recrystallized at high temperatures and pressures). There are a few interesting exceptions, such as lava flows and volcanic ashes that have trapped living creatures, and metamorphic rocks such as marbles that retain ghostly vestiges of fossils which were in the original (unmetamorphosed) rock.

Question 3.2 The events in order, starting with the oldest, are as follows. The *approximate* absolute dates are also given only if they are mentioned in the text.

- first fishes: late Cambrian
- start of main diversification of fishes: late Ordovician
- main invasion of the land by plants and invertebrates begins: middle Silurian (430 Ma ago)
- first amphibians: late Devonian
- first reptiles: early Carboniferous (350 Ma ago)
- first dinosaurs: middle Triassic
- first mammals: late Triassic (210 Ma ago)
- Jurassic fossils in the Kit: 165–155 Ma
- first birds: late Jurassic
- first flowering plants: early Cretaceous
- radiation of mammals: early Cenozoic
- first *Homo sapiens* (100 000–400 000 years ago)

Question 5.1 (a) A fine-grained igneous rock would have cooled rapidly and is likely to have been erupted at the Earth's surface or intruded near the surface as a small dyke or sill. A coarse-grained igneous rock would most likely have come from a pluton intruded at some considerable depth below the surface.

(b) A sill could be mistaken for a lava flow because they both lie parallel to the layering in the rocks above and below, and both are relatively fine-grained. A distinguishing feature is that top surfaces of lava flows are exposed immediately after eruption and tend to be uneven and weathered, whereas the surfaces of sills are generally flat because they are in contact with existing rocks, having been intruded along surfaces between beds. You might also expect the rocks adjacent to a hot body of magma to be affected by the heat. A lava flow would affect only those rocks below it; a sill would affect those above and below it.

Question 5.2 (a) The granite is composed of large crystals, randomly arranged. It crystallized slowly from magma, deep in the crust.

(b) The porphyry consists of large crystals set in a fine-grained groundmass. The large crystals formed first during slow cooling within a magma chamber. The groundmass cooled rapidly on eruption, or on solidification if it was intruded as a sill or dyke.

(c) The rhyolite is fine-grained throughout. Individual crystals are difficult to distinguish. It crystallized quite rapidly on eruption at the Earth's surface.

(d) The pumice is a rough-textured rock but few, if any, individual grains are visible. The roughness is due to innumerable holes. It solidified rapidly as gases were released on eruption, forming a honeycomb texture. In fact, this solid material is composed of glass.

(e) The obsidian is a glassy rock. It solidified very rapidly on eruption under water, or onto a cool land surface, to form smooth glass.

Question 5.3 (a) Granite and rhyolite contain the highest proportion of quartz.

(b) Gabbro and basalt contain the highest proportion of mafic minerals.

(c) Gabbro and basalt contain no alkali feldspar.

(d) Diorite may contain pyroxene, granite does not; diorite contains more plagioclase feldspar and amphibole than granite does; granite contains more alkali feldspar and quartz than diorite does.

(e) Diorite contains more silicon, sodium and potassium, but less magnesium, iron and calcium than gabbro.

Question 5.4 Quartz, alkali feldspars and pale mica tend to melt at low temperatures. These minerals have complex framework or sheet structures, made of connected SiO_4 tetrahedra, and they are rich in silicon (Section 4). Mafic minerals, especially olivine, require high temperatures to melt (Figure 5.10). Olivine is a magnesium- and iron-rich silicate mineral, its structure based on separate SiO_4 groups; pyroxene is also magnesium- and iron-rich, its structure based on SiO_4 chains (Section 4, Table 4.2). These are simpler structures, with less silicon than those of quartz or feldspar.

Question 5.5 Basaltic lavas can be formed either in a mid-plate (hot spot) or plate-boundary (mid-ocean ridge or volcanic arc) setting. Without additional evidence, such as ocean-floor sediments or rocks from the mantle, they are not diagnostic of any one setting. Large quantities of andesitic lavas are found mainly in volcanic arcs, and are indicative of such plate-boundary settings when found in the geological record, but independent evidence is normally sought before any setting can be confidently assigned.

Question 6.1 In hot, humid regions, chemical weathering is rapid, whereas in cold, wet regions it is very slow, but physical weathering, through repeated freezing and thawing (frost shattering), is much more important. Water is essential for both chemical and physical weathering; without it rocks are neither broken down nor decomposed. Although there are extremes of temperature on the Moon, because there is little or no water, very little weathering occurs there.

Question 6.2 Granite is a coarse-grained igneous rock composed mainly of feldspar, mica and quartz. Physical weathering breaks down the rock into smaller fragments and may release individual mineral grains. Chemical weathering decomposes unstable minerals such as feldspar and mica, forming stable clay minerals and soluble metal ions (e.g. Equation 6.2); it also liberates resistant quartz grains. {The disintegration of granite by physical and chemical weathering is shown in the video, 'A story in sand', in Activity 6.2.}

Question 6.3 Arid desert conditions in ancient sandstones are indicated by the presence of well-rounded, well-sorted, quartz grains, with pitted ('frosted') surfaces, reflecting wind transportation, and a red surface coating of iron oxide, reflecting oxidizing conditions.

Question 6.4 Chemical weathering provides a steady supply of soluble ions, especially Na^+, K^+, Ca^{2+}, Mg^{2+} and HCO_3^-. These ions are removed from seawater by: (i) the crystallization of salts, extracting Na^+ and Ca^{2+}, especially during the formation of evaporites, and (ii) the growth of marine organisms responsible for many limestones, which 'lock away' Ca^{2+} and CO_3^{2-} ions in calcium carbonate (mainly calcite).

Question 6.5 Note that the descriptions are *appropriate* to the rocks given, but do *not* represent definitions of those rocks; for example, not all conglomerates contain pebbles in a quartz cement.

(b) mudstone — contains a high proportion of clay minerals.

(c) breccia — contains large angular rock fragments.

(d) evaporite — contains interlocking crystals of water-soluble minerals.

(f) conglomerate — contains rounded pebbles cemented by quartz.

(g) limestone — contains remains of shelly organisms in fine-grained carbonate mud.

Question 7.1 Mudstone is converted to slate, to schist or to gneiss at progressively higher grades of metamorphism. The rocks produced at higher grades are increasingly coarse-grained. The minerals that form are progressively more anhydrous (like feldspars and garnets) as water is liberated when hydrous minerals (like clays and micas) break down. The texture changes from the smooth, even texture of a mudstone with fine clay mineral grains, to that of slate, with very fine-grained aligned mica flakes, allowing the rock to split along smooth parallel surfaces; to that of schist, with roughly aligned coarser-grained platy minerals, so that the rock splits along uneven surfaces; to that of gneiss, with rough mineral banding and fewer platy minerals, so it does not split as easily.

Question 7.2 (i) Figure 7.9a represents compression and Figure 7.9b represents tension. If you want to check this, take a strip of paper and make a diagonal cut across it. Starting from their uncut positions, move the two parts to match the arrangement shown in each of the figures. To match Figure 7.9a they must be pushed together sliding along the diagonal; to match Figure 7.9b they must be pulled apart sliding along the diagonal. Directions of movement are shown in Figures 7.13a and 7.13b.

(ii) The sandstone and mudstone are repeated in the sequence in Figure 7.9a, whereas the sandstone is missing from the sequence in Figure 7.9b.

(iii) The separation of the trees in Figure 7.9a is less than in Figure 7.9b; therefore compression results in overall shortening, and tension results in overall extension.

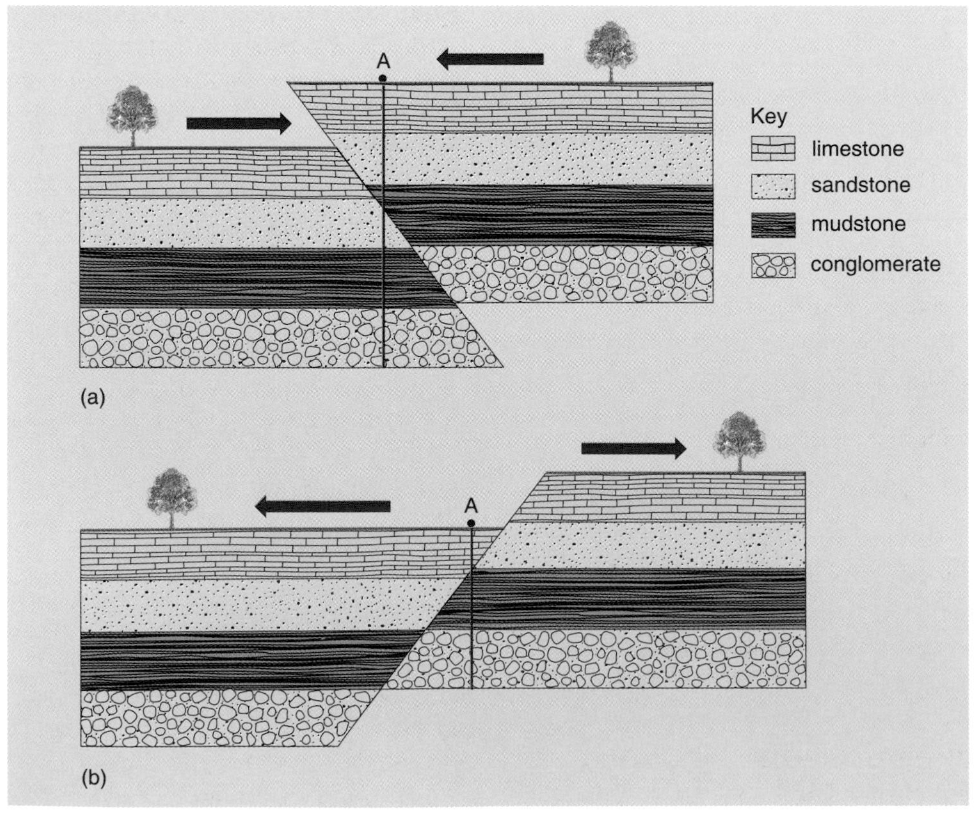

Figure 7.13 Repetition of Figure 7.9, with arrows showing boreholes and directions of horizontal movement.

Question 7.3 The presence in rock exposures of folds and faults, formed in response to either compression or tension, would be signs that earth movements had taken place. The presence of regional metamorphic rocks with visible metamorphic minerals and textures formed at considerable depth would also demonstrate that burial and uplift had taken place as a result of tectonic activity.

Question 7.4 Metamorphic belts are formed by regional metamorphism of pre-existing rocks that encounter high pressures and temperatures during mountain-building, which generally involves collision and crustal thickening at convergent plate boundaries. Erosion of mountains and the buoyant uplift of thickened crust are largely responsible for raising metamorphic belts to the surface and exposing their interiors.

Question 8.1 The volume of Etna is given in km^3 but you have calculated the rate of growth in $m^3\,y^{-1}$. You therefore need to convert the growth rate to $km^3\,y^{-1}$, or, alternatively, to convert the volume to m^3.

There are 10^9 cubic metres in a cubic kilometre. Imagine a cube 1 km × 1 km × 1 km; each side is 1 000 m long and so the cube has a volume of $1\,000 \times 1\,000 \times 1\,000\ m^3 = 10^9\ m^3$.

Therefore the rate of growth is:

$$\frac{5.0 \times 10^6}{10^9}\ km^3\,y^{-1} = 5.0 \times 10^{-3}\ km^3\,y^{-1}.$$

The age of Etna is now calculated by dividing the volume by the growth rate:

$$\text{age} = 350\ km^3/5.0 \times 10^{-3}\ km^3\,y^{-1} = 70\,000\ y.$$

Question 8.2 (a) The zircon in the granite has a ${}^{207}_{82}Pb/{}^{235}_{92}U$ value of 1.7. A D/P value of 1.7 is equivalent to about 1.4 half-lives (Figure 8.6). The half-life of ${}^{235}_{92}U$ is 704 Ma and so the age of the granite is:

$$1.4 \times 704\ Ma = 986\ Ma$$

$$= 990\ Ma \text{ to 2 significant figures.}$$

(b) The zircon in the second granite has a ${}^{238}_{92}U/{}^{206}_{82}Pb$ value of 2.5.

Note that in this case you have been given the parent/daughter (P/D) value.

If $P/D = 2.5$, then:

$$D/P = 1/2.5 = 0.40.$$

A D/P value of 0.40 represents about 0.50 half-lives (Figure 8.6). As the half-life of ${}^{238}_{92}U$ is 4 470 Ma, the age of the granite is:

$$0.50 \times 4\,470\ Ma = 2\,235\ Ma$$

$$= 2\,200\ Ma \text{ to 2 significant figures.}$$

Question 8.3 If the uncertainty of the final age is ±1%, the age of the first granite would be expressed as:

$$986\ Ma \pm (1\% \times 986) = 986\ Ma \pm 10\ Ma.$$

The age of the second granite would be expressed as:

$$2\,235\ Ma \pm (1\% \times 2\,235) = 2\,235\ Ma \pm 20\ Ma.$$

Question 9.1 Because of their great age, Precambrian rocks: (i) are usually devoid of fossils (Section 2.3), so biostratigraphic correlation is not possible; (ii) have, in many cases, been subjected to several episodes of tectonic deformation, and are thus highly metamorphosed and structurally complex, with most earlier features obliterated; (iii) are often obscured by a covering of younger rocks. In addition, the widely-separated nature of Precambrian outcrops makes their relationships difficult to interpret. You may also have thought of some other reasons which could be equally valid.

Question 9.2 The only paragraph that contains errors is number 6. Note that the corrected errors are identified here by *italics*, and that these comments also include some additional information that you have not been given before. As can be seen from Figures 9.1 and 9.3, the areas of the British Isles subject to the most intense Caledonian metamorphism were *the highlands of Scotland* and *northwest Ireland*. Early in the Caledonian Orogeny, some of the gneisses and schists in the Grampian Mountains reached a depth of *30 km* before being uplifted (burial to 3 km would *not* give high-grade metamorphism, Figure 7.1). Whatever these gneisses and schists were derived from, it was *not limestones*, which form marbles when metamorphosed (Section 7.1.1). The rocks of the Southern Uplands of Scotland, the Lake District, Wales, and eastern and southeast Ireland were affected later, but only by much lower-grade metamorphism. For example, it was lateral compression and relatively shallow burial to about 8 km that produced the famous slates of north Wales (originally Cambrian and Ordovician mudstones).

The prevailing trend both of the major faults and of the folds in the British Caledonides is *NE–SW*. Notice also on Figure 9.1 the band of Ordovician and Silurian rocks crossing NE–SW from southern Scotland into Ireland, and the NE–SW alignment of Ordovician and Silurian rocks in the Lake District. Finally, remember that the paragraphs in this question serve to tell an important story.

Acknowledgements

Grateful acknowledgement is made to the following sources for permission to reproduce material in this block:

Figures

Figure 2.1a: J. Chester Farnsworth, Princeton University Natural History Museum; *Figure 2.1b*: courtesy of Martin Lockley; *Figures 2.2 and 3.11*: Peter Sheldon; *Figure 2.3*: photograph by Frank M. Carpenter; Figure *2.4a and 2.6a*: courtesy of Heather Angel; *Figure 2.4b*: Clarkson, E. N. K. (1993) *Invertebrate Palaeontology and Evolution*, third edition, Chapman and Hall, by permission of the author; *Figures 2.5 and 2.6b*: Fish, J. D. and Fish, S. (1989) *A Student's Guide to the Seashore*, Unwin Hyman, International Thomson Publishing; *Figure 2.8a*: Donald R. Lowe; *Figure 2.8b*: Andrew Knoll, Harvard University; *Figure 2.9*: figure first published in Schopf, J. W. (1992) 'The oldest fossils and what they mean' in Schopf, J. W. (Editor) *Major Events in the History of Life*, Boston: Jones & Bartlett. Reproduced courtesy of J. W. Schopf; *Figure 2.10*: Chip Clark, National Museum of Natural History, Smithsonian Institution; *Figure 2.11*: Plates 1–3 of Matthews, S. and Missarzhevsky, V. (1975) *Journal of the Geological Society of London*, **131**, London; *Figure 2.12*: courtesy of John Sibbick; *Figure 3.1a*: Dianne Edwards; *Figure 3.1b*: courtesy of Jason Dunlop; *Figure 3.2*: courtesy of Wendy Webb; *Figure 3.3*: courtesy of Michael Coates; *Figure 3.4*: National Museum of Natural History, Smithsonian Institution; *Figure 3.5*: Benton, M. J., (1997) *Vertebrate Palaeontology*, second edition, Chapman and Hall, by permission of the author; *Figure 3.6a*: Alessandro Montanari/Osservatorio Geologico di Coldigioco; *Figure 3.6b*: Richard Grieve, Geological Survey of Canada; *Figure 3.6c*: Bruce F. Bohor, United States Geological Survey; *Figure 3.7*: Benton, M. J. (1993) 'Dinosaur summer' in Gould, S. J. (Editor) *The Book of Life*, Ebury Hutchinson, Random Group (UK) Ltd; *Figure 3.8*: Stanley, S. M. (1993) *Exploring Earth and Life Through Time*, p. 409, © W. H. Freeman & Company; *Figure 3.9*: Luria, S. E. et al. 1981, A View of Life, Benjamin/Cummings Publishing; Figure 3.10: Thewissen, J. G. M., Hussain, S. T. and Arif, M. (1994) 'Fossil evidence for the origin of aquatic locomotion in archaeocete whales', Science, 263, 14 January 1994, American Association for the Advancement of Science; *Figure 5.3*: courtesy of the Northern Ireland Tourist Board; *Figures 5.4, 9.3 and 9.9*: Dunning, F. W., Mercer, I. F., Owen, M. P., Roberts, R. H. and Lambert, J. L. M. (1978) *Britain Before Man*, Natural History Museum, London; *Figures 5.5a and 7.5*: Press, F. and Siever, R. (1994) *Understanding Earth*, W. H. Freeman & Company; *Figure 5.5b*: courtesy of Andy Tindle; *Figures 5.5c and 8.1*: English Heritage Photographic Library; *Figure 5.8*: adapted from Bott, M. H. P. (1982) *The Interior of the Earth, Its Structure, Constitution and Evolution*, Edward Arnold; *Figure 6.1a*: courtesy of Chris Wilson; *Figure 6.1b*: courtesy of Kevin Church; *Figure 6.1c*: courtesy of Angela Coe; *Figure 6.4*: courtesy of Evelyn Brown; *Figure 6.9a*: courtesy of J. G. Ogg; *Figure 7.6a*: courtesy of Nigel Harris; *Figure 7.6b*: courtesy of Jill Eyers; *Figure 7.6c*: courtesy of Chris Hawkesworth ; *Figure 7.8*: M. S. Paterson, Australian National University; *Figure 8.2*: courtesy of Hazel Rymer; *Figures 9.1 and 9.11*: BD/IPR/5-12, reproduced by permission of the Director, British Geological Survey. © NERC. All rights reserved; *Figure 9.2*: Mac Niocaill, C., van der Pluijm, B. A., Van der Voo, R. (1997) 'Ordovician paleogeography and the evolution of the Iapetus ocean', *Geology*, **25**(2), February 1997, p. 161, Geological Society of America; *Figures 9.4 and 9.8b*: Smith, A. (1996) *CD-ROM of Plate Reconstructions*, Cambridge Palaeomap Services Ltd; *Figure 9.5*: courtesy of Rodney Gayer; *Figure 9.9*: The Natural History Museum,

London; *Figures 10.1, 10.3, and 10.7*: Dave McGarvie; *Figure 10.4*: Strahler, A. (1973) *Earth Sciences*, Harper & Row, Harper Collins Publishers; *Figure 10.5*: Coffin, M. F. and Eldholm, O. (1993) 'Exploring large subsea igneous provinces', *Oceanus*, **36**(4), Woods Hole Oceanographic Institution; *Figure 10.6*: Haq, B. U. and Milliman, J. D. (Editors) 1984, *Marine Geology and Oceanography of Arabian Sea and Coastal Pakistan*, Van Nostrand Reinhold.

Every effort has been made to trace copyright owners, but if any have been inadvertently overlooked, the publishers will be pleased to make the necessary arrangements at the first opportunity.

Title page

Courtesy of John Sibbick.

Index

Entries and page numbers in **bold type** refer to key words which are printed in **bold** in the text and which are defined in the Glossary. These are terms that we expect you to be able to explain the meaning of, and use correctly, both during and at the end of the course. An entry followed by ^{G} indicates a term which is defined in the Glossary but which is not bold in the text. Where the page number is given in *italics*, the indexed information is carried mainly or wholly in an illustration or table. Section summaries and answers to questions are not indexed.

ACC. No: 02922270

SIMON AND SCHUSTER
First published in Great Britain in 2013 by Simon and Schuster UK Ltd
1st Floor, 222 Gray's Inn Road, London WC1X 8HB
A CBS Company

Copyright © 2013 HIT (MTK) Limited. Mike The Knight™ and logo
and Be A Knight, Do It Right!™ are trademarks of HIT (MTK) Limited.
All rights reserved, including the right of reproduction reserved in whole or in part in any form.

Based on the television series Mike the Knight
© 2013 HIT (MTK) Limited/Nelvana Limited. A United Kingdom-Canada Co-production.

ISBN 978-1-4711-1821-0
Printed and bound in China
10 9 8 7 6 5 4 3 2
www.simonandschuster.co.uk

© 2013 HIT Entertainment Limited.
HIT and the HIT logo are trademarks
of HIT Entertainment Limited.

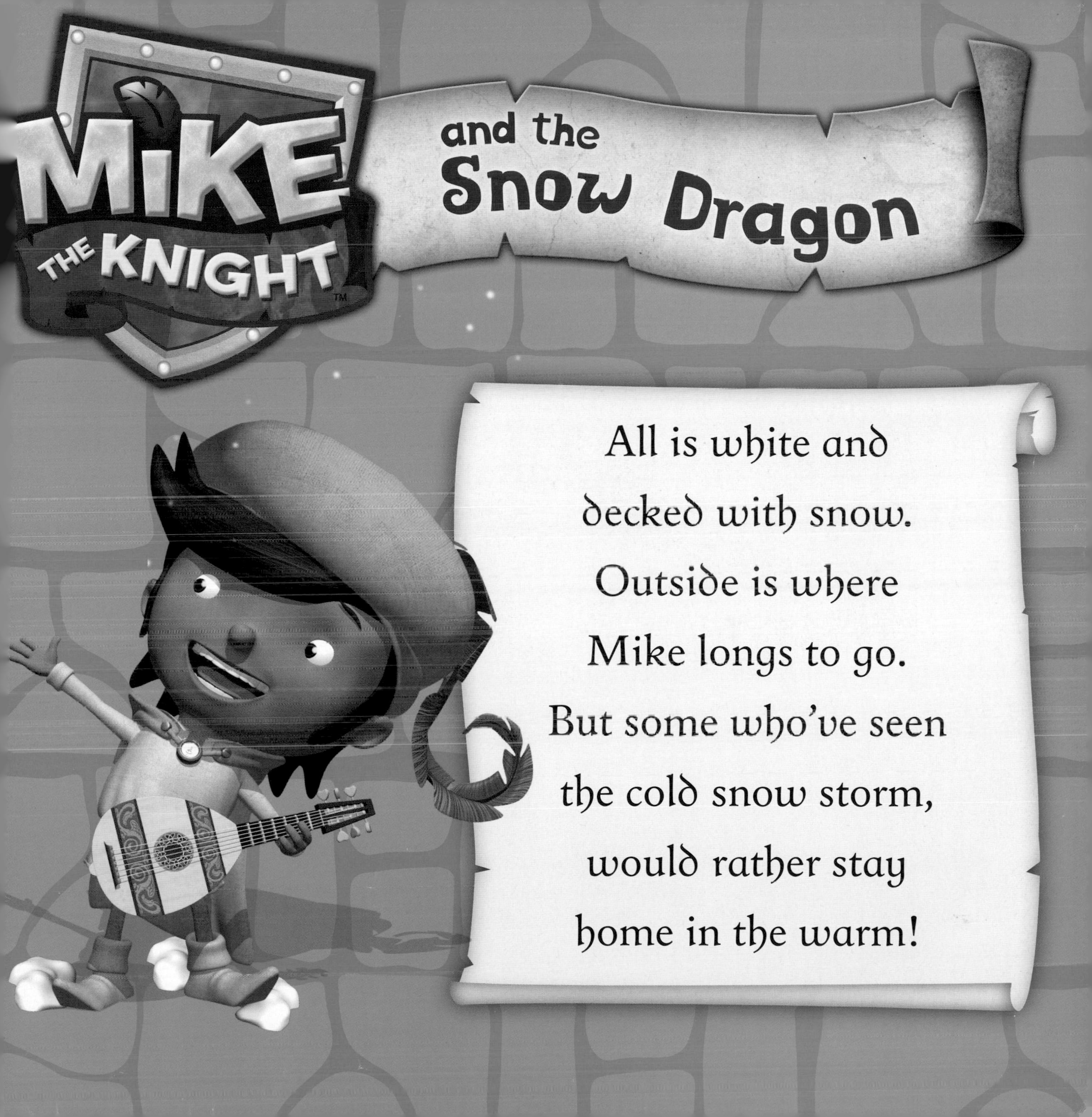
MIKE THE KNIGHT™
and the Snow Dragon
All is white and
decked with snow.
Outside is where
Mike longs to go.
But some who've seen
the cold snow storm,
would rather stay
home in the warm!

Noble knights are always ready for adventure, whatever the weather!

[illegible]

but Squire and Sparkie wanted to spend the day snuggled up with their favourite book.